The Penrose

Annual

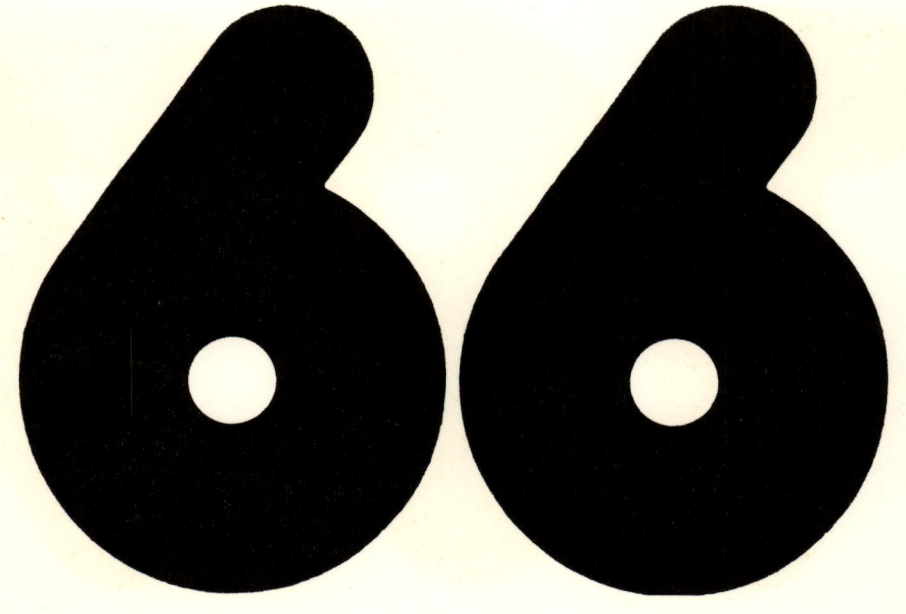

Graphic Arts International Annual

1973

The Penrose Annual 1973

Edited by **Herbert Spencer**

Published by **Visual Communication Books**
Hastings House, Publishers
New York 10016

Made and printed in Great Britain by
Lund Humphries
London and Bradford

Contents

Penrose 1973

Several of this year's twenty contributions deal with what can be called the sociology of printing and the graphic arts media. For the first time, the problem of eliminating from the printing processes the various sources of pollution of the environment figures prominently; Hugh Dunn's article on water-based printing inks and William A. Rocap's on press coatings hinge partly on this question, which is already of acute practical concern to the American industry and will become so for printers everywhere.

Also connecting with the social responsibilities of the graphic arts are a study by Theo H. Oltheten of the media in the developing countries and the central importance to them of the 'knowledge industry', an article on modern methods of 'humanizing' science teaching by Michael Shayer, and a critique by Romek Marber of current art school methods of training scientific and technical illustrators capable of resolving the presentation problems with which modern science, industry and marketing confront them.

In this field, too, may be placed the contribution by Herbert Jones on the challenge to the values of the established daily and weekly papers represented by the 'underground press' in Britain and the United States, both through its content and its design.

In newspaper typography the event of the year in Britain was perhaps the switch by *The Times* from the forty-year-old Times New Roman to Times Europa. John Dreyfus tells the story of Stanley Morison's world-famed typeface and assesses its future prospects, and Allen Hutt celebrates the distinguished career of Walter Tracy, designer of Jubilee, Linotype Modern, and now of the face that is replacing Times New Roman. The exacting métier of the journalist–designers whose graphics have done so much over the past fifteen years to alter the appearance and increase the eloquence of the daily and weekly press is analysed by Raymond Hawkey.

Five contributions deal mainly with varied aspects of the graphic design and printing of the past and its lessons for today.

James Moran takes a critical new look at accepted estimates of some of the leading British printers between 1900 and 1950 and finds some unsung heroes. Among those who have not had the recognition they deserve he places C. J. Jacobi, who redesigned THE PENROSE ANNUAL in 1915, and the annual's great founder-editor William Gamble.

In another assessment, Peter Guy reviews the twenty-five years of the Folio Society and its book-publishing achievement.

Geoff Weedon and John Gorham trace the development of the

popular decorative art serving the English fairground and discover the social roots of the changes which it has undergone over the last century or so. The highly specific design traditions of Poland are the subject of an article by Szymon Bojko. And Bernarda Shahn contributes a study of the lettering skills of Ben Shahn and the unique role which they played in his art.

One of the fresh dimensions opened up by technology for the graphic designer is described by Aaron Marcus in an article exploring the new and imaginative approaches to typographic composition made possible with photo-typesetters linked to a digital computer.

In a full-length treatment entitled 'Composition '72', L. W. Wallis finds that the past year was one of solid commercial progress in the application of new composing technology, as well as far-reaching technical innovation, especially in computer systems controlling visual display terminals and mass-storage peripherals for data entry retrieval and editing purposes.

The problem of good register in web-offset printing is examined by John R. Martin. He probes the mystery of the relationship between tension and stretch and describes the solution achieved with equipment produced by his firm, Martin Automatic. Another U.S. contributor, Collier A. Elliott, considers the developing use of cathode-ray tube systems in composition and their growing usefulness in enabling editors to see exactly what is in storage and make corrections more easily.

Dr N. K. Bridge of PIRA looks at the prospects for plastics papers and in particular the effect that synthetic pulp – likely to be recognized as a breakthrough in papermaking – will have on these prospects. Maurice Goldring and Angela Hackelsberger put forward proposals for a standard specifications system for print production.

The Survey with which this volume opens includes some examination of the opportunities and the risks which face the British printing industry in this first year of United Kingdom membership of the European Economic Community.

Penrose 1973

Plusieurs des vingt articles de cette année traitent de ce que l'on pourrait appeler la sociologie de l'imprimerie et des techniques des arts graphiques. Pour la première fois, le problème d'éliminer des procédés d'imprimerie les diverses sources de pollution de l'environnement figure de façon proéminente ; l'article de Hugh Dunn sur les encres d'imprimerie à base aqueuse et celui de William A. Rocap sur les couchages de presse roulent en partie sur cette question, qui est déjà pour l'industrie américaine une cause de grave préoccupation pratique et le deviendra également pour les imprimeurs dans le monde entier.

Toujours dans le cadre de leur responsabilité envers la société, nous avons une étude par Theo H. Oltheten sur les arts graphiques dans les pays en voie de développement et sur l'importance primordiale qu'a pour eux « l'industrie du savoir », un article sur les méthodes modernes « d'humanisation » de l'enseignement des sciences par Michael Shayer, et une étude critique par Romek Marber des méthodes actuelles utilisées dans les écoles de beaux-arts pour la formation d'illustrateurs scientifiques et techniques capables de résoudre les problèmes de présentation que leur posent la science moderne, l'industrie et le marketing.

Dans ce domaine peut aussi être placé l'article d'Herbert Jones sur le défi aux valeurs des quotidiens et des hebdomadaires que représente la « presse clandestine » en Grande-Bretagne et aux Etats-Unis, tant par son contenu que par sa présentation.

En typographie, dans le secteur journaux, l'événement de l'année en Grande-Bretagne a peut-être été l'abandon par *The Times* du Times New Roman, vieux de quarante ans, en faveur du Times Europa. John Dreyfus relate l'histoire de la série fameuse dans le monde entier de Stanley Morison et évalue ses perspectives d'avenir, et Allen Hutt rappelle la carrière distinguée de Walter Tracy, créateur du Jubilee, du Linotype Modern, et maintenant de la série remplaçant le Times New Roman. Les exigences du métier des journalistes–dessinateurs dont les créations graphiques ont tant contribué au cours des quinze dernières années à modifier l'apparence et à augmenter l'éloquence de la presse quotidienne et hebdomadaire font l'objet d'une analyse par Raymond Hawkey.

Cinq articles traitent principalement des divers aspects du dessin graphique et de l'imprimerie du passé et des leçons que l'on peut y trouver pour aujourd'hui.

James Moran examine de plus près l'opinion dans laquelle sont généralement tenus certains des principaux imprimeurs britanniques d'entre 1900 et 1950 et découvre quelques héros ignorés. Parmi ceux qui n'ont pas connu la renommée qu'ils méritent, il place C. J. Jacobi, qui renouvela en 1915 la forme de THE PENROSE ANNUAL, et le grand rédacteur-fondateur de l'annuaire, William Gamble.

D'un autre côté, Peter Guy passe en revue les vingt-cinq années de la Folio Society et ses réalisations dans le domaine de l'édition.

Geoff Weedon et John Gorham retracent l'histoire du développement de l'art décoratif populaire qui a trouvé son application dans les fêtes foraines anglaises et décèlent les origines sociales de l'évolution qu'il a subi depuis le début du siècle dernier environ. Les traditions très spécifiques du dessin en Pologne font l'objet d'un article par Szymon Bojko. Et Bernarda Shahn fournit une étude de la technique de l'emploi de caractères de Ben Shahn et du rôle unique qu'elle jouait dans son art.

Un des nouveaux horizons ouverts par la technologie au dessinateur graphique est décrit par Aaron Marcus dans un article qui explore les manières nouvelles et imaginatives d'aborder la composition typographique rendues possibles par les photocomposeuses reliées à un ordinateur digital.

Dans une longue étude intitulée « Composition '72 », D. W. Wallis aboutit à la conclusion que l'année dernière a été une période de réel progrès commercial dans l'application de la nouvelle technologie de la composition, ainsi qu'une période d'innovation technique lourde de conséquences pour l'avenir, particulièrement en ce qui concerne les systèmes d'ordinateurs contrôlant des appareils terminaux d'indication optique et des appareils périphériques de mémorisation en masse pour l'introduction, le relèvement et l'arrangement des données.

Le problème du bon repérage dans l'impression offset en continu est examiné par John R. Martin. Il étudie le mystère du rapport entre la tension et l'allongement et décrit la solution obtenue avec du matériel produit par sa firme, Martin Automatic. Un autre collaborateur américain, Collier A. Elliott, fait l'étude du développement de l'emploi des systèmes de tube cathodique en composition et leur utilité croissante grâce à la possibilité qu'ils donnent aux rédacteurs de voir exactement ce qui est en stockage et de faire plus facilement des corrections.

M. N. K. Bridge, de la PIRA, considère les perspectives d'avenir des papiers plastiques et en particulier les effets que la pâte synthétique – qui semble devoir être une découverte de majeure importance pour l'industrie papetière – aura sur cet avenir.

Penrose 1973

Mehrere der zwanzig Beiträge dieses Jahres befassen sich mit was man als die Soziologie des Druckereiwesens und der graphischen Medien bezeichnen kann. Erstmals nimmt das Problem der Ausschaltung von Quellen der Umweltverschmutzung aus dem Druckverfahren einen wichtigen Platz ein; die Artikel von Hugh Dunn über Druckfarben auf Wasserbasis und von William A. Rocap über Siegelaufstriche drehen sich teilweise um diese Frage, die in der amerikanischen Industrie bereits von brennendem praktischem Interesse ist und es für Druckereien überall werden wird.

Die sozialen Verantwortungen der Graphik lassen sich auch erkennen in einer Studie von Theo H. Oltheten über die Medien in den Entwicklungsländern und die wesentliche Bedeutung der „Wissensindustrie" für diese Länder, einem Artikel über moderne Methoden zur „Humanisierung" des Naturwissenschaftsunterrichtes von Michael Shayer, sowie einer Kritik von Romek Marber der zur Zeit in Kunstschulen angewendeten Methoden zur Schulung wissenschaftlicher und technischer Illustratoren, die imstande sein sollen, die sich bei der Darstellung wissenschaftlicher, industrieller oder mit dem Marketing verbundener Gegenstände ergebenden Probleme zu lösen. In dieses Gebiet gehört auch der Beitrag von Herbert Jones über die Herausforderung der Werte der bestehenden Tagespresse und der Wochenzeitungen, inhalts- und gestaltungsmässig, durch die „Untergrundpresse" in Grossbritannien und in den Vereinigten Staaten.

In der Zeitungstypographie war das Ereignis des Jahres vermutlich der Übergang der Tageszeitung *The Times* von ihrer vierzigjährigen Times New Roman auf Times Europa. John Dreyfus erzählt die Geschichte von Stanley Morisons weltberühmter Schrift und bewertet ihre Zukunftsaussichten. Allen Hutt würdigt die Laufbahn von Walter Tracy, dem Gestalter der Schriften Jubilee, Linotype Modern und der Schrift, die jetzt die Times New Roman ersetzt.

Der anspruchsvolle Beruf der journalistischen Graphiker, die im Laufe der letzten fünfzehn Jahre so viel geleistet haben, um die Tages- und Wochenzeitungen in ihrer äusseren Gestaltung zu wandeln und in ihrer Beredsamkeit zu stärken, wird von Raymond Hawkey untersucht.

Fünf Beiträge behandeln in erster Linie verschiedene Aspekte der graphischen Gestaltung und des Druckens in der Vergangenheit und was wir daraus heute lernen können.

In einer kritischen Betrachtung der überlieferungsmässigen Einschätzung einiger der führenden britischen Drucker zwischen

1900 und 1950 entdeckt James Moran bisher unbesungene Helden. Zu denjenigen, die noch nicht die ihnen gebührende Anerkennung gefunden haben, gehören seiner Meinung nach C. J. Jacobi, der 1915 THE PENROSE ANNUAL neu gestaltete, sowie William Gable, der bedeutende Gründer und Herausgeber des Annuals.

Die Folio Society und ihre Leistungen als Buchverlag über 25 Jahre werden in einem Überlick von Peter Guy gewürdigt.

Geoff Weedon und John Gorham gehen der Entwicklung der volkstümlichen angewandten Kunst auf englischen Jahrmärkten nach und entdecken die sozialen Wurzeln der Änderungen, die sie im Laufe der letzten hundert Jahre oder so erfahren hat. Die in hohem Masse eigenständige graphische Überlieferung Polens ist das Thema eines Artikels von Szymon Bojko. Und Bernarda Shahn schreibt über Ben Shahns Technik der Anwendung von Buchstabenkunst und die einmalige Rolle, die diese in seiner Kunst spielte.

Eine der neuen Dimensionen, die die Technik dem Graphiker eröffnet hat, wird von Aaron Marcus in einem Artikel beschrieben, in dem auf die neuen und phantasievollen Arten des typographischen Setzens hingewiesen wird, die durch Anschluss von Fotosetzmaschinen an Digitalcomputer ermöglicht werden.

In einer ausführlichen Abhandlung mit dem Titel „Composition ’72“ stellt L. W. Wallis massive kommerzielle Fortschritte in der Verbreitung neuer Satztechniken im letzten Jahre fest, sowie weitreichende technische Neuerungen, besonders in bezug auf durch den Computer gesteuerte Anzeigeeinheiten und periphere Gross-Speicher für Dateneingabe, -wiederauffindung und -aufarbeitung.

Das Problem der genauen Zurichtung im Rotations-Offsetdruck wird von John R. Martin untersucht. Er dringt in das Geheimnis der Beziehungen zwischen Spannung und Dehnung ein und beschreibt die Lösungen, die mit Hilfe der von seiner Firma, Martin Automatic, hergestellten Geräte erzielt werden konnten. Ein weiterer Beitrag aus den U.S.A., von Collier A. Elliott, befasst sich mit der steigenden Verwendung von Kathodenstrahlröhren beim Satz und sieht ihre wachsende Nützlichkeit darin, dass sie es dem Redakteur ermöglichen genau zu sehen, was sich im Speicher befindet, wodurch er leichter Korrekturen vornehmen kann.

Dr N. K. Bridge von PIRA betrachtet die Aussichten von Kunststoffpapieren und insbesondere die Wirkung von synthetischem Papierstoff, der vermutlich als umwälzende Neuerung in der Papierherstellung erkannt werden wird, auf diese Aussichten.

Notes on contributors

Biographical notes on some of the contributors to this volume.

Szymon Bojko

studied art history at Warsaw University and at the Institute of Social Sciences in Warsaw. He is a member of the editorial board of the art review *Projekt*. He has contributed to journals in Poland, France, Czechoslovakia, Italy, Denmark, and the Soviet Union, and is author of *Polish Poster Art* (Warsaw 1971) and *New Graphic Design in Revolutionary Russia* (Lund Humphries, London 1972).

N. K. Bridge

is now director of PIRA. He was previously manager of PIRA's Paper & Board Division. After being trained as a physical chemist and as an engineer, he began his career at the British Rayon Research Association, working mainly on the technology of the fading of dyestuffs and associated degradation of polymers. Subsequently he worked for the U.S. Atomic Energy Commission at the Argonne National Laboratory in Chicago. He joined Reed International in 1959 as head of the Formation Section in the Group Research Laboratories. Later he was in charge of the Paper and Boardmaking Process Group in the laboratories. In 1966 he moved to the Reed Empire Paper Mill to supervise the installation of the Group's first paper machine process control computer.

John Dreyfus

is president of the Association Typographique Internationale, and typographical adviser to Cambridge University Press and to the Monotype Corporation, European adviser to The Limited Editions Club of New York, and a director of the Curwen Press, London.

Hugh Dunn

is director of research and development in the printing and publishing area at Inmont Corporation. He is a chemical engineer, a graduate of Polytechnic Institute of Brooklyn, and has done postgraduate work at Harvard Business School, New York University, and Newark College of Engineering. He was until recently chairman of the Research Committee of the National Printing Ink Research Institute.

John Gorham

was born in 1937 and studied briefly at Harrow College of Art. In 1962 he joined the *Daily Mirror* Publicity Department and in 1964 worked as a designer with the *Sunday Times* Marketing Department. He was an art director with Cassons Advertising for two years before becoming a freelance designer in 1967. He has won many graphic design awards in Britain and abroad.

Peter Guy

worked in the production departments at Chatto & Windus and The Bodley Head before joining The Folio Society in 1964 as designer and production manager. He later became a director of the company but left in 1968 to become senior lecturer in Book Production and Publishing Techniques at the Oxford Polytechnic. Subsequently he was responsible for design and production of The Fraser Press limited editions and is now concerned with developing Gordon Fraser's book publishing interests. He is currently chairman of the Wynkyn de Worde Society.

Maurice Goldring

has had his own practice since 1965 concerned with information design, including the editing, design, and production supervision of scientific and technical printed information. Between 1960 and 1964 he set up and was head of the Technical Information Service of the Royal Institute of British Architects. He is chairman of BSI Technical Committees responsible for the production and revision of British Standards on copy preparation and proof correction, loose leaf binders, and personal stationery. He is a Fellow of the Society of Industrial Artists and Designers, Fellow of the Society of Typographic Designers, and Associate Member of the Institute of Printing.

Notes on contributors

Angela Hackelsberger

works together with her husband Maurice Goldring. She was educated in Germany and the USA, studied in the Department of Visual Communication at the Hochschule für Gestaltung in Ulm, Germany, where she subsequently became designer to the HfG's Optical Research Centre which she helped to set up. She worked as graphic designer and photographer in Rio de Janeiro and in Munich before coming to London.

Raymond Hawkey

was born in Cornwall in 1930. He trained first as an illustrator at Plymouth College of Art and then as a graphic designer at the Royal College of Art, London. It was at the Royal College of Art that he gained his first editorial experience as art editor of *Ark*. During his final year Hawkey won a *Vogue* talent contest and, on graduating in 1953, joined Condé Nast Publications as art director of their promotion department, later becoming art editor of a group of *Vogue* magazines.
In 1957 he left to become an art director at Colman Prentis & Varley. It was while with the agency that he was commissioned by Arthur Christiansen, then editorial director of Beaverbrook Newspapers, to restyle an arts magazine belonging to the group. This led to Hawkey being appointed, in 1958, design director of the *Daily Express*. He remained with the *Express* until 1964 when he left to become presentation director of *The Observer*. Hawkey has twice received the Newspaper Design Award on behalf of *The Observer* and, in 1971, was himself a judge of the competition.

Herbert Jones

after a lifetime in printing and publishing, is now working as a freelance designer and writer, mostly on printing and allied subjects. He is engaged on a study of the typography of the late Stanley Morison, hopefully to be published in 1974.

Romek Marber

graduated from the Royal College of Art in 1956. He has a design practice in London. In 1961 he designed the Penguin crime series covers and Penguin packaging and publicity. He also did three educational films for BBC/TV and film credits for Columbia pictures. In 1964 he joined *The Observer* as art director to start the colour supplement and the same year was appointed consultant designer to Harrison & Sons. He has been consultant designer to Nicholson Publications since 1966 and consultant head of the Department of Graphic Design at Hornsey College of Art since 1967. He is a member of the Graphic Design Panel of the Council for the Diplomas in Art and Design.

Aaron Marcus

is an assistant professor in the School of Architecture and Urban Planning and in the Visual Arts Program at Princeton University where he teaches basic design and graphic design. He completed the work described in this volume while he was on sabbatical leave at Yale Art School in the Department of Graphic Design, as a research associate in the arts.

John Martin

graduated from the University of Illinois, and has been designing equipment for the graphic arts industry since 1961. He is president of Martin Automatic Inc., formed in 1968.

William A. Rocap

has been director of research and engineering of Meredith Printing, Des Moines, Iowa, for seven years. He was previously director of research and development at Curtis Publishing Company, Philadelphia, and instructor of printing at the Des Moines Area College. He is a member of the Board of Directors of PERI.

Bernarda Shahn

the wife of the late Ben Shahn, is both an illustrator and writer. During the early thirties she was a columnist and reviewer for the Ohio State *Journal*, and later an illustrator for *Fortune* Magazine, *Harper's* and *Scientific American*. She has written and illustrated several books of legends, and has just completed and published a large illustrated volume on the paintings, drawings, and murals of Ben Shahn (Abrams, New York).

L. W. Wallis

is composition consultant at PIRA. Previously photo-typesetting systems adviser at Crosfield Electronics Ltd and before that systems adviser with The Monotype Corporation Ltd. He has lectured widely on composition techniques and has written many articles for the trade press. Among his more durable writings are *Filmsetting in Focus* and *Precision in Map Making*, both editions of *The Monotype Recorder* in the middle 1960s.

A. E. Walsh

has had a lifetime of practical experience in the marketing of British goods in Europe. Since 1957, he has been co-editor with John Paxton of *Euromarket Surveys* and is also co-author with him of *Trade in the Common Market Countries* and *Trade and Industrial Resources of the Common Market and EFTA Countries*, and of the recently published *Into Europe* (Hutchinson, London).

Geoff Weedon

was born in 1944 and studied graphic design at the London College of Printing. He has worked as a designer for the *Daily Mirror* Publicity Group, and as an art director for Saward Baker and S. H. Benson. He is currently with Young & Rubican.

Acknowledgements

The printing, except where otherwise
stated, and the binding are by
Lund Humphries
The Country Press, Bradford BD8 8DH
and at
12 Bedford Square, London WC1B 3JB

The types used are 'Monotype'
Times New Roman Book (series 627)
Times New Roman (series 327)
Times New Roman Semi-bold (series 421)
Univers Light (series 685)
Univers Bold (series 693)

The jacket design is by
Christine Charlton

In the main this edition has been printed
on Evensyde Process Litho 140 g/m²
supplied by John Dickinson & Co. Ltd,
Croxley Mills, Watford, Hertfordshire
and Stargloss Art Paper 140 g/m²
supplied by Star Paper Sales Ltd,
Feniscowles, Blackburn

The summaries on pp.9–16 are on
Glastonbury Antique Laid 122 g/m²
supplied by Grosvenor Chater & Co. Ltd,
68 Cannon Street, London EC4N 6AN

The colour reproductions on pp.167–70
are on
Translucent Polyart 97 g/m² and
Standard White Polyart 115 g/m²
supplied by Bakelite Xylonite Ltd,
Lawford Place, Manningtree,
Essex CO11 2NA

The prelims and survey are on
Antique White Wove 164 g/m²
supplied by Spicer-Cowan Ltd,
New Hythe House, Larkfield,
Maidstone, Kent ME20 7PD

The inks used for the text, letterpress
illustrations, and advertisements were
made by
Ault & Wiborg Ltd,
71 Standen Road, London SW18 5TJ and
Croda Polymers Ltd, Ink Division,
Flemings of Edinburgh
170 Glasgow Road, Edinburgh EH12 9BE

The hardback edition has been bound
using Art Canvas supplied by
Winterbottom Products Ltd,
Lonsdale Chambers, 27 Chancery Lane,
London WC2 1NF and
Eska binders' board supplied by
Spicer-Cowan Ltd,
New Hythe House, Larkfield,
Maidstone, Kent ME20 7PD

Hardback cover screen printing by
Northern Screen Prints Ltd,
Crawshaw Hill, Pudsey
Yorkshire LS28 7BP

Endsheets are Strathmore Artlaid
Indian Gold 104 g/m² supplied by
G. F. Smith & Son (London) Ltd,
Lockwood Street, Hull HU2 0HL

The cover of the paperback edition is
Snolin 400 Shantung supplied by
The Grange Fibre Co. Ltd,
20 Princess Street, Manchester M14 LU

The jacket is ISB One-sided Strongart
supplied by W. Rowlandson & Co. Ltd,
10–16 Lafone Street, London SE1 2LY

Dean Valley Ltd, Lowerhouse Mills,
West Bollington, Macclesfield laminated
the jacket using film supplied by
British Celanese Ltd, Celanese House,
22 Hanover Square, London W1A 1BS

The publishers and the editor acknowledge
their indebtedness to all those who have
provided advice and assistance; to the
authors, artists, and institutions; and to
the engravers and printers who have
contributed to this volume including:

Art Reprographic (London) Ltd,
46–52 Banner Street, London EC1Y 8SS

Jesse Broad Ltd,
Atlantic Street, Broadheath,
Altrincham, Cheshire WA14 5EB

City Engraving Co. (Hull) Ltd,
Ryde House, Hull HU5 1QE
Curwen Press Ltd,
9 North Street, Plaistow
London E13 9HJ

Friarsgate Studio Ltd,
Barmston Road, Swinemoor Lane,
Beverley, E. Yorkshire HU17 0LA

Gilchrist Brothers Ltd,
Claypit Lane, Leeds LS1 1NN

Hislop & Day Ltd,
9 Albany Street, Edinburgh EH1 3PY

Kings Town Engraving Co. Ltd,
Leads Road, Stoneferry, Hull HU8 0DA

Leeds Engraving Co. Ltd,
62 Mabgate, Leeds LS9 7DZ
Leyton Studios Ltd,
Longley Lane, Manchester M22 4SY
London & Provincial Reproduction Co. Ltd,
Nesfield Street, Bradford BD1 3ET
The Lyth Engraving Co. Ltd,
23–25 Gun Street, Manchester M4 5DL

W. & J. Mackay Ltd,
Lordswood, Chatham, Kent

Philipson & Son, Ltd,
Albany House, West Blandford Street,
Newcastle upon Tyne NE1 4HZ

V. Siviter Smith & Co. Ltd,
Siviter House, Moseley Street,
Birmingham B12 0RX

Vantage Engraving Co. Ltd,
90 Wardour Street, London W1V 4AJ

The Penrose Survey

Contributors: Michael Bruno, Allen Hutt, James Moran, A. E. Walsh

The British printing industry is now embarked on the chancy waters of
Britain's entry into the European Economic Community and our
survey almost necessarily starts this year with a look at the trim of the
vessel as it enters this period of great change and great opportunity.
The event occurs at a time when the trade is also being exposed to
Government action in industrial relations – action which the printing
trade union leaders are among the strongest in opposing. And the
outcome of the efforts to bring British industrial relations under
control will in its turn affect British ability to cope with competition
inside the Common Market.

There are both positive and negative aspects of entry into the
Market to be considered. The negative side became only too apparent
when it was realized that there would be a great increase of officials,
working from Luxembourg, who could interfere with the domestic
affairs of companies. The Value Added Tax, while said not to be a part
of Britain's entry, will also add to an already inflated bureaucracy; it is
calculated that 6000 inspectors will be needed to implement this tax.

This imposition will fall particularly heavily on smaller businesses
and most printers are in this category. While it was being forged a new
statutory inquiry into printing ink, bookbinding, and paper goods
machinery, paper and board was initiated by the Business Statistics
Office. The benefits of these compulsory inquiries are often illusory and
appear to go to civil servants rather than to the industry concerned.

The Market produced hours of discussion at conferences and
columns of printed matter, but it all boiled down to the fact that
Europe was simply a bigger, if somewhat more complicated, economic
unit than Britain and that an inefficient, harassed, under-capitalized
printing firm with bad staff relations and without sense of direction was
in the same position in Britain as in France or Holland. Those Scottish
printers who penetrated the expanding English book market in the
nineteenth century were able to do so because they were efficient and
quality-conscious, not because they were Scottish. A medium-sized
firm, of whatever nationality, with ideas, quality, service, enlightened
management, and devoted technicians can beat a slovenly giant,
bulging with money, overburdened with 'executives', short on ideas,
and riddled with vested interests in its staff.

The problem facing Britain, however, is not shortage of ideas but
industrial organization. The path for the printing industry is
straightforward, although hard. It has to work out for itself a *modus
vivendi*. This calls for some form of continuous discussion between the

various interests away from the wages and conditions negotiating board. These interests should not be seen as simply those of capital and labour. What is required is a deep, objective examination of the conflicting elements among the employing groups and among the various kinds of operative. Some of the conflicts may be natural, permanent and, indeed, salutary, but others arise from the British industry's peculiar structure, which can put it at a disadvantage when faced with competition from other members of the Common Market. A dispute over a British Rail magazine being printed in Holland reflected the situation neatly. Publishers are concerned with price, quality, and service and in reply to protests British Rail pointed this out; it also promised that tenders for the magazine would be asked for toward the end of the year. It did not say that these would be restricted to British firms and both employers and unions would do well to think about this. British firms may soon be called upon to quote for the publications of State boards in other countries and they will have to show that they are capable of meeting the customers' requirements. Resolutions of protest are no substitute for service.

It might be urged that the Institute of Printing should act as a neutral forum where many of the industry's problems could be tackled, but the Institute has decided to limit full membership to specialists in aspects of printing technique or holders of academic qualifications rather than initiators or executants. As it withdraws into itself and becomes more parochial the very name of the Institute becomes debatable. It is to be hoped that more constructive thought will be given to its role in the not too distant future.

Problems facing British industry
The British industry faced the same problems in 1972 as in immediately previous years but in an intensified form. The most difficult concerned labour relations; the problem was only part of the general political and economic situation in the country, although for historical reasons it had a special relevance in printing.

Nearly a whole year was taken up with the 'ritual dance' of wage negotiations, including offers by the employers, counter-demands by the unions, overtime and productivity bans, new offers and ballots of members in unions which did not agree among themselves. The result was predictable: at exhaustion point there was eventual agreement, which was regarded as out of date not long after it was reached. Was this the way to negotiate wages and conditions in the 1970s? The question was increasingly asked by printers, trade union leaders, and particularly by print users who had been inconvenienced during what was called a 'marathon' negotiation. The question was particularly urgent in view of the imminent entry into the Market.

The answer was that while industry in general was run on these lines, and while trade unions rejected any system except that based on bargaining from strength, there was no alternative. Whether printing trade employees shared their union leaders' hostility to the legislation on industrial relations is doubtful. The membership of the National Union of Journalists in a ballot voted in favour of remaining a registered union under the Industrial Relations Act, despite decisions to the contrary by the union's national executive and annual conference. The ballot decision was over-ruled by a special conference; this saved the union from expulsion by the Trades Union Congress which had ruled earlier that no registered union could remain affiliated. The National Graphical Association went the other way, despite its leaders' opposition to the Act, when the membership voted to remain on the register of the Registrar of Trade Unions, and the NGA accepted this decision and resigned from the TUC.

The matter of registration, with the benefits entailed – exemption from income-tax, among others – was not a major issue until the TUC made it the criterion by which unions were judged; but the question of the 'closed' and 'agency' shop was felt to be a basic one in printing union circles. The NGA declared that it would resist any attempt to destroy the principle of the closed shop. In much of printing there has always been a resistance to outsiders, whatever the state of the law, and many managements would not be eager to change the situation, particularly as they would be unable to obtain skilled labour except through the unions.

But there are those at various levels who are attracted to the agency shop, in which employees vote for the union they wish to represent them. A minor breach occurred when the Wallpaper Workers Union – a small union not in the mainstream of printing – signed an agency shop agreement. To confuse matters, some of the workers in the factory concerned demanded that a general workers' union represent them. This presents a dilemma for the closely-knit printing unions, which have always endeavoured to keep out non-printing unions. Outside unions could claim to give better service than the traditional printing unions, and this has happened in a limited sector. The Printing and Kindred Trades Federation has had to ask book publishers not to recognize a non-printing union which is appealing to editorial staff. Paradoxically – and the Industrial Relations Act has produced a whole series of paradoxes – the union concerned, while making use of the agency shop proviso, is supposed to be utterly opposed to the Government's industrial relations policy.

It may well be that the printing unions will have to think deeply about their policies rather than reacting emotionally to get the best out of an existing situation, in which it would be wiser also for employers to resist the age-old temptation to play off union against union, however attractive this may seem in a period when traditional methods of printing are being abandoned in some publishing activities. It would be more sensible, if the unions were willing, to discuss the whole range of implications of the Government's policy in an endeavour to see where the industry might act in a unified way to avoid self-injury.

The Common Market challenge
How does British printing stand in relation to the single market of 250 million consumers which it is the central purpose of the Treaty of Rome to create? Narrowed down further, what does entry into the Market mean to an individual producer of print in Britain?

The penetration of this market on equal terms of entry with competitors in eight other countries is a challenge. The opening up of the domestic market on the same terms is an even greater one. The Printing and Publishing EDC, now disbanded, produced in 1970 a remarkable report – which people in the British industry should read from cover to cover – surveying the state of printing and publishing in Britain, Italy, West Germany, the Netherlands, and the United States. The investigation was undertaken in 1968, at a time when the enlargement of the European Economic Community was in doubt, and the report was not, therefore, concerned with the impact that joining the Market would have on Britain. Most of what it says about the countries with which Britain is now joined is of greater importance now, because its examination of the attitudes of the overseas firms which the members of the team visited serves once again to emphasize what the report so effectively sums up in the words 'the approach to business'. If belief in expansion is the common philosophy of so many top managers in the industry in Europe, if the quality of firms abroad, both in technical skill and management proficiency, was impressive in comparison with some British managements five years ago when the report was compiled, these qualities will now be all the more redoubtable in a single larger market with producers competing on equal terms.

Appendices to the report show that in new investment per employee, Britain is bottom of the table at £112, the USA is top at £300, with the Netherlands at £280 running it a close second. In output per employee, Britain and West Germany are lowest at £2,280 and £2,222 respectively, with Italy £3,066, the Netherlands £4,200 and the USA £8,333.

Some significant changes in the pattern of Britain's trade with the Common Market, however, have occurred in the past year or two. Imports of books, booklets, trade catalogues and similar products, from the Common Market countries to pre-entry Britain fell from £6,700,000 in 1966 to £6,026,000 in 1971 – a 10 % decrease. British exports to the Common Market countries, however, rose from £2,500,000 in 1966 to £6,037,000 in 1971 – an increase of 141 %.

The export-import ratio in trade in these items, having moved from 100:145 in 1962 to 100:265 in 1966 went back, for 1971, to the more acceptable level of 100:100. This seems to bear out the principle that attack is the best form of defence and that the more you can penetrate into competitive markets the better the protection of your own home ground.

In the new European Economic Community, Britain has yet to learn the art of selling internationally, with its prerequisite of international marketing research. The problem is to find the highest common denominator for trade throughout this vast field and to learn how to specialize in both marketing and production to fulfil the requirements of that denominator.

The second October Revolution

Symbolic of the new times was the new dress with which *The Times* was already adorned at the moment of entry into Europe. Exactly forty years after its first October Revolution, the newspaper last year successfully carried through its second – the change of its body type from Times Roman to Times Europa, first exclusively announced in the Penrose Survey for 1972. Examined in more detail in the article elsewhere in this issue on Walter Tracy, Europa's designer, the new face has been widely welcomed for its improved legibility. The three sizes of Europa in use are 9, 8, and 7 point (the last a notably brilliant performance, as the Parliamentary reports, the Court page and much of the Business News have shown). For the classified advertisements and long run-on lists of names the $5\frac{1}{2}$ and $4\frac{3}{4}$ point of Times Roman continue in use, as does the Times Bold for the news headlines. The inevitable wordiness of the condensed Times Bold lowercase in multi-column headlines, however, has encouraged speculation that a wider face will have to be designed.

Times Europa was designed with the whole of Times Newspapers, not just Printing House Square, in mind; but *The Sunday Times* is inhibited from installing it while it has the contract for the daily printing of *The Guardian*, which uses Royal. Since *The Observer* continues to be printed by *The Times* the quaint consequence is that the traditional competitor of *The Sunday Times* has gone over to Europa while *The Sunday Times* perforce stays in Royal. Still, this will not last since *The Observer* has given notice to end its contract with *The Times* and transfer its printing to plants equipped with Royal.

The *Observer* move, due to take effect this summer, is interesting because it envisages printing in two centres, London and Leeds, making use of facsimile transmission and web-offset printing for a portion of its run. The plan is that some half-million of the paper's 800,000 run shall be produced in London by the *Financial Times* (this would be the run for London and the South, broadly) while the northern run of some 300,000 will be produced by Yorkshire Post Newspapers in Leeds. *The Observer* does not normally run more than forty pages, which is the capacity of the *Financial Times* and *Yorkshire Post* presses; but it is intended to exploit the web-offset capacity of the 'hybrid' press lines at Leeds. In short, feature and other early pages will be sent in matrix form to Leeds on Friday, to be stereocast in the ordinary way up to the twenty-four-page capacity of the Wellington Street letterpress units; on Saturday up to sixteen late news pages will be facsimile-transmitted, to be reproduced as litho plates for the two web-offset units in each Leeds press line. The Tokyo-Sappuro facsimile experience of the Japanese and the parallel Manchester-Belfast experience of the *Daily Mirror* have shown that facsimile transmission from repro-proofed hot-metal works most efficiently when translated into web-offset at the receiving end.

On the national front *The Times* and *The Guardian* are running neck-and-neck; last year *The Guardian* made a striking breakthrough to 335,000, its highest circulation ever, while the latest figure for *The Times*, including a modest increase, was 338,000. Nevertheless the loss rate of *The Guardian* had increased while that of *The Times* was reported to have shown a further drop. Last summer planning permission was granted for the imposing new headquarters offices and plant of Times Newspapers, greatly extending the present *Sunday Times* building in Gray's Inn Road; but no firm dates are yet known for the completion of this work and the transfer of *The Times* from Printing House Square. Maintenance of the *Sunday Telegraph* has been increasing the losses of the *Daily Telegraph*; but Associated Newspapers reported a stable circulation figure for the tabloid *Daily Mail* in excess of its final circulation as a broadsheet and had a gratifying increase of over 50 % in its pre-tax profits (to £6,330,000). The Associated group was nevertheless taking elaborate steps to tackle the ailing condition of the London *Evening News*; circulation has dipped well below the million mark (not so many years ago it was in sight of 1,750,000) while advertising, and the paging that it produces, lags badly behind the rival *Evening Standard*, which has a substantially smaller circulation. The *Standard* has been regularly running fifty-six pages (tabloid, equal to twenty-eight pages broadsheet), and carrying much high-quality gravure preprint, while the *News* can only occasionally reach twenty-four pages; no wonder the *Standard* is reported to be making large contributions to Beaverbrook profits.

No large daily newspaper concerns have shown any signs of following I P C's Glasgow *Daily Record/Sunday Mail* photo-set, web-offset example. Two substantial new plants now under construction are both hot-metal and rotary letterpress. They are the new Merseyside headquarters of the *Liverpool Daily Post* (which last year for the first time passed the 100,000 mark) and its evening the *Liverpool Echo*, always one of the top three provincial evenings, and the new establishment on the outskirts of Bristol of the morning *Western Daily Press* and the *Evening Post*. Liverpool starts operating this year – with its twenty-eight new Goss double-width units, costing £1,750,000 – and Bristol early next.

The financial position of most provincial newspapers of any size continued buoyant; and with evenings of 50,000 a day or less, together with weeklies, photo-setting and web-offset printing were still advancing. In Oxford the Westminster Press successfully changed over its evening and weekly. The solidly entrenched *Barnsley Chronicle* did likewise, interestingly insisting on Linotype Modern for its text (the face had to be re-drawn for the paper's V-I-P photosetter). The *Kent Messenger* group, whose evening and weeklies have for some time been web-offset, completed the changeover to photo-setting for all text and display, and auctioned off its extensive linecaster and Ludlow equipment. The Kent County Newspapers group of four weeklies,

headed by the 255-year-old *Kentish Gazette* of Canterbury, convert to
photo-setting and web-offset this year. In Carlisle the small but
progressive Cumberland Newspapers group – a 30,000-run evening and
three weeklies – was an early pioneer of computerized typesetting and
web-offset printing; now it has added a Typeset-8 computerized
editorial/classified storage system.

Offset-lithography marches on
A number of economic factors as well as technological and market
developments contributed to the continued growth of offset-
lithography, especially web-offset, during the year. In the United States
the printing industry as a whole made a respectable recovery from the
recession that dominated all American industry in 1971 and early 1972.
DRUPA, the largest exhibition of printing equipment ever held,
stimulated many manufacturers to produce new products and
equipment for display and, as in other recent shows, the major
emphasis was on lithography. High cost of labour, especially in the
preparatory areas of type composition, proofreading, colour
separation, imposition or stripping, and platemaking have led users
and manufacturers alike to search for new and less costly ways of
performing these functions. In addition, the Environmental Protection
Agency (EPA) and the Occupational Health and Safety Act (OSHA)
exerted tremendous pressures on the printing industry and its suppliers
to eliminate or relieve areas of violations.

The net result has been an increase in the use of offset-lithography
as this process has proved more flexible and adaptable to changing
needs. Some of the areas in which lithography is growing are newspaper,
magazine, and book publishing and commercial printing.

Daily newspapers were one of the most rapid growth areas in this
field. The Goss Metro press, which prints four newspaper pages wide
with the capability of 60,000–65,000 newspapers per hour, has opened
up the medium- to long-run daily newspaper market to offset-
lithography. Over 100 US newspapers have already converted to
web-offset using this equipment. In Ontario, Canada, *The Ottawa
Citizen* is installing a specially designed twelve-unit Goss Metro in a
new plant and will phase out its letterpress operation when this press
and the other equipment in the new plant go into full-scale operation in
July 1973. The Goss Division of MGD Graphic Systems announced the
largest order it had ever received for offset equipment. The Oregonian
Publishing Company (Portland, Oregon) ordered thirty-six Metro units

with six folders and other auxiliary equipment worth $13 million altogether.

A serious problem attending the conversion of newspapers from letterpress to offset has been the accumulation of lint on the blankets of the offset press. This has been reduced considerably by the use of newsprint made on machines with twin-wire screens in place of the conventional single screen used on Fourdrinier machines. The twin-wire machines, like the Vertiformer, produce a sheet with essentially two wire sides so that there is less loose lint or fines to collect on the blanket. Relief is also coming in the development by chemical manufacturers of alkaline fountain etches which reduce the accumulation of lint on the blankets, and the introduction by at least one ink manufacturer of a so-called 'lint-free' ink.

The general interest magazine is still suffering from reduced readership and advertising revenues. Special interest magazines, on the other hand, are increasing in number, size, and circulation. About half of these are printed by web-offset and the list grows monthly. At a meeting of the Association of Publication Production Managers in New York City in 1972, it was stated that the costs of printing magazines in the US in 1970, including paper, was $1 billion. About 55 % of this was spent on letterpress, 37 % on web-offset, and 8 % on gravure.

Business Week has introduced an interesting concept which is used by other McGraw Hill publications and could spread to other publishers. All type is photo-set and page layouts are composed in the publishing headquarters in New York. The punched tapes for the type are transmitted by Dataphone and the page layouts are broadcast by facsimile to two printing locations in Albany, New York and Milwaukee, Wisconsin, where the magazine is composed and printed. It also will not be long before the black-and-white and colour illustrations will be transmitted along with the text and layouts.

Printing Developments, Inc. (PDI), a subsidiary of Time Inc., has developed a system combining the capabilities of photo-typesetting and single and multicolour picture generation that can transmit complete page formats by facsimile anywhere. The main obstacle is the absence of a reasonably priced transmission system able to handle the amount of information that needs to be transmitted. PDI engineers have succeeded in reducing the amount of information to be transmitted by blurring the yellow separation, transmitting sharp magenta and cyan images, producing the black separation and screening all separations on the receiving end, transmitting at one-third the scanning rate, reducing the scanning lines to 500 instead of 1000, and reducing the grey scale to six or seven bits instead of the usual eight. With all these modifications and compressions it will be possible to use the telephone company's Dataphone-50 – the simplest transmission system at present available – and transmit images from city to city with acceptable quality for reproduction.

Over 75 % of all books published in the us in 1971 were printed by offset-lithography, about half by web-offset, and the remainder on sheet-fed perfectors. Most of the other 25 % were paperbacks which are generally printed from moulded rubber relief plates using oil-based inks. Book publishing is also considering some new concepts that will revolutionize this old art. The author will compose on typewriters equipped with magnetic tape, which will be transmitted and stored in a computer from which the editor, production manager, illustrator and art director can extract the copy and work on it. When the book is complete, it will be stored in page formats in the memory of the computer. The publisher, instead of trying to anticipate print orders for the book and inventorying them, will print on demand. Book stores will take orders for the book and direct them to a satellite printing plant in the area. The plant will contact the data bank in the computer which will transmit the page formats in sequential order so that a complete book will be printed in each pass through the press.

The concept is not so far out as it appears. We already have the Cameron book (belt) press, which prints a complete book in one pass through the press. Six of these belt presses are in use or being installed in the us. The method is gaining in popularity and use, but could become even more practical and economical with the use of the new electrostatic or jet printing systems, now being developed, which can use computer memories to supply the sequential page layouts.

In commercial printing a growth rate of 14 % per year over the next ten-year period is predicted for offset. Much of this growth is in web-offset and in small- and medium-size multi-colour sheet-fed presses especially in the 25 in. × 38 in. to 38 in. × 50 in. sizes. Companies with large sheet-fed presses in 60 in. to 78 in. sizes are having trouble finding commercial printing to keep them busy. The large sheet-fed presses are still used extensively in specialty printing like greetings cards, labels, packaging, posters, maps, and books, but the trend seems to be away from the large 77 in. and 78 in. sizes to the intermediate 60 in. size.

In web-offset there is a trend toward the common-impression

cylinder (CIC) press. At least five new Halley-Aller presses have been installed in the US by Baker-Perkins during the past year, mostly in the Midwest. These presses are used for book, magazine, and catalogue printing. A new narrow-width Harris-Cottrell 30 in. blanket to blanket web-offset press has been installed by Fawcett Publishing in its Rockville, Maryland, plant to print signatures for the *National Geographic Magazine* at a rated speed of 1800 ft per minute.

New developments in equipment and materials
Some significant developments in graphic arts equipment and materials in 1972 will have an important effect on the course that the printing industry will follow in the next few years.

Since the introduction of direct screening on scanners last year, the use of scanners has increased and a number of innovations have been introduced. Scanner speeds have doubled and will continue to increase until separations will be made in seconds instead of minutes and hours as at present. At DRUPA, Dr Hell introduced a system for producing half-tones on his chromograph colour scanner DC300 using lasers. PDI has produced a set of screened separations using the electronic dot generator announced at IPEX last year. PDI has also introduced a Colour Coded Knockout Drum for its MRD colour scanner. This is a second glass drum added to the scanning pick-up system which uses colour coded masks to allow the insertion of colour type and the combination of several picture elements at different magnification ratios so that a complete positive or negative page make-up is produced containing all elements to size, in position, and in register. The same group has abandoned the Flying Spot Scanner announced last year because of difficulty in obtaining cathode-ray tubes within proper tolerances. The Colour Coded Knockout Drum makes the need for the Flying Spot Scanner less urgent.

Hunter Associates Laboratory has developed on-line colour monitoring instruments which are being used to control automatically the colour of paper, pulp and coated metals in manufacture. So far, they have not been used for printing as the sample area required – 2 in. $\times 2\frac{1}{2}$ in. – is quite large. Hunter has also developed a very sensitive densitometer which can read colour blocks on a press at time intervals of 0·00004 (40 millionths) of a second with an accuracy of 0·001 to 0·002 of a density unit. This is ten times as accurate as densitometers now in use. Macbeth, a division of Kollmorgen Corporation, has also developed an automatic system for colour measurement, control, and research. Known as the KCS-40, it is an automatic Colour Eye which uses a dedicated mini-computer to compare a colour with a standard, or control, and judge it in a manner similar to the way the eye sees and matches colour. The instrument is capable of an accuracy unheard of in densitometers.

At the Annual Symposium of the Society of Photographic Scientists and Engineers (SPSE) on New Photo-Technology Trends in the Graphic Arts, 25–27 October 1972 in Washington, D.C., a whole session was devoted to automated or micro stripping. These systems are similar to the Matrographics system for automatic step and repeat described last year, except that the two systems described are still in use and Matrographics is no longer in operation. The two systems were Opti-Copy by Western Blue Print Company of Kansas City, Missouri, and the Latady Projection Platemaker by Latady Instruments, Randolph, Massachusetts. The Opti-Copy system reduces copy 2 × to 4 × and projects the images in position on new projection speed negative working plates. At the time of the meeting it was in use in thirty commercial installations.

Photopolymer plates is a field in which there was more development for letterpress than for offset during the year. Kodak and Du Pont both introduced medium-run varieties of their photopolymer plates for offset-lithography, while the Japanese introduced five new photopolymer plates for letterpress, most of them for the newspaper market. The conventional letterpress market appears to be dominated by the BASF Nyloprint plate. This plate coupled with magnetic cylinders is revitalizing letterpress for publication printing and could slow down the rate of conversion of periodicals from letterpress to web-offset.

While 3M is still searching for an optimum ink to improve the performance of its driographic plates, the Scott Paper Company has been issued two patents on similar processes. One is by Harry F. Gipe who has a British patent that predated the Curtin 3M patent by fifteen months. The other, by T. Doggett, is for a process employing a silicone gum that is cured *in situ*. This is claimed to result in a much more wear-resistant surface that makes the plate easy to handle and practical for long runs. It will be interesting to see how the new Scott plates behave with respect to the ink problems encountered with the 3M plates.

At the annual meeting of the GATF Research Committee, 20–21 March 1972 in Pittsburgh, George Jorgensen reported on a computer simulation of a single-colour offset press, which mimics the behaviour of an actual press. The programme utilizes six variables under the control of the pressman and nine printing characteristics which the pressman has to evaluate in terms of the quality of the print. The operator can control the levels of the six input variables and the computer indicates the resulting change in the output variables. The six input variables are ink feed, water feed, press speed, impression pressure, number of sheets in the delivery pile, and ink tack. The nine printing characteristics or outputs are ink thickness, resolution, pick, ink set-off and blocking, wash marks, snowflaky solids, ghost images, sheet flatness, and plate dry-up. The operator's proficiency in manipulating the six input variables to achieve satisfactory levels of the output variables is determined by the press time consumed and waste incurred, which are tabulated with the computer output. Other work on computer models of printing presses is being done by INCA-FIEJ (the European newspaper research group) for newspaper presses and GRI (Gravure Research Institute) for gravure presses.

At its annual meeting in Key Biscayne, Florida, in November 1971, GRI announced results of its research on a wrap-around gravure system, which uses direct etched trimetallic plates of chrome-plated copper on a steel base mounted on a magnetic cylinder. The edges of the plates are cut at 5° to the axis of the cylinder and the plates staggered to minimize doctor blade bounce at the gaps, which are filled with fast curing epoxy cement. The most promising approach to eliminating the gap problem has been the use of off-set gravure with the blanket undercut in the gap area.

In the ink field a number of gravure printers have been interested in water-based inks for at least two reasons – ecology and explosion resistance. Solvent recovery and/or incineration of conventional inks are very expensive and explosions are disastrous. Most of the tests have been done in the Midwest. One printer conducted two reasonably successful tests and printed part of a mail-order catalogue with these inks. A third test by the same printer was unsuccessful. The inks are certainly not ready for commercial application yet, but the concentrated effort being exerted may lead to a breakthrough not too far ahead.

In the heat-cured catalytic inks, a number of low-solvent hybrid systems which cure at lower temperatures than the solventless type have been formulated and are being used in areas where the Environmental Protection Agency (EPA) regulations are strictly enforced. Universal acceptance is still hindered by the increased costs of the inks (36–80 % higher than heat-set) and lower value of the waste because of the difficulty in repulping it.

Interest in U V cured inks is increasing. Ten web-offset presses and almost as many sheet-fed presses were due to be equipped by the end of 1972 with high-intensity U V radiation sources to cure U V inks. Miehle has sold and built several sheet-fed presses in sizes from 38 in. to 77 in. designed specifically for use with U V inks. While there are still problems, such as compatibility of inks with roller and blanket materials, repulping of waste and costs of inks, interest continues to increase in this means of reducing ecological problems and achieving improved efficiency and quality.

Project G R O W (Get Rid of Wax which later became Get Rid of Waste) was initiated by I N M O N T almost ten years ago. It involved the application of water-soluble resin to the printed sheet in-line. The water-soluble resin which dried readily, kept the wet ink underneath from smearing or setting-off in the delivery, so no spray or wax was needed to prevent set-off. At first the mixture was applied through a conventional dampening system but this did not work well. About three years ago, the J. H. Dusenberry Company designed a unit called the Dusencoater for accomplishing the same result. After several false starts, the firm worked out the bugs in the system and an installation at Album Graphics in Chicago has been operating well since November 1971.

The use of an overcoating could be a more practical and economical answer to the effluent and spray problems than U V or catalytic inks, and is worth some investigation. Criticism of the original I N M O N T concept was that it used a unit on the press, limiting its capacity. The Dusencoater, or other application device, is a separate unit that is put in line with the press. If the concept works, if it allows the use of high-gloss resins enabling off-press varnishing and lacquering to be eliminated, and if it protects the ink well enough to keep it from smearing in folding or finishing operations, so that in-line operation can be considered in sheet-fed, and expensive dryers and incinerators can be eliminated in web printing, these new systems can be real winners.

A new system of printing without contact or plates, called jet printing, was presented by the Batelle Memorial Institute, in its report at C O M P R I N T 90, as the most promising printing process of the future. Ink jet printing applies ink to paper by squirting it directly onto the sheet. The squirting can be done in two ways. A single nozzle actuated by a computer can oscillate back and forth over a sheet, much as an electron beam produces an image on a TV screen. This is the technique used in the Teletype Inktronic and the A. B. Dick Videojet Systems. The other way is to use a bank of nozzles each of which is digitally controlled by a computer program. As many as 200–500 jets/in., which can form droplets at speeds as high as 80,000 per second, are used.

Such a system was announced by the Mead Corporation in its last annual report. It was developed by the Data Corporation of Dayton, Ohio, a Mead subsidiary, which has worked on it for over seven years. Known as the Dijit printer, it is claimed that it can match the speed of the computer and can image as many as 150,000 characters per second, or 70,000 lines of type and figures a minute. Process colour prints have been produced experimentally by this method. How long it will take this system to achieve the quality of conventional printing is anybody's guess. Such a process, when commercial, could be the answer to book publishing's problem of printing sequential pages so that a complete book can be printed in one pass through the press without the awkwardness of plate belts. It could even be the answer to speeding up the publishing of newspapers and magazines, and newspaper publishers are already taking a close look at it.

English fairground decoration

Geoff Weedon and John Gorham

'Proud Old Time Riding Horses, Rode by All with Joy . . .' much of the fun of the fair was provided by the rides and their graphic adornments. Styles in this century-old popular art form changed constantly as the showmen followed their competitive urge to be 'modern' at all costs. This article tells the story of the gallopers, switchbacks, gondolas, scenic railways, Noah's arks, dodgems, swirls, and more recent moon rockets and space ships and the art that furbished them for the fairground public.

The colour illustrations in this article were reproduced offset-litho by Friarsgate Studio Ltd and the monochrome by Lund Humphries.

On St Valentine's Day (February 14) the fair season begins and for the next nine months high streets, parks, and waste land all over Britain will have their brief moments of glory. For a few days they will harbour a fantasy world of flashing lights, raucous music, and swirling rides. Giant letterforms will leap from the hoardings and golden horses, lions, tigers, and Mickey Mouse will mingle with kings and queens.

The decoration of fairground rides, stalls, and booths is the pictorial record of our popular culture, the flotsam of the popular imagination of the last hundred years. Look carefully in any big fair and you'll find Winston Churchill rubbing shoulders with a pin-up from the fifties, an Esso tiger, Batman, and jungle scenes from the Empire beside rocket ships heading for the moon. Wherever you turn, the shows, stalls, and rides compete with each other; the louder the music and the brighter the colours, the bigger the crowds they draw. The fairground is intensely competitive and its decoration has a very real job to do. It's all a matter of packaging.

In 1953, when the present Queen was crowned, a number of showmen redecorating their rides renamed them 'Coronation' speedways and adorned the proscenium arches with giant portraits of the happy royal couple. When rock 'n' roll took the country by storm, guitarists, teddy boys, and bobby soxers graced booths and rides. Because the showman likes above all to be 'modern', he usually picks his motifs from topical themes and current fashions when ordering a new ride or redecorating an old one. Fortunately his choice may be preserved, for economic reasons, for many years.

The fair as we know it, with its fast rides, began in the latter part of the last century. Previously, rides had been hand or horse driven and the entertainments fairly simple. There were usually a few shows manned by itinerant players, and booths with peep-shows, menageries, and so on and a variety of food and drink. Their usual decoration consisted of large painted canvas banners hanging above the entrance, like the banner for 'The Two-headed Cuban Giant', which was in use until quite recently. By 1865, however, steam power had been harnessed to roundabouts and the modern fair was born. The great pioneer was Frederick Savage, a manufacturer of agricultural machinery from King's Lynn, in Norfolk. He recognized the potential of steam traction and over the next forty years developed many ingenious rides and a world-wide market for them.

The rides gradually became more elaborate and so did their decoration. The horses on the gallopers were carved more richly with

Canvas banner for The Two-headed Cuban Giant, hung above the entrance to the booth.

Above: Details of horses on George Whittle's Gallopers, carved by Andersons. Left: Detail of the proscenium arch to Tommy Benson's Swirl, by Edwin Hall.

rolling manes, glass eyes, and horsehair tails, and then sumptuously painted. Some of the finest sets came from Anderson's workshops in Bristol, where craftsmen carved wild animals, portraits, and wildly curling foliage into the necks and flanks of the horses. On one of the horses on Irvin's gallopers there is even an Edwardian pin-up, painted reclining a little below the saddle. Other horses carried names and Union Jacks and one set of gallopers included a number of centaurs, the human parts modelled after heroes of the Boer War. Good company for the bears, pigs, turkeys, ostriches, cockerels, peacocks, and bat-winged dragons that now rode the gallopers.

The power to drive these rides came from a truck-mounted engine, placed in the centre of the ride, which was concealed by richly decorated shutters called the 'bottom centre'. Like the horses, they were often deeply carved with portraits and baroque foliage, sometimes studded with cut-glass mirrors or perhaps displaying paintings of battle or jungle scenes. Higher up was the 'top centre', similarly adorned; sometimes it bore portraits of contemporary beauties or personalities, like the top centre in Beach's gallopers at Kew which was redecorated in the thirties with portraits of the latest film stars.

All the carving, statuary, twisting brass rods and ornate mirrors reflecting the naphtha flares by night, must have looked very modern to the Victorians. Yet at the top of every set of gallopers is a relic of pre-mechanical days. The radial arms known as 'swifts' which stretch out from the top centre to support the rounding boards and cranks from which the horses are suspended are carved and painted in traditional style like the substructure of gipsy caravans and old farm vehicles and the frames of the swingboats, a very early fairground ride.

The rounding boards began simply with delicate letterforms, or perhaps a number of carefully painted jungle or battle scenes. Gradually they were made fatter, with domes added to the top, and scalloped droppers, often carrying mirrors, to the bottom. The lettering with its message grew bolder and more extravagant: 'James Noyce & Sons, Proud Old Time Riding Horses, Rode by All with Joy'; 'Pettigrove's 20th Century, Grand Golden Galloping Horses. The Ride to Suit All Ages. A Thrill of a Lifetime. The Pride of the South'; 'Swale Forrest's Grand Stud of Racing Horses and Flying Cockerels. The Greatest Sensation of the Century.' Which should remind us that all fairground decoration, whether pictorial or verbal, is an advertisement for its ride or show. A 1914 photograph of

Opposite page: Detail from rounding board
of George Whittle's Gallopers (above) and
of W. Ashley's Gallopers (below, left).
Below right: Detail of the Gavioli organ on
Sally Beach's Gallopers.

Page 38: Hermes motifs on booth fronts,
round stalls and Swirl and Waltzer rides.
By Edwin Hall and Freddie Fowle.
Page 39: Round stall decorations
employing variations on the 20th Century
Fox symbol, by Freddie Fowle and
imitators.

Charles Thurston's Great Show with its
120 key Marenghi organ in 1912.

Strickland's gallopers shows the rounding board decorated with a
blatant call for hire: 'Galas, School Festivals, Clubs, Fêtes . . .'.

By the turn of the century the fairground was as ornate as the music
halls and public houses with which it competed. Wonderfully carved
organs with automation figurines had been imported from Continental
dance halls to play in the centre of the rides, manufacturers such as
Marenghi had set up workshops in London, and with the help of the
wood carvers at Orton Sons & Spooner, the wildly burgeoning classical
forms of the organs had spread throughout the fairground. The power
of the organs to draw crowds was well understood by the showmen,
who incorporated them into the extravagantly fronted walk-up shows.
Coloured lights that flashed in time to the music were added and
together with the paraders and the pitch getter, guaranteed a good
crowd. The shows offered melodramas, circuses, bioscope shows,
menageries, and concert parties and the decoration of their massive
fronts took fairground baroque to its glorious limit, outshining the
most ornate music halls.

Contemporary with the shows were the switchbacks, mostly built by
Savages and sumptuously carved, gilded, and upholstered in velvet by
the Venetian craftsmen whom he had brought to his workshops in

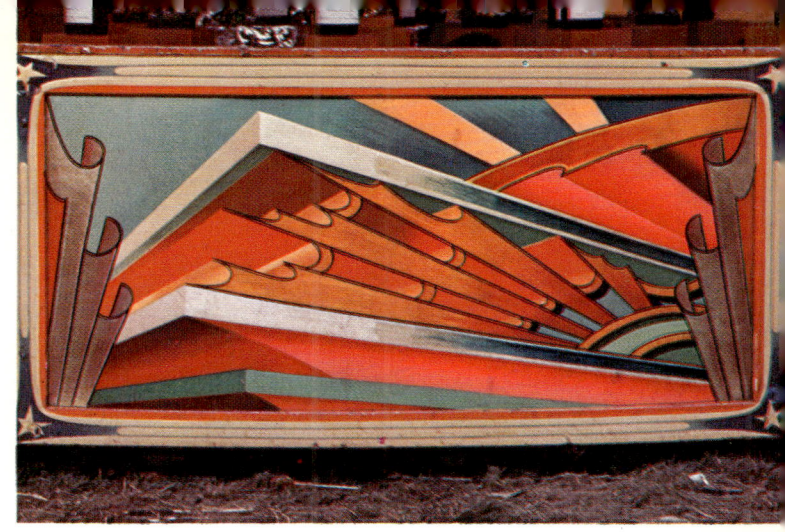

John Murphy's Scenic with imitation motorcars, built and decorated by Orton Sons & Spooner.

Early National Benzole symbol.

Mercer Car symbol.

Islington, London. The early rides carried chariot-shaped vehicles or gondolas often carved with portraits of royalty or current heroes. When motoring became popular, some of these were replaced by clever replicas of the latest automobiles. In 1909, for instance, Thurston's Gondolas became 'The White City Mountain Motors', though the caryatids and scenes of Venice were nevertheless retained.

During the brief reign of Edward VII (1901–1910), the English travelling fair was at its zenith. It is difficult to imagine the impression a large fair made on the public. The splendid shows, the glittering rides, the organs piping out popular melodies, must have presented a glamorous and exciting world, very different from the shabby hardworking lives of so many of the people who came to them. And by night everywhere reflected the naphtha flares – and sometimes there were real electric lights as well! Electricity brought great changes. By 1914 most switchbacks were being converted to electric traction and the removal of their large steam centre engines left gaps in the middle of the rides. The war and later the establishment of cinemas affected the bioscope shows and gradually their organs became available to be built into the centres of the switchbacks. Showmen added some scenery, a few fountains, or perhaps a waterfall and pond with real ducks, and the scenic railway was born.

As new scenics were built they grew larger and more fantastic. Gondolas and motor cars gave way to whales, dragons, dolphins, and peacocks and the rounding boards were heightened and painted with jungle scenes. The proscenium arches deepened to carry Neptune and some classical goddesses, painted to simulate statuary, which on this scale would have been too heavy to support and by now too expensive to commission. The scenics represent the last flowering of fairground baroque. But it became unprofitable to transport, build up, and dismantle fifty tons of low-relief, organ and mechanical effects and in 1928 the last of the scenics was built. By then showmen were facing the great depression and the baroque tradition of the decorations gave way to the airbrush techniques of the thirties. Art deco had arrived and fairground decorators, like designers and architects, absorbed its

White Bros. Ben Hur Speedway decorated
by Edwin Hall at Lakins.

quasi-geometrical styles and abstractions to give the fairground a
'futuristic' look.

This revolution was spawned in the workshops of Lakins, a firm of
showmen's builders and decorators, which had recently broken away
from Orton Sons & Spooner, By the early thirties the firm was claiming
the lion's share of the market and each ride bore the stamp of its young
chief decorator Edwin Hall. Trained as a traditional decorator, Hall
nevertheless found that many of his young assistants could not
decorate quickly enough in the old manner for the work to be
profitable. Reluctantly he devised a method of stencilled patterns that
could be easily copied and coloured by his assistants and were ideally
suited to the new streamlined rides coming into being.

The scenics were replaced by smaller, faster machines, some
imported from America, which sported in their centres just a simple
paybox and a panatrope to broadcast the latest hit records. First
came the Noah's Ark, which carried flat-carved animals to ride on,
and was decorated with jungle scenes. The screen success of *Ben Hur*
led to a brief re-introduction of classical motifs and to chariots
replacing animals. The proscenium arches were adorned with vastly

Detail of Botton's Dodgems at Battersea decorated by Freddie Fowle, top, and an Esso advertisement of 1954.

Opposite : The Esso tiger developed by Freddie Fowle decorating Traylen's Speedway and W. Nichol's Speedway, Shooting Gallery Fronts including two poor imitations of Fowle's Esso tiger, a traditional Bengal tiger and an heraldic lion by Fowle. Also an early neo-architectural classical lion motif.

enlarged copies of *The Charioteers*, a painting by a Victorian artist called Wagner. Edwin Hall made his copies from a squared-up postcard of the painting, and was soon able to complete a proscenium in two-and-a-half days from memory. This was no mean feat, because the proscenium was painted in sections and slotted together after it had left the workshop. Later in the thirties, an enterprising showman called Corrigan, who had noted the popularity of speedway racing, ordered a set of flat carved motorbikes to replace the animals on his Noah's Ark. Lakins built the ride and adopted the idea, for which Corrigan received a royalty. An excellent example of this evolution is White Bros. Ben Hur Speedway, photographed in 1939. Basically this is an old scenic with the original jungle rounding boards, a charioteer proscenium flanked by motorcyclists and motorbikes for the customers to ride on.

The introduction in the twenties of rides like the dodgems, the whip and its successor the swirl, the waltzer and the autodrome with their simply shaped metal cars, helped the new movement toward abstract 'futuristic' patterns. For these faster rides, Hall adapted brightly coloured and highly varnished popular symbols of speed. Two favourites were lightning flashes (the swirl became known as the 'lightning swirl') and the god Hermes or Mercury, symbol of the National Benzole Petroleum Company and the Mercer Car Company, as well as being the god of the fair and protector of travellers. Other devices bore wings in the same manner as the old AA badge or the symbol of Bentley Motor-cars. The winged disc, symbol of an Egyptian sun god possibly inspired by the opening of Tutankhamun's tomb in the twenties, became a winged wheel and decorated dogdems, racing cars, and Mont Blancs.

Later American rides like the moon rocket and the space ships were decorated, naturally enough, after the current interest in science fiction. Edwin Hall treated the subject humorously: he has a rocket landing in the eye of the moon, and cartoon-style characters flying into space, complete with pet dog. Another new ride, the caterpillar, suggested a lighthearted treatment and by the mid forties, fairs were alive with cartoon characters of the day; R A F types, G I S, W R A C S, and of course Walt Disney's growing family.

After the war, Hall's brother William and another of his assistants at Lakins, Freddie Fowle, set up their own firm of decorators. Fowle, the main designer of the team, developed Edwin Hall's motifs, adding new ones of his own, to create designs that have not only been imitated

20th Century Fox symbol anc, below, Freddie Fowle's 3D lettering on Botton's Supersonic Jets.

throughout the fairground, but borrowed by Bond Street artists like Peter Blake and Peter Phillips and designers like Binder, Edwards, and Vaughan. Like Edwin Hall, Fowle is a talented representational painter, as is demonstrated by the two giant lions flanking Botton's dodgems at Battersea Pleasure Gardens. Not untypically, these were inspired by an illustration in a small double-column advertisement for a safari film in an evening paper. Like a true 'pop' artist, Fowle un-selfconsciously uses mass media images, particularly the cinema and its advertising, as inspiration for his work. The 20th Century Fox symbol standing on a pedestal with searchlights in the sky behind, has inspired many a design for round stalls and booths. It is seen in most fairs in a variety of disguises. Sometimes it is a monolithic carved wing, sometimes a 3D lightning flash, sometimes massive architectural shapes and frequently it is plagiarized by other decorators, sometimes with amusing results.

The cinematic 3D craze in the fifties had a marked effect on Fowle's

Two examples of Freddie Fowle's treatment of cars on Irvin's Swirl and Botton's Waltzer.

Page 46 : Carved portraits of Harold Lloyd and Churchill decorating the cars on Billy Manning's Scenic. Portraits of Tito and Stalin from the war heroes who adorn J. Harvey's very patriotic Juvenile.

work. His lettering began to leap from the rides and his designs break out of their two-dimensional world, to express speed and energy. It is not surprising that he was attracted by the fifties poster of the Esso tiger leaping from the hoardings. Taking it much as it was, he made this symbol of power and speed work for waltzers, swirls, ghost trains, and other rides, sometimes giving it wings for even greater speed! Perhaps Fowle's greatest gift is his ability to express the movement and excitement of a ride in his motifs or lettering; the decoration of Botton's waltzer cars, for example, mimics perfectly the rotary movement of the ride. Fowle is not averse to using slogans as decoration, a device as old as the first showman getting up a pitch. Like the showman he tries to keep up to date; when he decorated Pat Collin's twist at Battersea he employed the 'hip' language of the day, e.g. 'It's a Gas' 'Yeah! Yeah! Yeah!' and 'Get with it. It's the Gear'. Even more dated now are the slogan banners on Harry Gray's swirl. Catchphrases from Wilfred Pickles (Have a Go Joe) and Tommy

STALIN

TITO

THE BIG SHOW HA[LL]

REDWARDS CHARIOT

R. Edwards & Sons Ltd. 68. Ferndale Rd. Swindon. Wilts.
Secty V Edwards   Plate 31-Oc-Oo-Oo

Detail of one of R. Edwards beautifully
lettered wagons.

Page 47: Panel originally from a Crazy
House or booth with a wire machine,
photographed as part of a round stall at
Nottingham Goose Fair.

Trinder (You Lucky People) decorate the ride together with a variety
of rhymes: 'Don't be Shy, Have a Try', 'Bring Your Girl, on the Swirl'.

Strangely, some of the best examples of sloganeering are to be found
around the edges of the fairground, particularly those fairs attended by
R. Edwards' rides and the beautifully decorated wagons that carry
them. Painted by a local Swindon signwriter employed by British Rail,
they use traditional coachwork colours of maroon, golden yellow, and
white but are a graphic feast worthy of the best designers in Britain.
Not only do they announce the arrival of the fair, but when everything
is loaded up and the fair moves on, the back of the last wagon bears the
message: 'Cheerio, We Hope to be Back Soon'.

Sadly today there are very few skilled decorators left, many recent
rides require little surface decoration, and anyhow the showmen cannot
often afford to redecorate their rides. However, there are still many
talented – and some plain hopeful – amateurs among the showmen
who continue to enrich the fairground with contemporary images and
unwittingly keep alive one of Britain's few remaining popular art forms.

Don't overlook the underground press

Herbert Jones

Any half-dozen active people can produce their own paper, as this takes no special journalistic or technical skills, opines one British example of the 'underground press'. Not many of all the hundreds of products in this genre of the Western press take the same 'instant journalism' approach, but many of them claim to be trend-setters in various ways. The claims, in their typographical and make-up aspect are here examined, with some reflections on the sociological significance of the challenge offered to the established daily newspapers and weeklies.

Illustrations in this article were engraved by Art Reprographic (London) Ltd, pages 52, 53, 54, *right* 55, 56, and 61 and by London & Provincial Reproduction Co. Ltd, pages 50, 51, *left* 55, 57, 59 and 60.

Thanks to the *OZ* trial, which dragged on for over five weeks in the summer of 1971, few people in Britain can be unaware of the existence of the 'underground press', although there must be wide differences of opinion as to what the term means. Because it suggests that the publications to which the label is applied are illegal, the term is a misleading one. There is also a tendency to assume that the underground press automatically includes pornography, which it does not. There is a separate underground sex press, but that is not our concern here. The underground press of the Western world embraces hundreds of little papers – little in financial status and usually in circulation – but it has one thing in common: dissatisfaction with things as they are.

Some of these papers have a comet-like existence, flashing on the scene with great brilliance and then disappearing, to endure long in the memory and become a legend. A few, like their astronomical counterparts, have a dateline significance and are used as a measure against which others are assessed and from which lessons are often to be learned.

In America the new radical press took its impetus in the early 1960s from the reaction to McCarthyism, from disillusionment with the Vietnam war, and from the general frustrations, confusions, and social tensions that were spreading over the entire continent. In France, the general strike and the student demonstrations in the streets of Paris in 1968 threw up a series of publications, some possessing a vigour that was sufficient to carry them on for long afterwards, and some still firmly established. Britain has always had a number of left-wing papers produced by small groups for a limited though committed readership, but *Private Eye*, *The Black Dwarf*, *The Red Mole*, and *OZ* introduced a new element of sophisticated satire.

Many explanations have been offered for the growth and apparent success of the underground press, but whether it created an entirely new audience or merely fulfilled the need of one brought about by social conditions must remain a matter of opinion. It existed, wrote Tony Palmer, in his book *The Trials of OZ*, 'because it believed that proper newspapers either ignored what was really happening or else distorted it . . . *Private Eye* indicated that there was much to be told that somehow, mystery upon mysteries, never reached the daylight of print . . . its challenge to other newspapers was simply that, frequently, it was better informed than they were'. Harold Evans, editor of *The Sunday Times*, said in a television interview that there was 'too much opinion and not enough news in the established press'. Some people believe that the trouble with the established press is that it has too little originality and that when one paper has a new idea all the other Fleet Street papers copy it. Others have sounded a warning note. C. Denis Hamilton, chairman and editor-in-chief of Times Newspapers, said at a conference in Copenhagen that the growth of the underground press was part of the growing competition facing established newspapers. Anthony Howard, now editor of the weekly *New Statesman*, said in a BBC programme that in face of the challenge from the alternative press 'the weeklies must not lose their nerve'. In France

THE PAPER THAT SAYS: GET THE TORIES OUT IN 1972!

Tribune

LABOUR'S INDEPENDENT WEEKLY	7p	Vol 36 No 18 May 5, 1972

NO SURRENDER!
To the Tory legal sanctions

IF THE Labour movement can maintain its unity, it can force the Conservative Government into a general election, suggested Vic Feather, general secretary of the TUC, at a May Day rally last weekend. Not one voice within the Labour movement will dissent from that sentiment, but many of them will ask, "How?"

Mr Feather did not have any immediate answers. But underlying his words was an acceptance that the trade union movement is now forced directly into the political arena. The Conservative Government has seen to that. The introduction of the Industrial

press and other media in recruiting "public opinion" to their side.

Furthermore there will almost certainly be some backsliding by a number of unions (like the Union of Shop Distributive and Allied Workers which last weekend voted in favour of staying on the Government-inspired register). Such evidence will be used by the press to embroider and exploit the disunity within the trade union movement.

So what is needed is a positive answer to all those inside the Labour movement who ask: how can the movement force a general

which the Conservative Party has carefully laid. For the last two months it has been running an all-out campaign to persuade the public that, if an election comes, it is to be fought on the issue of whether it is the elected Government or the trade unions which should run the country. As every political sophisticate knows, that is not the issue, but it is one on which the Conservative Party — with the gleeful aid of the media — would be delighted to fight.

Of course we want a general election — but we also want to win a general election. Some of

this is a short-cut to political suicide. To throw down all our defences at this moment when they are under such severe attack would drive the British working class into a state of deep despair.

It follows from this that the Labour movement must take up the Conservative challenge at a political level. To do this it is vital that there should be a united policy of opposition to the Government's attack. The best way to bring this about would be by a speedy recall of the Trades Union Congress followed by a recall conference of the Labour Party. The first would ensure that

EEC VOTE NO!

DON'T BETRAY THE INTERNEES!

How big an anti-EEC vote in Ireland's referendum?

Freedom
anarchist weekly   9D.

FEBRUARY 14 1970 Vol 31 No 5

VOTE—WHAT FOR?

AT ANY TIME during the next fourteen months the Prime Minister may announce the date for the General Election. As the leader of the party governing this country, it is up to Harold Wilson to decide on the time, as and when it suits their chances.

Having done so, the whole circus will once again roll into town, with the candidates of all parties, vieing with each other for the support of the public. For them it is an important time for, depending upon the number of crosses placed against their names, it will determine their whole life for the next five years.

For the wooed electorate, the chances are that very little change will take place in the following five years, no matter which candidates receive the most votes. Elections for them are but a brief period of illusion that they are deciding who governs the country. It is the only time that the public is asked its opinion and to actually participate.

Having gained victory many candidates are not seen again until the following election and the party that forms the Government proceeds to

election, the public is wooed with promises for this, that and the other. It is a time when all sorts of restrictions are lifted and people are given a false impression that everything is rosy. Already the creating of this impression has started with the lifting of the travel allowance restrictions, and the forthcoming budget is likely to give further spending power to the public. However, Wilson's dilemma is to achieve a balance. He cannot afford too much of a give-away budget, because, together with the wage increases, it could affect the trading position and therefore the balance of payments.

From now on all parties will be playing politics. Each one will be seeking popularity with electoral bribes. The uncertainty about the date will also create tension and

couragement and their only chance seems to be in holding on to power for the full constitutional period.

Already the ground on which the election will be fought has been staked out by the Tories—taxation, imposed wage settlements, law and order and immigration. In general they are trying to put over a tough image against the so-called 'permissive society'. Most of this is just emotion, using the public's irritation and frustration for electoral gain, for there are plenty of harsh laws already on the statute book to deal with demonstrators and to strengthen these would mean restrictions on our liberties.

Unlike many on the 'left', we do not think the Labour Government has failed. Before the 1964 and 1966 elections we said that Labour's priorities were with the economy of

Whichever party gets hold of the reins of power, they will put the economic system before the social needs of people. Whichever party wins the next election, legislation will be introduced to restrict wage increases and an attempt will be made to curtail the bargaining power of the unions.

As a trading country, with a possible recession in America, cost per unit of production has got to be controlled. Tough action will be required and this seems to be an economic fact of life in the present-day capitalist society. However no politician is going to say this in public, just as during the March 1966 election, no Labour MP said that in the July a full freeze on wages would become law. Prior to an election all governments (that is those that have to go through these

returned to power, there will be little difference made to the lives of the majority of people. If anything, the two main parties are moving towards a more authoritarian position and those who argue for voting for the lesser evil are only fooling themselves. It is up to the individuals to free themselves from this illusion. The conscious refusal to vote is a positive step and a sign of social responsibility, because one cares too much to give power to the politicians and the state.

A period prior to a general election is a good time to mount a campaign to propagate anarchism, using the refusal to vote as its main theme. Many people are becoming disillusioned with politicians and their parties. More and more are turning to themselves and are taking direct action to achieve demands, whether in the area of industry, housing or universities. Manchester comrades have started by duplicating a leaflet and in London posters have been printed. We shall also be printing anti-election articles which could be used as leaflets.

The politicians have started their

the brilliant *Le Monde* declared: 'the press is sick, the press is dying'.

It will be helpful in this look at the design of the underground press, to divide it into two broad categories: the older, straight, political papers and those that concentrate on cultural or philosophical aspects or have specialist interests, such as rock music, sexual freedom, and so on. Generally the straight political papers are fairly conventional in appearance, most of them taking the tabloid, or half-sheet newspaper as their model. When Francis Meynell became involved in the production of *The Communist* (a weekly newspaper) in the twenties, he specified Caslon Old Face for headings – and today the journalists who

Part of the front page of three British publications – *Tribune*, the anarchist journal *Freedom*, and *The Red Mole* – and one American socialist paper, *Bulletin*.

Bulletin
weekly organ of the workers league

VOLUME EIGHT NUMBER FORTY 249   JUNE 12, 1972   103   FIFTEEN CENTS

Nixon Takes Pay From Workers' Pockets

STRIKE THE BOARD!

The Government's offensive against the working class and its trade unions has entered into a critical stage. Nixon—acting in the interests of the employing class—has ordered a frontal assault on the trade unions with the objective of smash-

The Red Mole

No. 41 1 May 1972   Price 7½ p.

produce *The Morning Star* would not be offended if they won awards for the best-designed newspaper, meaning best on strictly traditional lines, as this newspaper's predecessor the *Daily Worker* did. *Tribune*, barely 'underground', is an example of a well-established periodical of the left which has changed its style from the plain and decent, three-columns-to-the-page quarto weekly review, to a boldly displayed, completely styleless, tabloid newspaper similar to many trade union journals and hundreds of advertising news-sheets whose authors imagine that the form will persuade the readers to devour the contents as avidly as they do those of the strongly tabloid, mass circulation daily newspaper *The Sun*.

With *The Red Mole*, boasting an editorial board headed by the redoubtable Tariq Ali, one might have expected some typographical fireworks. However, apart from the quite dramatic poster technique of the front page, we are given a fairly commonplace use of sans serif headings with unjustified text. *Rouge* is its ideological French counterpart and is practically identical in style. *The Red Mole* is almost a prototype and a few facts about its production may be of interest. The fortnightly journal of the International Marxist League, the British section of the Fourth International, it started publication in March 1970 with a circulation of 6,000 which has grown to 10,000. It has one full-time and one part-time journalist. A professional designer makes up each issue, using IBM output and transfer headings. It is printed on a Solna 125, and production costs of a twelve-page issue are about £300

plus £150 for salaries. At a selling price of $7\frac{1}{2}$p, it just about breaks even.

    The Black Dwarf has some striking covers and the short-lived *Seven Days* can claim the credit for printing some of the most startling photographs of current events ever seen in the British press. There is little else in their design that is remarkable. The same can be said about the American socialist papers *Bulletin* and *The Militant* although they are slightly more professional looking. *Freedom*, the anarchist journal

Above and opposite, the front pages of three British journals and one French ; and, right, the cover of the monthly publication *Inside Story*.

53

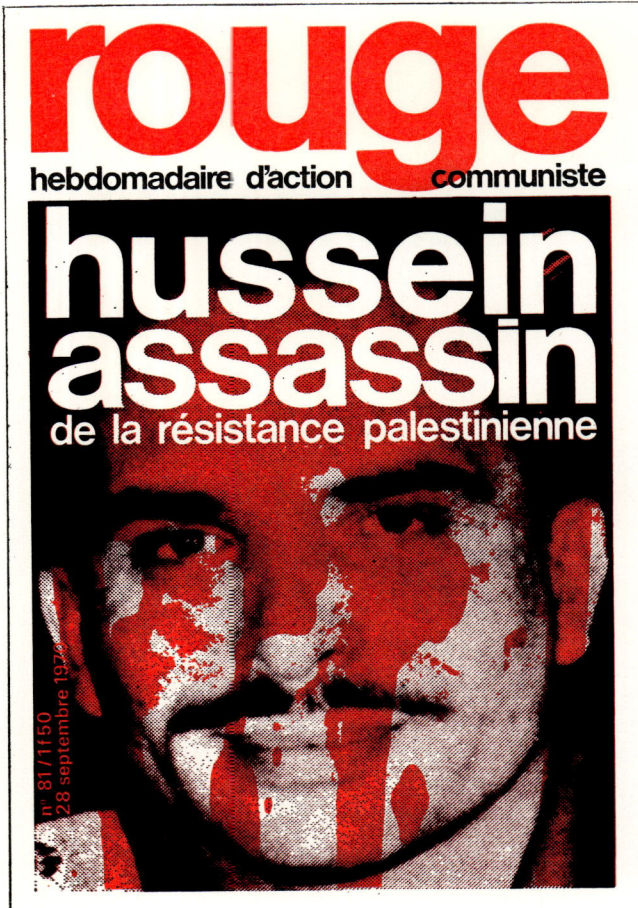

Front page of the French communist weekly *Rouge* and of the short-lived British journal *7 Days*.

which has been in the business by far the longest and has by far the most radical political outlook, sets its type squared up, seldom goes above 60 point for its headlines, is mostly unillustrated, eschews crossheads, never uses swearwords, and looks more sober than any issue of the 'quality' Sunday paper *The Observer*. Most of the straight political journals stick more or less closely to already well-tried variations of newspaper format. They experiment little, if at all, and never surpass in technical competence the best of the established press, though this can sometimes be due to sheer lack of money.

Only when the underground press adopts the illustrated magazine concept does it really seem to be attempting to break new ground. In the 1920s artists like McKnight Kauffer drew freely on the work of post-Impressionist and abstract painters such as Léger, Braque, and Picasso to develop a style which, together with the influence of the Bauhaus in typography, completely changed the look of commercial printing. Today, in the designs of the underground press, it is easy to see the influence of op, pop, and other contemporary schools of painters. Lichtenstein, Warhol, and Allen Jones are among the artists whose work has impressed its approach to design on printing as clearly and as emphatically as did their predecessors nearly half a century ago.

This is how Ethel Grodzins Romm in her book *The Open Conspiracy* describes one of the most talked about underground papers in America, *The San Francisco Oracle:* 'It was mystical and magical. It preached salvation through drugs. Issues 7, 8, and 9 sold more than 750,000

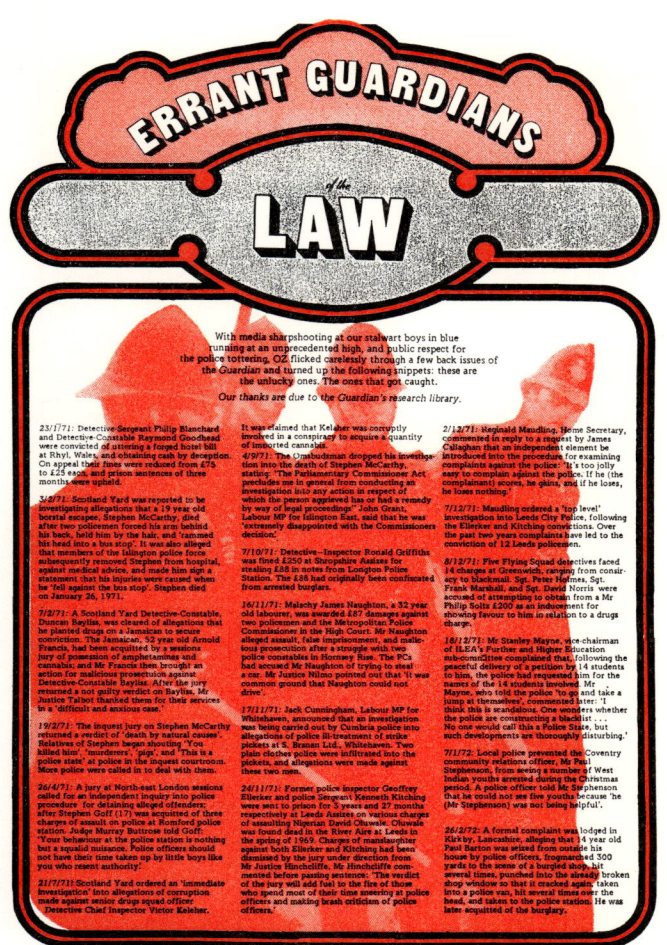

Inside page from *OZ* and the front page of the University of London Union journal, *Sennet*.

copies. The *Oracle*'s exuberant experimentation with layout and split-fountain was the trend-setter for later protest papers and influenced poster art and magazine and advertising layout for the next few years. Content was erotic and adolescent but the editors never asked to have their paper judged by content. Each *Oracle* page was designed first for composition. The decorative area was given to an artist while the prose or poetry went to the typist who patiently set it inside the drawn pattern. The text floated up the page in bubbles or poured over it in rainbow spray.'

Old hands in printing and publishing, or anyone who has done a little research in this field, may smile at the trend-setting claim, since almost all the pictorial or patterned effects achieved by the *Oracle* can be seen in nineteenth-century jobbing work. Looking at the psychedelic designs of today, one is also immediately reminded of the Art Nouveau of the last century. In 1900 John Southward wrote: 'A word may be said in protest against the increasing practice of printing the text of magazines and even of books in coloured inks. It is quite a recent innovation, but is now degrading otherwise excellent printing. The use of colours in book work is not a mark of progress, but a violation of the recognised canons of typographic art'. In Britain his words fell on deaf ears so far as Horatio Bottomley was concerned, for in 1902 he printed his newspaper, *The Sun*, in green ink, to distinguish it from its competitors. Time passes and we have the Dadaists, parodied by Philip Owen in his novel of the twenties *The Hobohemians*:

'Sleeping in one corner was the poet from Antwerp who had exchanged agitation in the streets for upheaval in typography. His manifestoes to the masses concerning the new poetry were printed upside down or sideways or both in obviously important passages. This, he maintained, drew the attention of the people to them.'

In Britain *OZ* is the most ambitiously presented product of the underground press. I put to Richard Neville, the editor, the point that the overriding aim of typography as regards text matter is legibility and that the use of black ink on white paper provides the most likely means of achieving that result. He simply did not agree that this had been proved in any way. On the contrary, he asked, who would not prefer a colour television set to the black-and-white version? There had been accidents he conceded. Indeed. It sometimes seemed as if all the elements of printing were put in a bag, so to speak, and given a good shaking. However, what came out was quite often an astonishingly compelling synthesis, albeit accidentally achieved. More important, it was one which appealed to the restless audience at which it was aimed. This is the heart of the matter – the understanding of the new culture of youth which holds, among other things, that it has to shock to get attention, to be obscene to be believed. Perhaps the most extreme examples of shock tactics come from France in the form of *Zinc* and *L'Egout* (The Sewer), which in a juvenile context might be called comics since they consist only of drawings with all text hand drawn, a fact proudly announced on the cover of *L'Egout*. Inside this paper,

Front pages of *Private Eye* (original in two colours), above, and of the American bi-weekly *Changes*, and the French publication *L'Egout*.

Part of the front page of each of four
newspaper-format journals, three American
and one, *The Black Dwarf*, published
in Britain.

MAY 5, 1972   25 CENTS   VOLUME 36/NUMBER 17

THE MILITANT

A SOCIALIST NEWSWEEKLY/PUBLISHED IN THE INTERESTS OF THE WORKING PEOPLE

Nixon vows more bombing
Protest on May 4!

—page 6

THE BLACK PANTHER

INTERCOMMUNAL NEWS SERVICE 25 cents

VOL. VIII NO. 3   Copyright © 1971 by Huey P. Newton   SATURDAY, APRIL 8, 1972

PUBLISHED WEEKLY   THE BLACK PANTHER PARTY   MINISTRY OF INFORMATION BOX 2967, CUSTOM HOUSE SAN FRANCISCO, CA 94126

"THIS WILL TIDE ME OVER"

The Black Dwarf

Established 1817 Vol. 14 No. 23   October 1st 1969   Fortnightly 1/6

If the people at the bottom of the pile stopped grinning and let go, what would happen?

thevillage VOICE

35¢

Great Britain   30 Pence
France   2.50 fr.
Mexico   5 Pesos

a nine-letter word for &%$!—page 22

Copyright © 1972, The Village Voice Inc.   THE WEEKLY NEWSPAPER OF NEW YORK   ● Vol. XVII, No. 24 ● New York, N. Y. ● June 16-22, 1972

Myrna Loy
**Repressed
years of**

Opposite page: miniature reproduction of a fully-opened sheet of *Rolling Stone* (original size 430×570 mm, 17×22½ in) showing the two 'front page' alternatives.

with its nihilistic view of late capitalism, there is nothing funny however.

What the underground press looks like is a sore point with many critics. In an article in *The Listener* about the alternative press, D. A. N. Jones complains: 'The *IT* representative on "Man Alive" said that he had heard a middle-aged businessman telling his friends that he was going home to read *OZ* in the toilet; he suggested that "in that close secretive environment", the paper's message would "get across" to the businessman, and the writer could "relate to him at that level".' 'But surely', Mr Jones went on, 'the main point of the anecdote is that the businessman would be ashamed to be seen reading *OZ* in public not so much because of the verbal content but because of the look of the thing.' That is a view which appears to do little justice to the businessman and somehow to confuse, deliberately or otherwise, the political with the sex underground.

As well as the extremes of style there are the extremes of resources. From America we have two interesting cases of underground papers turning into commercial successes. *The Village Voice*, once an occasional six-page paper of protest, is now a ninety-six page weekly packed with advertising and a toned-down editorial. *Rolling Stone* started out talking to the young about music with modest success and now appears as an eighty-page fortnightly filled to the brim with the sales talk of the record companies and boasting a worldwide circulation reaching out to half a million. Neither of them is more than competent typographically but *Rolling Stone* has devised a method of packaging itself that has been copied several times. Printed as a folio measuring 430×285 mm ($17 \times 11\frac{1}{4}$ inches) it makes up the last page of text as two quarto pages, the right-hand one being a title-page. The whole paper can be folded as a quarto, a point which must surely make it more acceptable for display at news stands where space is at a premium in almost every big city in the world. A clear case of 'if you can't lick 'em, take 'em over'.

Time Out is a bright light in the underground with an interesting history. For many years the weekly publication *What's On* listed for Londoners and others the films, plays, exhibitions, and restaurants in town. It did the job well enough, and even threw in a very *avant-garde* art critic. Into this monopolised field burst *Time Out*. It gave the basic data but also commented on the social and political scene with considerable revolutionary flair, and it has never looked back. An example of the influence that a comparatively insignificant publication

ROLLING STONE

'All the News that Fits'

Issue No. 106
April 13, 1972

Judee Sill is a songwriter, and she has a tale to tell: It's an exorcism of low-riding smack-shooting ghosts. See page 24.

WILL MARIJUANA BE LEGALIZED IN CALIFORNIA?

BY PATRICK SULLIVAN

SAN FRANCISCO — 1972 may turn out to be more than just another presidential election year for California voters. This time they may have a chance to decide whether the use of marijuana is a crime.

A statewide campaign called the California Marijuana Initiative has been organized to place on the November ballot a measure which, if approved, would wipe out penalties for the personal use of cannabis by anyone 18 or older. The organizers of the drive are, in their words, "a broad-based group of physicians, attorneys, civil libertarians and everyday Californians." The state coordinator is Robert Ashford, 28, a Harvard educated lawyer.

A campaign with similar intentions failed to generate any momentum several years ago, but the 1972 effort appears to be a strong one. And the energy is not confined to California. Efforts are underway in Washington, Oregon and Arizona to put pot on the ballot.

More than 75,000 persons (registered voters) have signed the California petition in the first six weeks of the campaign. The organizers have until July 3rd, the deadline to file 326,408 valid signatures with the state registrar of voters to qualify the measure for the ballot.

Petition circulators are fanning out to office buildings, campuses, downtown streets and shopping centers to obtain signatures. On a recent Sunday a young woman petitioner picked up an easy dozen signatures during a ten-minute tour of a suburban playground, where young mothers were sitting in the sun while their children played.

Pat Farrington, assistant coordinator of the California campaign, would have fit directly in the suburban park scene. She is a mother of three. "I feel confident we're going to make the ballot,"

she said at the CMI office in San Francisco's Marina district, an affluent neighborhood with views of the Golden Gate Bridge from almost every corner.

"The Marina just does not seem like the place where a bunch of people would locate to work on cannabis law reform. On one of the main drags, Union Street, there are a lot of singles bars, boutiques, antique shops and coffee houses, and every fourth car seems to be someone's burnt orange Porsche with a ski rack. But it is five years later and three miles away from the Haight and Golden Gate Park, where bands used to play for free

—Continued on Page 16

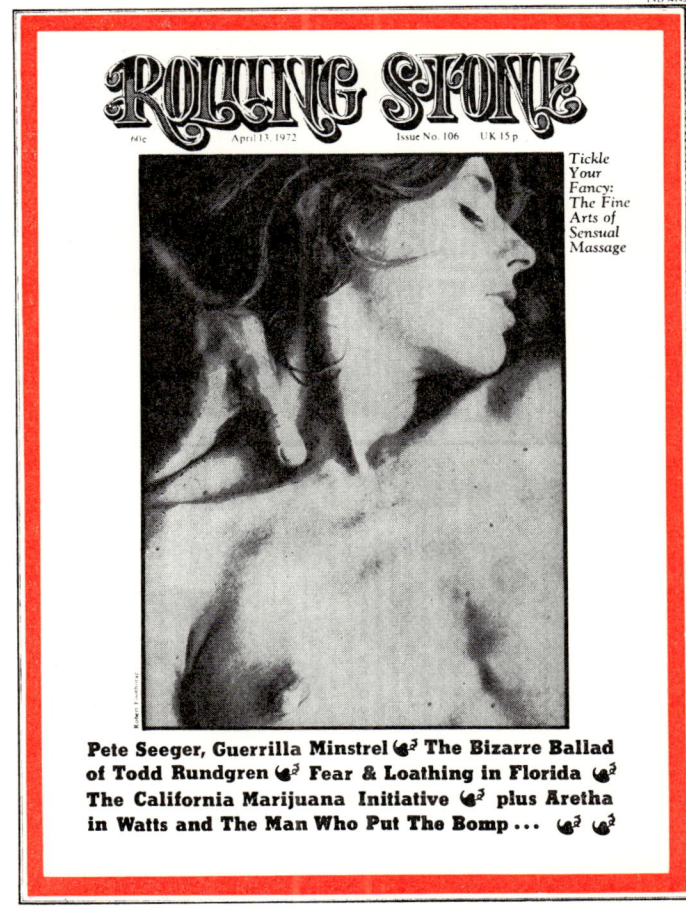

ROLLING STONE
60¢   April 13, 1972   Issue No. 106   UK 15p

Tickle Your Fancy: The Fine Arts of Sensual Massage

Pete Seeger, Guerrilla Minstrel 🌿 The Bizarre Ballad of Todd Rundgren 🌿 Fear & Loathing in Florida 🌿 The California Marijuana Initiative 🌿 plus Aretha in Watts and The Man Who Put The Bomp ... 🌿 🌿

Both *Crawdaddy* and *it* follow the pattern of *Rolling Stone*.

can have was provided in its issue of 8 September 1972; the press, it claimed, was not reporting the trial of the Stoke Newington Eight. *The Guardian* on the following day printed a letter from Dr Alex Comfort on this subject and on 10 September the BBC had Dr Comfort talking about the case in its programme 'The World this Weekend'.

It is at the other end of the scale, where money is short, that one comes across a presentation which shows that, as ever, necessity is the mother of invention. In this area *Inside Story* manages to make a readable job with a little Letraset and a lot of well-thumped-out-typewriter. This existentialist attitude to printing as a means to an end comes out well in a note from *Come Together*, put out by the Camden Gay Liberation Front in London. It reads: 'How to make a Newspaper: Any GLF Group with half a dozen active people can produce their own paper. It takes no special journalistic or technical skills. We set aside a weekend and two other days to work on this *Come Together*. At one time there were 2 people around, but mostly just 6 to 8. During this time most of the articles were written, and all typing, artwork and paste-up done. You don't need any leaders. All decisions are made by the people there at the time. Here are some technical hints:

ACTION

N° 34 ● MARDI 26 NOVEMBRE 1968 ● PRIX : 0,50 F ● REALISE AU SERVICE DES COMITES D'ACTION ● ACTION : 52, RUE GALANDE, PARIS-5°, Tél. 633-76-61 et 633-26-67

LES GAUCHISTES EXPLIQUENT :

LE CAPITAL A PEUR
LA BOURGEOISIE VEUT SA REVANCHE
LES TRAVAILLEURS DOIVENT PAYER
DE GAULLE LACHE SES FLICS
NOUS NE MARCHONS PAS

Front page of a typical issue of the French journal *Action*, printed in two colours in newspaper format.

(1) This paper was printed by the photolitho method. That means that you yourselves lay out the copy exactly as you want the finished product to look, and it is reproduced photographically. (2) Copy generally includes words, photos and drawings. Words can be typed on an ordinary typewriter (as here), preferably with a new black ribbon. For added professionalism, use an IBM typesetter (try your local underground paper). Decide in advance on column widths. Headings can be done in Letraset, or drawn. Use black ink, preferably Indian. (3) Paste copy onto white card, at lease double page size, using Cow gum. Draw double page outline in very pale blue. Leave at least $\frac{1}{2}''$ margin around each page, except centre spread. Page size must be established with printers in advance. Last minute drawing can be done directly on card. Photos should *not* be pasted down. Keep separate and mark photos and appropriate spaces.'

This note on instant journalism goes on to say that 4,000 copies of an eight-page paper $15\frac{1}{2} \times 12$ in. would cost £75. At 5p a copy the publishers of *Come Together* stand to make a gay little profit, if they sell out.

The underground press has transformed university papers in Britain and America both in form and content. In its review of John Birmingham's book *Our Time is Now*, a collection of articles from high school underground newspapers, the *Chicago Sunday Times* said that 'this new perspective . . . may change the face of America itself'. The paper put out by the University of London Union, *Sennet*, contains articles on the conditions and wages of women cleaners, the abortion racket, and an account of Derry's 'Bloody Sunday' by three eye-witnesses from the London School of Economics, containing information not printed in any British newspaper.

It is impossible to put a limit to the development of the underground press, either as regards its sponsors or the style of production. At the moment the category most likely to grow is perhaps the neighbourhood paper, though it remains to be seen how long the current urge to produce such papers will last. Perhaps changes in normal newspaper publishing – more local newspapers, more local radio – will provide the kind of communication, less authoritative in tone, that people want. Even though the underground press has so far brought about no revolution in the art of printing (whatever it has achieved in other directions), it is certain that no future history of the press will be complete if it fails to deal with the most impassioned and challenging use made of it in our time.

Twenty-five years of the Folio Society

Peter Guy

A celebration of twenty-five years of book production by the Folio Society, and an attempt to assess the overall achievement in its production, design, and illustrative aspects.

The illustrations insets facing page 64 and page 70 were contributed by Curwen Press Ltd and W. & J. Mackay Ltd respectively. Paper for both was supplied by William Sommerville & Son Ltd.

The Folio Society recently celebrated twenty-five years of existence. For a book club whose aim is the production of books to a high standard of design and manufacture, this relative longevity is in itself a cause for congratulation. How far in achieving this success has its original aim 'to produce editions of the world's great literature in a format worthy of the contents, at a price within the reach of everyman' been realized?

The Society has never been content merely to produce 'shelf furniture'. There is a high proportion of the major classics (and here the texts are chosen with care) but the editorial policy has been widened to include lesser-known works of importance, new translations, unpublished eye-witness accounts of history in the making, memoirs – in fact original publishing of a high order. This careful editorial balance must be borne in mind in any consideration of the Society's design and production, for the texts are regarded as the *raison d'être* for the books' physical form. This formula, which accounts for no small part of the Society's success, does not, however, allow for more than two twentieth-century works at most in each programme, and thus the overwhelming majority of its books, having an allusive quality in design, appear in firmly traditional form.

The price a member pays for his edition is seldom much more than he would spend on a more pedestrian offering available through the trade. The Society has been concerned to present value for money and this, combined with the basic tenet that the text should be presented without distraction and in its most readable form, has prevented its editions from becoming the lavish portfolios with peripheral text which so often pass for fine editions. One of the reasons for consistency here is that design has, with very few exceptions, been carried out within the house. A record of the personalities involved, together with other historical data and illustrations, is to be found in *Folio 21* and *Folio 25* published on those anniversaries by the Society.

Partly for economy and partly for convenience, the formats have mostly been standard crown, demy, medium, and royal octavos with demy sometimes in narrower and sometimes in shorter variations. Bastard formats and the occasional quarto have been used where desirable and the selection has been usually unobjectionable except possibly with the poetry titles for which crown octavo became almost standard. This is curious, for surely poetry, more than any other form of the printed word, demands that the shape of the page be carefully considered in relation to the area of the space occupied by the words.

The Society has seldom bought print abroad; when it has done so it has almost always been for specific purposes – restrictions on print in post-war England, the quest for collotype, and direct copperplate printing for illustrations and so on. Therefore text type-faces have usually been selected from the range available among the best British book printers, and very largely from the Monotype repertoire. The choice has been governed by the practicalities of availability and suitability for production as well as aesthetic preferences. The majority of texts are set in sizes slightly larger than are to be found in books from the more distinguished British publishing houses. Margins, too, are usually slightly larger and almost invariably in conventional proportions. Occasionally, however, the Society (which seems, for some reason, to have an antipathy to really thin papers) has resorted to uncomfortably small type sizes to avoid unduly bulky books for long texts. A detailed analysis of the Society's use of text faces was made in *Monotype Newsletter 84*, from which one may conclude that if the Society's designers have not been consistent in their choices, neither have their reactions been reflex. Yet a cavalier approach to the marriage of text and type has not prevented some faces from seldom being put to bed – Lutetia and Dante for instance.

The Society's usual adherence to renaissance principles of disposition may partly account for the relative failure of too high a proportion of its departures into asymmetry; the Brontë series for instance and *A Portrait of the Artist as a Young Man* have a rather half-hearted air. On too many occasions, the text is set out according to traditional proportions while the prelims seem to be a last-minute concession to the twentieth century; there is a failure to consider the entire typographic treatment as a unity. As yet only one title, *The Trial*, has appeared with unjustified setting and one in a sans serif face, *Brave New World*, set in Univers Light (Monotype Series 685). In matters of display the Society has been frequently adventurous though seldom intrepid. One or two of its intended *jeux d'esprit* have been a little solemn – the way in which the arabesque is used in *At the Court of the Borgia* may seem a trifle heavy – yet others have succeeded well. Display in more serious mood, as in *A Journal of the Terror*, has been suitably impressive in its restraint. In this instance the rococo ornament is effective without the whole design suggesting pastiche – a snare which the Society has mostly, though not always, avoided. These criticisms notwithstanding, there is not a Folio Society volume which does not set out the author's text clearly and lucidly, an admirable record for a

Opposite page:
Chapter opening from
Merchant Venturers.

existence is the original illustration of adult books. The list of artists is long and impressive: Edward Ardizzone, Michael Ayrton, Edward Bawden, John Bratby, Eric Fraser, Barnett Freedman, Robert Gibbings, Duncan Grant, Joan Hassall – the list runs on alphabetically with equal distinction. These artists have been given the opportunity to illustrate great and small masterpieces of literature. In doing so, in widely differing styles and techniques, they have shown that there is still vigour in the tradition of book illustration and demonstrated to a new generation that at its best it can illuminate and complement even the greatest texts. Of course the standard has been uneven, but the less happy instances have more often been the result of an unsuccessful bold approach rather than of timidity. Even during its first year the Society produced some notable work; Edward Bawden made a gloriously imaginative set of twelve six-colour lithographs for *Gulliver's Travels to Lilliput and Brobdingnag.* The richness and subtlety of the medium were combined with a powerful and witty draftsmanship eminently suited to Swift's text. Four months later *Dr Jekyll and Mr Hyde* appeared with brush-drawn illustrations in two colours by Mervyn Peake, his vital line reproduced by letterpress. By the twelfth publication, the media used also included pen and pencil drawings, wood engravings, scraper-board, and copper engravings reproduced by collotype.

The tradition of diversity of style and technique was thus early established. The following years saw further successes .The Society became particularly strong in its wood-engraved illustration, occasionally printing from the wood, but more usually from electros. A natural concern in commissioning work has been to avoid the obvious in both choice of artist and the artist's approach to the text. In retrospect, however, it is difficult to think of Joan Hassall as anything but the obvious illustrator for Jane Austen: her superb engravings made the Society's edition one of the most delightful collected works of that author. Derrick Harris produced three joyfully witty sets for *Joseph Andrews, Humphry Clinker,* and *Tom Jones,* and one wonders if the Society would have looked further for illustrators of the eighteenth-century English novel if it had not been for his untimely death. Frank Martin was not so happy with this period but produced sensitive and deeply thought-out engravings for *Scarlet and Black*, which retained all the ease and fluency of the pen-drawn line while still deriving a crispness and power from the quality of the wood. Despite the fact that the medium is slow, expensive (the price of boxwood for a substantial text is about £30) and unfashionable, young engravers have been coming

DRAKE'S RAID ON CADIZ

Anonymous

Sir Francis Drake had already left behind him his brilliant career as a lone privateer, or pirate. On his devastating raid on the West Indies in 1585–6, and all his later voyages, he was a naval officer commanding powerful fleets. But, except in battle with the Armada, he was still expected to bring home a profit, for the expeditions, however official, were always financed by private subscribers. The Queen contributed by lending her ships, and she too expected a profit. For Cadiz, London privateering merchants supplied eight well-armed ships and two pinnaces, which they had fitted out to raid Spanish shipping, and they were a valuable addition to the fleet, but they were half-independent and left Drake as soon as it suited them knowing that they would get their share of all the plunder.

The ships which Philip was gathering were still scattered among various Spanish and Portuguese harbours. Drake's orders were to destroy as many as he could, to disrupt the preparations in general, and to take valuable prizes.

A brief relation of the notable service performed by Sir Francis Drake upon the Spanish Fleet prepared in the Road of Cadiz: and of his destroying of 100 sail of barks; passing from thence all along the coast to Cape Sacre, where also he took certain forts: and so to the mouth of the River of Lisbon, and thence crossing over to the isle of Saint Michael surprised a mighty carrack, called the *Saint Philip*, coming out of the East India, which was the first of that kind that ever was seen in England: performed in the year 1587.

HER MAJESTY, being informed of a mighty preparation by sea begun in Spain for the invasion of England, by good advice of her grave and prudent Council thought it expedient to prevent the same. Whereupon she caused a fleet of some 30 sails to be rigged and furnished with all things necessary. Over that fleet she appointed General Sir Francis Drake (of whose manifold former good services she had sufficient proof), to whom she caused four ships of her Navy Royal to be delivered, to wit, the *Bonaventure* wherein himself went as General, the *Lion*, under the conduct of Master William Borough,

Wood Engravings by Derrick Harris
for *Tom Jones* (above)
and Peter Reddick
for Thomas Hardy's
The Mayor of Casterbridge (right)

One of Lynton Lamb's illustrations
for *The Compleat Angler*

Two drawings by John Lawrence
for *The Diary of a Nobody*

serious determination, and was equal even to encounter her father. They walked off, utterly heedless of Mr Rushworth's repeated question of, 'Shall I go too? Had not I better go too? Will not it be right for me to go too?' but they were no sooner through the door than Henry Crawford undertook to answer the anxious inquiry, and encouraging him by all means to pay his respects to Sir Thomas without delay, sent him after the others with delighted haste.

Fanny was left with only the Crawfords and Mr Yates. She had been quite overlooked by her cousins; and as her own opinion of her claims on Sir Thomas's affection was much too humble to give her any idea of classing herself with his children, she was glad to remain behind and gain a little breathing time. Her agitation and alarm exceeded all that was endured by the rest, by the right of a disposition which not even innocence could keep from suffering. She was nearly fainting: all her former habitual dread of her uncle was returning, and with it compassion for him and for almost every one of the party on the development before him—with solicitude on Edmund's account indescribable. She had found a seat, where in excessive trembling she was enduring all these fearful thoughts, while the other three, no longer under any restraint, were giving vent to their feelings of vexation, lamenting over such an unlooked-for premature arrival as a most

133

forward with an equal mastery of technique – Peter Reddick, Garrick Palmer (with a particularly remarkable series for *Three Stories* by Herman Melville), and John Lawrence.

It was John Lawrence who undertook the daunting task of re-illustrating *The Diary of a Nobody*. Weedon Grossmith's illustrations, almost inseparable from the text, had given Mr Pooter his well-defined visual form but their draftsmanship leaves very much to be desired. The new interpretation was remarkably successful – the same hapless Pooter recreated in a controlled, vigorous line. Line-drawings have been commissioned for a wide variety of texts from Lynton Lamb's *Compleat Angler* to John Bratby's *Horse's Mouth* and Felix Topolski's *War and Peace*. Usually these have been printed by letterpress line-blocks with the text, but in Charles Raymond's elegant evocation of the twenties for *The Great Gatsby* the extreme delicacy and precision of line was produced by photo-offset, the plates wrapped into the text.

Lithography has meant autographic techniques – drawing on film for contacting down to the plate or on transfer paper. Beside the Bawden *Gulliver* may stand Barnett Freedman's *Ghost Stories* as a fine use of the medium in two colours. Another outstanding example is Charles Keeping's *All Quiet on the Western Front* where, unbelievably, he managed to heighten the terrors of the text. In addition to his gift for dramatic composition he is also a skilful and inventive craftsman when he draws on film, which is a material inviting experiment. Clarke Hutton used a wide range of methods for treating the surface of the film in his series for *Villette*, as did Anthony Colbert for *Jane Eyre*. Artists new to the medium do not always exploit its possibilities to the full; some find it unsympathetic while others who draw with a rather taut line can be almost afraid of the freedom afforded them.

Until recently, the various intaglio methods were reproduced by collotype and in consequence lost a good deal of their immediacy. Nevertheless, delightful work was produced in this way until, in 1969, it at last became possible to use a direct plate process perfected by security printers in Budapest. This technique, which has been widely used by Hungarian artists, was used for the first time in Britain by Nigel Lambourne for an edition of *The Georgics*. Lambourne's versatility as an illustrator is evident in many Folio Society editions and it was he who produced abstract photograms for Kafka's *The Trial*. Here was an attempt to insinuate a suitably menacing quality on the periphery of the page; while the artist would be the last to claim that the enterprise was successful it was at least a wholehearted attempt to find a suitable way of complementing the text.

The Society has also sought out artists from overseas; among them Sem Hartz, János Kass (who produced most accomplished lithographs for *Thérèse Raquin*), Karel Svolinsky, Philippe Jullian, and Ru van Rossem. To this list may be added perhaps some of the artists represented in the stage designs for the Society's Shakespeare – a series which will incidentally provide interesting documentation of the theatre costume of our time.

Other avenues in illustration might have been explored but it should be remembered that the Society's editions are frequently printed in initial runs of 10,000 copies and may then go into further impressions. This alone excludes some media.

The Folio Society has been almost the only publisher to make full use of the Heath Robinson process of case binding. Even in its most mundane form, case-making is still a complex and fairly costly process. The Society has used a wide range of materials and variety of blockings which, although costlier than those used in the average trade edition, are worth the extra expense because of their enhancement of the visual impact. Sometimes the designs have been erroneously devised in typographic terms, ignoring the three-dimensional nature of both the blocking and the case, but there have been a number of successful designs commissioned from craft bookbinders. Materials have included silks, wood veneers, vellums, leathers, decorative papers, and pictorial and patterned designs printed on cloth. Some of these have been fragile and on occasion brash; some have been ill-suited to the text. Others might have served as elegant reminders to general publishers of what is possible with a little imagination and even less investment.

Probably for many readers of THE PENROSE ANNUAL one of the least attractive features of Folio Society design over the years would be the frequent adaptation of old, hand-tooled bindings into regularized patterns for machine blocking on buckram, yet these books have been bought by Folio members in their tens of thousands. This has been the Society's strength: although it never seems exactly to have defined its market, it has almost unfailingly produced what that market wants.

No doubt the energetic new management will continue to follow that example and, in doing so, will explore the possibilities for production and design created by the changing techniques available to them. If they do, then the Folio Society's contribution to book production in its second twenty-five years will be no less than in its first.

Unsung heroes of printing, 1900–50

James Moran

The author takes a new look at the 'greats' of printing in the first half of the century and finds that some of them have either been overlooked or undervalued by historians of printing. Among those who have not received the attention they deserve he lists Cooper and Budd, of Peckham, pioneers of the printer's house journal, Sir Herbert Morgan, C. H. St John Hornby, the Scottish firm of Dobson Molle & Co., C. J. Jacobi, who redesigned The Penrose Annual in 1915, the annual's great founder-editor William Gamble, and the many master printers who were devoted to what they called 'the craft' and tried to propagate the cause of good printing design according to their lights and the taste of the day.

Let us begin with a quotation from Francis Meynell's *My Lives*: 'Today, looking back, I think the historians of English Printing have been over-generous in their judgment of the Pelican Press. The Westminster Press and the Arden Press, its forerunner, and the Curwen Press, its contemporary, did fine work more consistently.' Francis Meynell draws attention here to a perennial problem for seekers after knowledge. Throughout history, one man has had a 'better press' than another, and it is hard work to establish even an approximation of what really happened at a given time.

When we are discussing printing in the first half of the twentieth century 'historians' is perhaps too grand a word to use. We might substitute 'bards', those who sing the praises of a particular hero and, in this respect, the Pelican Press had an excellent singer in the person of Meynell himself. I do not say this in any slighting way. On the contrary, it was a highly necessary activity for a new, young firm and evokes our admiration today. Readers may be familiar with the distinguished volume *Typography*, compiled by him in 1923, and which tells us that Mr Meynell is in constant attendance as 'architypographer' and manifesto-maker. Less familiar may be Meynell's delightful series of *Printer's Miscellanies* from 1921 onward.

It is true that the Pelican Press has been over-exposed since then, but in the first issue of the *Miscellanies* there is a paragraph which hints at what role the Pelican Press will be remembered for in the long run. It reads: 'When you see a newspaper advertisement outstanding for its typography, the odds are heavy on the Pelican Press having had some hand in it.' By 1929, in fact, those running the press were emphasizing that they were 'Advertisement Display Experts'. So the Pelican Press was a pioneer in that small but significant field which flourished while metal type prevailed – newspaper advertisement setting – in which such firms as the Fanfare Press (specially established for the purpose) and C. and E. Layton (originally general printers) made such a mark. This might attract the attention of a printing historian in the future.

Our problem in assessing the period 1900–50 is bound up in the fact that the bards – a good example is Holbrook Jackson – tended naturally to sing the praises of their friends. The casual enquirer, decades later, rarely comes across the name of say Cooper and Budd, of Peckham, devoted to good printing since 1876. This firm was not backward in issuing publicity. Its specimen book in the 1920s was attractive and the firm was among the pioneers of the printer's house journal, but somehow its name is not on the lips of teachers of typography.

Moreover, we have to overcome those generalizations which are passed on from generation to generation of students; for example, the popular idea that after Koenig invented the cylinder press printing underwent a great technical change and only printing of a low standard was produced until the emergence of William Morris. For an earlier period we owe much to Ruari McLean who has shown how wrong this notion is, not only bringing to light a number of good, if obscure printers, but enlightening us on the work of Clowes, Clay, Evans, Day & Son, R. & R. Clark, Ben Fawcett, and Griggs, among others. The generalizers confuse the undoubted development of rapid printing and cheap literature with the continuing tradition of good bookwork. A printer such as Stephen Austin, of Hertford, was quite clear in his mind – he installed a cylinder press for his newspaper but used a slow working bed-and-platen press for his excellent bookwork.

The tradition of good printing did not die and was carried over into the twentieth century, through the agency of a number of Scottish houses and such firms as the Chiswick Press. While it would be wrong to ignore the deterioration in standards which occurred toward the end of the nineteenth century, it would be unwise to believe that no improvements were made until the founding of the Double Crown Club.

Several figures, not all of them printers, have not perhaps received the attention they deserve. A man who carried out an Emery Walker-like role in bringing people together was Joseph Thorp. He was a clerk in The Art and Book Company, joining the printing side, the Arden Press, in 1903, when he had a few months instruction in printing from Bernard Newdigate and Frank Goeby (afterwards printer of *Punch*). He became a not very successful traveller for the W. H. Smith printing department and then managed to get transferred to what was known as the studio to work under R. P. Gossop, right-hand man to the controller of printing, H. E. Morgan.

The entry for Sir Herbert Morgan in *Who was Who* (he died in 1951) gives the extraordinary list of directorships and honorary and Government posts which he held. Only two small items reveal, and then only indirectly, that he had anything to do with printing. One is: 'attached to W. H. Smith since 1906' and the other: 'first President of the Society of Industrial Artists'. Yet under Morgan, the W. H. Smith printing department – its bindery was under the direction of Douglas Cockerell – became a powerful factor in good printing. Very little known is the fact that Morgan, before joining W. H. Smith & Son in

1906, had been with the printing firm of Spottiswoode's, which as early as 1904 was well ahead of other printers with its studio and layout services to customers.

Let us not forget one of the W. H. Smith partners – C. H. St John Hornby of the Ashendene Press. Beatrice Warde recalled a 1927 conversation with a well-known printer when she learned for the first time that the great St John Hornby of the Ashendene Press was also a director of W. H. Smith & Son; while her *vis-à-vis* learned for the first time with mild astonishment that the great St John Hornby of W. H. Smith & Son was also the owner of a private press.

Thorp was thoroughly aware of St John Hornby's dual role, and it was he who suggested to St John Hornby that Smiths acquire the Arden Press. This freed Newdigate from financial responsibility and in Thorp's view prepared him for the later splendid work at the Shakespeare Head Press. Thorp also wrote *Printing for Business* (the title was suggested by Morgan), and while today it cannot compare with the many books produced on printing, it was the first attempt to introduce the theory and practice of printing to the layman, and hopefully, to show him what was good and bad.

Thorp went on to become a consultant to Curwen Press for three years, introducing Lovat Fraser to Harold Curwen. He worked for the Design and Industries Association and was one of the members of the Government Committee on type-faces and later suggested a classification for type-faces long before Vox and others. Thorp gave the chief credit for the improvement in business printing to Herbert Morgan, but his two chief heroes of the period 1900–14 were Newdigate and Gerard Meynell, with the possible addition of G. W. Jones, whose main work, however, came later. The same might be said of Newdigate whose great impact was after 1920, when he joined the Shakespeare Head Press, acquired by Basil Blackwell from the executors of the late A. H. Bullen, a scholarly printer.

There were, as both Herbert Simon and Noel Carrington have made clear to me, two great influences in the 1920s. The first was that of the private presses, enjoying all the prestige of the Arts and Crafts movement, and the other the Design and Industries Association, which paid some attention to jobbing work. There were about a dozen printer members of the DIA, of which Harold Curwen was the most respected and influential, but Fred Phillips, of the Baynard Press, was also an important figure.

I have read various versions of the founding of the Westminster

Press but clearly the important date is 1899 when Gerard Meynell assumed the management. With Claude Gibson, he bought the business from Wilfrid Meynell and J. G. Snead-Cox the next year. Wilfrid Meynell, father of Francis, is well known as a publisher who insisted on high standards of printing, using the services of both the Arden and Westminster Presses, but it is fascinating to realize that his interest in printing derived from the work of Andrew Tuer and the Leadenhall Press. The Westminster Press progressed under Gerard Meynell and took offices in Covent Garden in 1912, and the next year *The Imprint* was published. Much has been written on this publication and its associates, and my intention here is rather to draw attention to Gerard Meynell. In 1914 posters drawn by the Senefelder Club were printed by the Westminster Press for the London Underground, and here we can only briefly refer to another great friend of good printing, Frank Pick of the London Underground. The Westminster Press also worked for the most discriminating book publishers. But Gerard Meynell was not only a pugnacious fighter on behalf of good-looking printing, he was a pioneer of business methods, and, in particular, the printers' costing system. He was joint founder and editor, with R. A. Austen-Leigh, of the *Master Printers Annual*, which he printed, and Austen-Leigh's firm, Spottiswoode Ballantyne, published. Nor was Meynell's interest limited to his own firm, as for some years he was adviser to the Sun Engraving Co., and initiated *Illustration*, an occasional miscellany, for this firm.

Mention of R. A. Austen-Leigh takes us to Spottiswoode Ballantyne, in which Edward and Richard Austen-Leigh were prominent. Although primarily a London firm, it may well have inherited Scottish traditions of good printing – a subject that deserves a great deal more attention than it has been given but for which I have not space here. One great printer was W. B. Blaikie of Constable's, and other names which occur to us are R. & R. Clark (although a certain amount has been written about this firm), Pillans and Wilsons and Ballantyne. Robert Maclehose & Co. are also well known, but perhaps the late John Easton, a director from 1925, may tend to be forgotten. He was one of those inspirers of good typography, and is known in philatelic circles for his books on postage stamp design and printing. But how many of us have heard of Dobson Molle & Co. of Edinburgh? Their distinguished type book, dated 1916, is so striking for the period that one wonders what happened to them. While they had to cope with the ubiquitous Cheltenham, nevertheless they used Caslon Old Face very effectively and had Goudy's Forum capitals in six sizes and Kennerley in three – an unusual investment at that time in American typefaces.

Founded in 1827, Dobson Molle by 1916 had offices in Edinburgh, Glasgow, Liverpool, Belfast, and London, but went into liquidation in 1929. The leading light was Gardner Sinclair (the headquarters were at St Clair Works) but apparently the firm, which was well known for its high-quality work, overreached itself with the purchase of a large amount of litho plant, for which there was insufficient work.

Literary students will know of Sir Walter Scott's involvement in Ballantyne's, and the subsequent decline of the firm. New life was breathed into it by Edward Hanson, famous as a master of printing house management; and in 1878 a London branch was formed by acquiring Saville Edwards & Co. in Tavistock Street, Covent Garden. Horace Hart, the famous Oxford University Printer, was manager, a position later occupied, coincidentally, by Walter Lewis, University Printer at Cambridge. The goodwill of Ballantyne Hanson was bought by Spottiswoode's in 1915, the firm becoming Spottiswoode Ballantyne.

Spottiswoode's derives from William Strahan (born Strachan) who took the high road to England – 'the noblest prospect which a Scotsman ever sees' – and lived to become one of England's most successful printers, incidentally printing the works of the gentleman who coined the phrase about the high road. He had his own printing business and a share in the King's patent. His daughter Margaret married John Spottiswoode of Spottiswoode, and her grandsons divided the inheritance, one becoming a partner in Eyre and Spottiswoode, King's printers, and the other a partner in Spottiswoode & Co., which was joined in 1862 by Cholmeley Austen-Leigh, descendant of Jane Austen's brother. The firm was devoted to good quality printing, originally occupying itself with book-work but branching out into periodicals and, in particular, publicity work. Its 1912 book, *The Story of a Printing House*, is a creditable production for the time. Opposite page 12 there is an illustration of the gateway to His Majesty's Printers with a large Royal coat-of-arms, which now adorns the entrance to the Eyre and Spottiswoode office in Serjeants Inn.

Spottiswoode Ballantyne was, in the words of Beatrice Warde, one of those creative printing offices which were determined not to let the traditional responsibility of the printer for typographic style pass wholly into the hands of the print buyer and advertising agent. It established a studio in 1904, but John Spottiswoode, the only remaining

Spottiswoode director, broke away to form one of those very agencies which were 'taking the bread out of the printer's mouth' – Spottiswoode Advertising; and Herbert Morgan took the rest of the studio staff to W. H. Smith. This did not deter Spottiswoode's, the printers, and this firm gradually achieved a reputation for creative printing, building up by the 1920s a team of typographers and writers which excited Beatrice Warde's admiration. A booklet, dated 1920, set in Kennerley type, was written by William Warbis.

Another of the team was William Tucker, who, Herbert Simon tells me, was a born reformer, but who was not supported in the firm, particularly by a Mr Seabright, the overseer of the big machine room, who 'felt there was some relation between typography and femininity'. Another member was Pynson Epps, who, after leaving Headley Bros. in 1902 was a pioneer advertising manager for Austin Reed. After 1908 he decided to work as a printing designer. He apparently did not like his own name of Percy and substituted the name of Henry VIII's printer, perhaps because it began with a 'p', for Pynson was not a particularly good printer.

Spottiswoode Ballantyne worked with a pioneer advertising agency – Stuarts – to produce the entertaining *Commentaries of Fortnum and Mason* in the twenties. Exactly what the division of responsibility was is now difficult to determine, but the imprint on the first is 'Produced by Stuart's Advertising Agency Ltd . . . and arranged and printed by Spottiswoode, Ballantyne and Co. Ltd', and it has a distinctively Will Ransom look about it (or for that matter an Andrew Tuer appearance).

Arising from this article many others suggest themselves – the development of advertisement typesetting; the emergence of the 'typographer' in the modern sense; the prevalence of the Scottish tradition; the change in the role of the advertising agency; and the interaction between the private presses and commercial printing. Charles Ricketts, for example, who edited *The Dial* with his friend Charles Shannon, ran the Vale Press until 1904, but the printing was done by Ballantyne. When Walter Lewis was setting up the Cloister Press in 1920 he wrote: 'I hope that I shall never print on "Art" paper unless it be Matt, and with some of the old Ballantyne Craftsmen have every confidence of producing work similar to the old private presses.' Obviously in Lewis's mind at that point the work of the private presses provided a standard at which to aim. C. J. Jacobi, at the Chiswick Press, had, of course, printed for William Morris, but was also responsible for the work of the Florence and Riccardi Presses. The general feeling about Jacobi was expressed by Thorp to the effect that he was a sound master printer, sitting docilely at the feet of Morris and his friends, and a receiver rather than a giver of ideas. If he were sent 'copy' for three booklets on a new face cream, a bicycle, and a recovered Codex, he would produce three faultless pieces of printing in Caslon Old Face and all precisely the same. At the same time he was in Thorp's list of the elect, and one can see why. Among other things Jacobi redesigned THE PENROSE ANNUAL in 1915, an event which has received less attention than the later changes made by Stanley Morison in 1924. Jacobi within his private press standards, brought some discipline into PENROSE and really laid down the pattern for Morison to follow. Mention of THE PENROSE ANNUAL, which Lund Humphries, the printers, took over from A. W. Penrose, the process suppliers, early in the century, leads us to consider William Gamble, the founder-editor. I have recently been looking through the annual's sixty-five volumes and have come to the conclusion that Gamble was one of the most extraordinarily well-informed men of his day on all aspects of printing, and again a man about whom little has been said. His typographical taste was not too well formed, it is true, but he had enough sense to consult such people as Jacobi, and in Lund Humphries he had an excellent firm of printers.

A man who was firmly connected with the great private press days and who was certainly a giver of ideas was J. H. Mason and here we begin to move into the realm of typographical teaching, the results of which are often hard to assess. This is particularly so with Mason who was active for half a century and who seemed to the young, I believe, toward the end of his teaching career to be somebody from another world. And perhaps he was – a world of much greater discipline and attention to detail. By accident he was apprenticed to one of the firms mentioned earlier – Ballantyne's, where he saw the work of the Vale Press and where he met Ricketts. He worked for Cobden-Sanderson at the Doves Press, and became a teacher at the Central School of Arts and Crafts. He is known naturally as one of Gerard Meynell's collaborators on *The Imprint* and the actual designer of the Imprint type, the first specifically designed for the 'Monotype'. One gets the impression also that he did most of the work on *The Imprint*. Then he set up the Cranach Press for Count Kessler at Weimar. In 1938 he became one of the first Royal Designers for Industry. Mason's typographic style was well known and his title-pages have had great influence. His prospectus for 1928 when he was head of the printing department at the Central School states: 'Great stress is laid on the layout as a means of training the display compositor, and some of our students have taken to this side of the printing trade permanently.' This is the origin of one generation of typographers. The prospectus also mentioned that the school was the only one where Greek and Hebrew printing were taught. I wonder if this is still so and whether any other working compositor ever achieved mastery of Greek and Latin as J. H. Mason did.

The third press mentioned by Francis Meynell in my original quotation was the Curwen Press, and it is hardly necessary to refer to it as 'unsung'; but for a time it was not sufficiently realized how far back the good work of Harold Curwen extended. This may have been due to one of the main recorders of the period, Holbrook Jackson. Jackson was primarily a journalist, although at the age of 29, in 1903, in Leeds, he arranged what was said to be the first exhibition of 'fine printing' in the provinces. While he was responsible for some good printing later in life his first efforts as a printer at the New Age Press, with his friend, A. R. Orage, who ended up as a Greenshirt, were not very remarkable.

This is a diversion, but Holbrook Jackson gave the impression, I think, that Harold Curwen sprang fully armed as a printer from the head of Edward Johnston, after attending classes in calligraphy. In fact, Curwen joined the Press at Plaistow as far back as 1908, after training at Leipzig, and the Press produced quite good work even before 1916 when Curwen began to extend his influence. This has all been put right in a delightful small history of the Curwen Press produced in 1970.

The Curwen Press is inseparably tied to the name of Simon and there is no need to repeat the story. But surprisingly little has been written about the period 1922–33 when Herbert Simon was in charge of the Kynoch Press, Birmingham, part of Imperial Chemical Industries. Kynoch had begun with an 'Arab' treadle platen printing labels for gun dealers to put on the cartridges they sold. The firm was bought by Arthur Chamberlain (brother of the famous Joe) and later the cartridge department was put in the charge of Donald Hope, who got to know Emery Walker, and from then on the Kynoch Press blossomed out – a further, lesser-known example of Emery Walker's remarkable influence. The fact that Herbert Simon, then 22, and filled with enthusiasm for printing by his brother Oliver, managed in 1920 to persuade William Rudge in New York, to take him on as a learner and then two years later became manager of Kynoch is some indication that we are dealing with a man of outstanding ability. From the *Kynoch*

Book of Type Specimens of 1927, one can get the flavour of this press more than forty years ago. The 1930 *Supplement* designed by Harry Carter has an interesting change of design emphasis on the cover.

It is appropriate at this point to mention Harry Carter, very much an unsung hero. A learner at Monotype for a year, he was at Kynoch Press from 1929 to 1937. In the Double Crown Club's last register he modestly described himself as being in 1932 a 'printer's office worker (mainly layout)' although another hand had described him in the 1949 register as production manager. In fact, Harry Carter has been more of a 'compleat typographer' than most people in the printing trade. He has set types and printed them, he has sold printing, he has designed type, including Russian and Hebrew, and has engraved punches, designed books and jobbing work for everything from the Nonesuch Press to Her Majesty's Stationery Office, where he served as head of the layout section. A gifted linguist, he is our greatest typographical historian. Yet only a meagre amount has ever appeared about his work. This should be remedied. While discussing Kynoch it is not inappropriate either to mention Noel Carrington, one who has done a great deal not merely for good book design but for industrial design in general. He was London representative of Kynoch and typographer in 1928, and went on to a wider career in publishing.

Henderson & Spalding was a firm which went out of business after the bombing of 1940, and in consequence little has been said about its contribution to printing in the period under review. An old firm, it had works in Sylvan Grove, off the Old Kent Road. This gave rise to the name Sylvan Press and a delightful printer's mark. (It was also, however, right next to the South London gas works.) Under the guidance of Harold Strong and Hubert J. Foss, the Double Crown Club's co-founder, the staff were imbued with the idea of good printing and the little book produced by Foss in 1926, although not in itself a very remarkable piece of work, shows how thorough this process was.

For the public, *Good Printing* was issued earlier. In a recent bookseller's catalogue this is stated to have been 'almost certainly' designed by Stanley Morison. Apart from the ambiguity of 'almost certainly' – it is like saying 'almost unique' or 'nearly absolute' – this is a little unfair on Strong and Foss. There is a danger of attributing all kinds of pieces of printing to Morison in the twenties. Although I gave rather a lavish show to the famous Pelican Press specimen in my book on Morison, I am glad I did not specifically state that he designed it as I discovered later that Francis Meynell was responsible for the design much earlier and that Morison was only involved in getting the 1921 edition off the machine and despatching it.

The same bookseller says of the *Manchester Guardian Advertising Review*, produced in 1924, after Morison had left the Cloister Press, that 'one feels strongly that it is Morison's work'. This ignores the fact that it was arranged and produced by Charles W. Hobson's agency, where the designer and studio director was William Grimmond, another man who has not received the credit he deserves.

Whatever one may think about these earlier Henderson & Spalding productions, I suggest that the firm's calendar is quite outstanding for the year 1932. Our problem today is that we are familiar with similar productions and too many years have passed for us to know what sort of reaction it produced in its recipients. My guess is that of all the calendars received that year Henderson & Spalding's did not end up in the waste-paper basket.

George W. Jones, who printed at the Sign of the Dolphin in Gough Square, was not exactly unsung. In the Midlands and in the US he was considered England's greatest printer, but he did not appeal to the younger men who founded the Double Crown Club, and for some years his work has been under a cloud. His career, however, covers a vital period in English printing design, and when he finally settled on what he thought was the way to print he did not change. He began in the so-called 'Leicester Free Style' school. In an excellent article 'Artistic Printing', in *Alphabet and Image*, January 1948, Vivian Ridler has examined this last independent flowering of the compositor's art. Jones went on to become a major educational influence in printing. William Maxwell, of R. & R. Clark, went so far in 1930 as to say that the two printer-craftsmen who had influenced his working life were Christopher Plantin and G. W. Jones.

Jones owned the periodical *Printing World* for a time and whatever one may say of its general make-up, the excellent presswork and its legibility and readability were far in advance of the other trade journals of the day; but it is equally interesting to go through the volumes to perceive the changes in his style as he progressed from 'artistic printing' to his established style, which was influenced by sixteenth-century French printing. But he was not in the Morris hand-craft tradition as he was a great admirer of the Miehle printing machine and the Linotype typesetter; it was from his confident use of these that he became Linotype adviser in September 1921, eventually producing a series of excellent book faces, of which Granjon is perhaps the most outstanding. Jones was one of those rare printers who had his own decorative material designed, engraved and cast, using borders modelled on those of Geofroy Tory, de Colines, de Tournes, and Granjon. He used contemporary artists to design initial letters, perhaps not always to our taste, but often remarkable pieces of technical virtuosity. Among those so employed were Robert Horne and Albert Turboyne. Jones also had a liking for Civilité as a display letter. In March 1938 he parted with the goodwill of the Sign of the Dolphin to Hunt, Barnard of Aylesbury, another firm which should have received more credit for its good work. Why Jones was not liked in Double Crown Club circles is not difficult to discover. He was considered pompous by the younger men, and there was rivalry between him and Morison in the type-design field, not unassociated with the fact that they worked for different companies. He was also what is called an Establishment figure – although I am not always sure what that means – being a prominent Mason, holding high office in the Grand Lodge of England, and being a leading City of London figure. All this should not concern us really, any more than the fact that Jacobi was considered a bore by some. It is by their work we should judge them.

I am reminded here of Louisa, daughter of John Fairbrother, printer of Bow Street. She was an actress before becoming Mrs Fitzgeorge, wife of the Duke of Cambridge. Her father opposed her choice of the stage as a career, believing that actresses were wanton women. Louisa did not deny that some were so but simply observed that he had not yet contemplated abandoning his own profession because there were villainous printers.

So we should take the work of printers – villainous, virtuous, or otherwise – like Honor Tracy's priest taking the straight and narrow path between good and evil and try to assess their work against the background of their time. Not all master printers were Philistines – indeed an objective view would indicate the contrary. Many, large and small, were devoted to what they called 'the craft', and if we do not always admire the results of their work it is because we are living in a different period from the point of view of taste.

There were the twenty master printers, some bearing famous family names – Bemrose, Clay, Clowes, Harrison, Keliher, Truscott, and Viney – who founded *Printing Review* in an effort to propagate the cause of good printing design. They were very sincere, but discovered that the production of a magnificent periodical costs money, that a single-minded person is needed to direct it, and that sharing out the printing involves unnecessary difficulties. One of them was Alfred Langley, who was instrumental in getting Morison to address the Master Printers' publicity conference in 1928. Some were outraged by Morison's controversial layout of the programme – it would hardly cause a raised eyebrow today – because they thought it betrayed all the hard work that such men as J. G. Riddell, principal of the London School of Printing, and G. W. Jones had put in to educate craftsmen in good design. The whole affair was one in which emotions and personal antagonisms clouded the basic fact that there could be different kinds of good printing.

A few smaller printers whose work seems to be worthy of mention have disappeared without trace. C. R. Heiser, of Aldersgate Street, must have been a neat, if rather dull printer if his production of J. H. Mason's *Printing Considered as an Industrial Art* is anything to go by. Incidentally, Charles Pickering's students at Medway produced a much livelier version, in the Masonian manner, some years later. I would like to know a lot more about George Roberts, of Cursitor Street, who printed so well for the Franfrolico Press in 1927; but we do know something about the firm of Strangeways, which operated near Seven Dials, but was absorbed into Billings in the war. Here the young Reginald Hutchings did some excellent work.

I have not referred to those younger men – printer and designers – who were gradually emerging in the 1940s and 50s. This is not to spare their blushes, but because firstly there has already been a little singing of their praises, and secondly because they do not really belong to the period under review. It will be time enough to assess their contribution twenty years hence, and if I am still around I will be glad to do so.

Postscript: This article began life as a paper read to members of the Double Crown Club in London, in which I drew attention to some figures and firms who, in my opinion, had either been overlooked or not fully appreciated for their work during the first half of the century. These were necessarily limited to England and Scotland, although I fully appreciated that much praiseworthy printing had been carried out in the United States and in various countries of Europe. The paper prompted a number of valuable comments and I have therefore occasionally amended the wording or added to it. I also did a small amount of additional research. This is the background to what is clearly not a comprehensive survey and which represents a personal viewpoint. I am indebted to those who favoured me with their comments and supplied me with additional material, in particular to Sir Francis Meynell, Dr Berthold Wolpe, Herbert Simon, Noel Carrington, Walter Tracy, and Herbert Jones; and to John Shepherd and Barrie Abbott of the British Federation of Master Printers and the Society of Master Printers of Scotland respectively. I am also grateful to William Hummerstone, of the Stellar Press, who printed my design for an invitation card and who so readily and effectively entered into the spirit of my pastiche of a George W. Jones menu.   J.M.

Ben Shahn and lettering

Bernarda Shahn

A study of the lettering skills as an integral element in the art of Ben Shahn, with a step-by-step account of how he gained his fabulous width of abilities and freedom of motion as an artist, constantly developing in the half century of creative activities that followed his apprenticeship at fourteen to a New York lithographer.

The illustrations in this article were reproduced by Leyton Studios Ltd and the twelve page section was printed offset-litho by Jesse Broad Ltd.

Lettering performed a unique role in the art of Ben Shahn who died in 1969. Although he had drawn pictures from infancy onward, letters were his first learned skill. He had barely completed his elementary schooling and was still under the age of 14 when he was removed from school to be apprenticed to a lithographer in the shop of Hessenberg on Beekman Street in the heart of New York's printing trades district. It was a bitter blow to him to be denied that academic future which seemed to him, as an immigrant boy, to be the very essence of the good American life. But he had already begun to dream of being an artist and the lithographic shop might at least provide him with an entrée into art. Later he recalled: 'The first tool I was given was a broom'. His first tasks were to fetch beer for the lithographers and carry the heavy lithographic stones – expertly, so as not to break or damage them. He learned to mix acids, to grain the surfaces of stones to a flawless, smoothness, prepare them, store them, and, with a little practice, apply an etch. Only after months of such labours was he judged fit to begin some training – not as an artist-lithographer, not even to work on stone, but in the rudiments of lettering. He said: 'I began with the "A" alone, just "A". And when I had spent what seemed weeks on that and could turn out an acceptable "A", I matriculated into "B".' And so on laboriously he worked his way through the alphabet,

mastering each letter, spending additional hours and days on the 'O's and 'S's because they were notoriously the hardest to make and the most frequently bungled.

Learning the rudimentary forms was only an initiation; next came styles. He must now depart from the basic austere and beautiful Roman to learn by heart, one after another, those Victorian extravaganzas in letter-styles that still thrived in the early 1900s, letters made of trailing vines, birds, and cupids, rustic letters made of crossed logs, letters with windows and lattice-work, Circus, Girder with its black-shadowed serifs. And besides all that he had to learn the classic forms with historiated capitals, medieval uncials, scripts, illegible gothic, suitable for bibles and newspaper mastheads, flowing scripts proper for banknotes and wedding invitations and, with modern times advancing, the limp shapes of art nouveau.

Yet even all this was only a beginning. Next he had to learn spacing – the ultimate test of the letterer. There was only one rule for spacing, he said, and that was that there was no rule at all. It was a matter of the eye alone. His shop foreman explained to him: 'Imagine you have in your hand a glass that will hold only so much water. Now, you must provide space between your letters – whatever their slants and curves may be – to hold just that much water – no more, no less.'

The lithographic shop would hardly have qualified as an art school, but it was a kind of school. Devoid of glamour or romance, parsimonious in praise, uninterested in art, unaware of aesthetics, it still exercised an unbending discipline. Craftsmanship was supreme because it was indispensable; to deliver an impeccable piece of work was the highest objective and no-one cared whether the artist liked it or not. So Ben Shahn as a youth made perfect perspectives of chain factories or woollen mills to be used as letterheads, finely engraved on stone and surrounded by clouds of script or fine lines, minute faces to be embossed on cigar labels, and gigantic faces to be spread in 24-sheet size on Broadway.

One might think that these rigorous years would turn any aspiring young person away from art forever, particularly when they could have been spent in acquiring the education for which the young Ben yearned. But by the age of 19, already a journeyman lithographer and a master of skills, he had finished high school through night courses. He went on to attend two colleges in succession, paying his way by lithography, won coveted scholarships in biology, proved himself as a student, and could turn back to art with a good conscience.

Below : page in tempera and gold-leaf,
God's admonitition to Job
(Book of Job XXXVIII 4–7).

Overleaf :
Ben Shahn's *Passion of Sacco-Vanzetti*,
1958, and a poster for a religious
conference.

IF IT HAD NOT BEEN FOR THESE THING, I MIGHT HAVE LIVE OUT MY LIFE TALKING AT STREET CORNERS TO SCORNING MEN. I MIGHT HAVE DIE, UNMARKED, UNKNOWN A FAILURE. NOW WE ARE NOT A FAILURE. THIS IS OUR CAREER AND OUR TRIUMPH. NEVER IN OUR FULL LIFE COULD WE HOPE TO DO SUCH WORK FOR TOLERANCE, FOR JOOSTICE, FOR MAN'S ONDERSTANDING OF MAN AS NOW WE DO BY ACCIDENT. OUR WORDS - OUR LIVES - OUR PAINS NOTHING! THE TAKING OF OUR LIVES- LIVES OF A GOOD SHOEMAKER AND A POOR FISH PEDDLER-ALL! THAT LAST MOMENT BELONGS TO US- THAT AGONY IS OUR TRIUMPH.

APRIL 26-29

BIENNIAL RELIGIOUS CONFERENCE INTEGRATION CONSCIENCE IN CRISIS

Ben Shahn

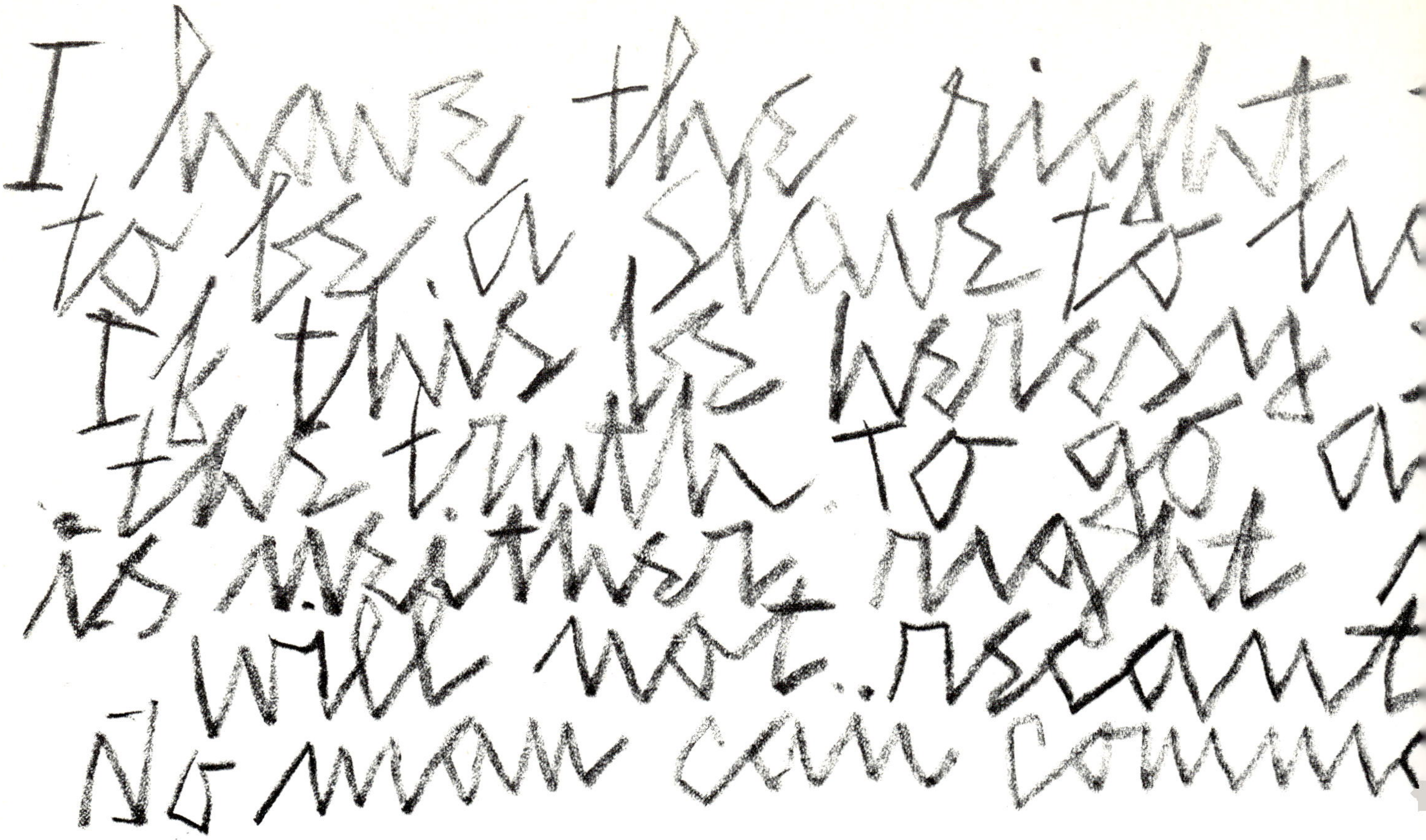

I have the right
to be a slave to the
If this be heresy
the truth to go
is neither right
will not recant
No man can comm

Two examples of pencil-drawn lettering
by Ben Shahn.

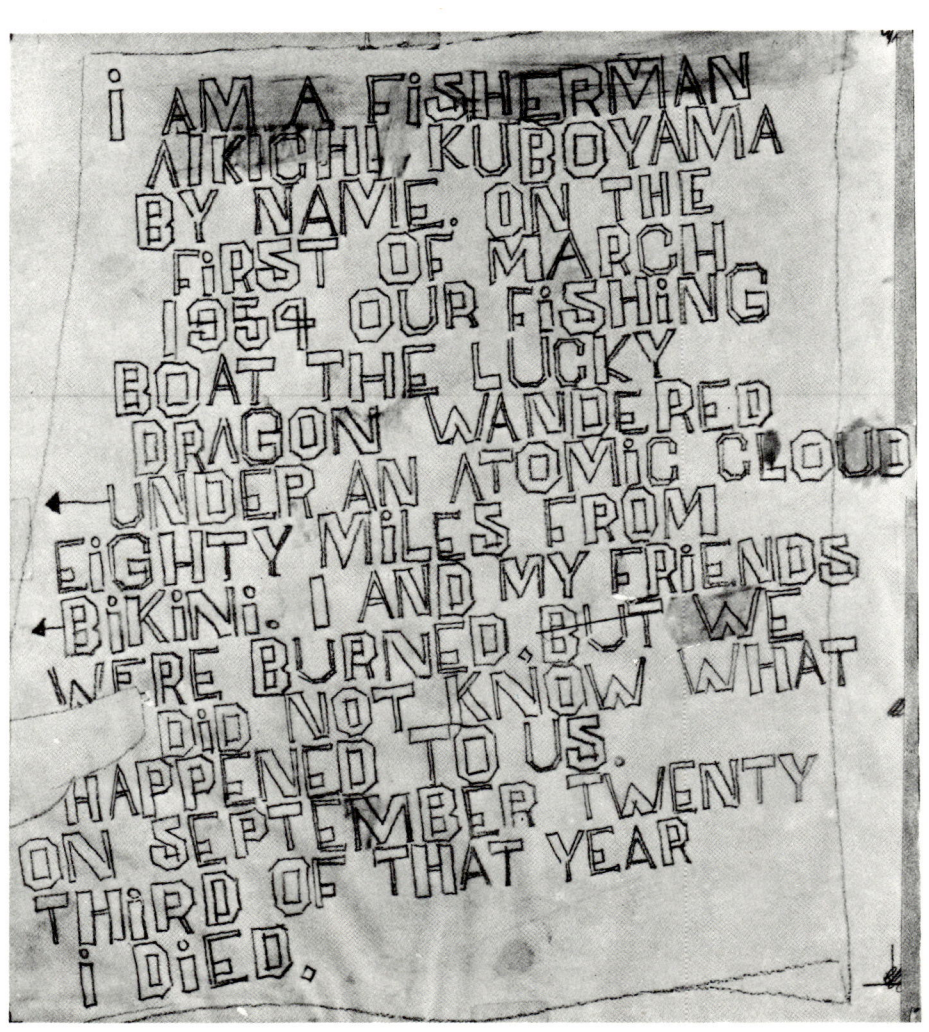

I AM A FISHERMAN
AIKICHI KUBOYAMA
BY NAME. ON THE
FIRST OF MARCH
1954 OUR FISHING
BOAT THE LUCKY
DRAGON WANDERED
UNDER AN ATOMIC CLOUD
EIGHTY MILES FROM
BIKINI. I AND MY FRIENDS
WERE BURNED, BUT WE
DID NOT KNOW WHAT
HAPPENED TO US.
ON SEPTEMBER TWENTY
THIRD OF THAT YEAR
I DIED.

Only after periods in several art schools and some years in Paris where he made his first acquaintance with the *avant-garde* of that time did he begin to use his lettering skill as part of his art. At first this was as an adjunct only, as in the Dreyfus case paintings of 1932 and the portraits of Huey Long. He took pleasure in the humorous use of lettering, often creating the most elaborate doodles entirely to entertain himself and his friends.

In 1954 he came across a colourful legend from the ancient Hebrew *Zohar* – The Book of Splendour – called *The Alphabet of Creation*. He set to work to reword, illustrate, and create beautiful Hebrew letters for this poetic tale and published it with the help of friends. Entranced by the Hebrew letters that he had reshaped for this work, he went on to make many versions of it, a large and handsome serigraph of the same name, drawings, paintings, and a pendant in gold. Next he recreated a number of Christmas carols as small books, using free variations on the Carolingian styles or inventing styles of his own.

One might say that the alphabet had been liberated within his consciousness. Increasingly he used it as an integral element of his painting, now as a setting or frame (as in the two mosaic murals *Atomic table* and *Tree of Life*), now as an interwoven pictorial element. It was a beautiful element too, providing for him a certain change of pace, a flash of gold here, or there an area of precise colour pattern or a structural member.

During the thirties, while he was on several photographic missions for one of the Roosevelt government agencies, he recorded a vast number of rural and highway signs painfully executed by amateur

96

From *The Alphabet of Creation*, left;
a cover design, original in gouache and
gold leaf, right; and, below, a verbatim
quotation from a series of interviews with
children asking their opinions about God.

WHO IS GOD? WELL IT IS AN INVISIBLE
PERSON AND HE LIVES UP IN HEAVEN
I GUESS UP IN OUTER SPACE HE
MADE THE EARTH AND THE HEAVEN &
THE STARS AND THE SUN AND THE
PEOPLE HE MADE LIGHT HE MADE DAY
HE MADE NIGHT HE HAS SUCH POWER-
FUL EYES HE DOESN'T HAVE MILLIONS
AND THOUSANDS AND BILLIONS AND HE
CAN STILL SEE US WHEN WE'RE BAD
HE STARTED ALL THE PLANTS GROWING TO
ME I THINK OF HIM WHO MAKES FLOWERS
& GREEN GRASS & THE BLUE SKY &
THE YELLOW SUN GOD IS EVERYWHERE
& I DON'T KNOW HOW HE COULD DO IT

Bernarda Shahn: Ben Shahn and lettering

letterers. He enjoyed the pictures and studied them. From them he began to develop what he was later to call his folk alphabet, at first only feeling his way toward it, possibly humorously, then, becoming serious, he turned into a fresh lettering style which, bright and staccato in its effect, violated every established canon of lettering. Where tradition said that the letters should be thick, they are thin; where they should be thin they are thick; where they ought to be round they are square, and so on. They are surprising in their effect, sparkling, often gaudy, always commanding. The folk alphabet has now been so widely adopted by letterers who may never have heard of its author that it might be said to have returned to its proper folk origins. Some of the striking uses made of it by Ben Shahn are in the serigraph *Immortal Words*, the poster *Ballets USA*, and a serigraph based on the Stephen Spender poem, '*I Think Continually of Those Who Were Truly Great*'.

In Paris in the late twenties, and again in the Orient in 1960, Ben Shahn became interested in and memorized a variety of Chinese calligraphic figures. Apart from the pleasure that he took in repeating them, he found in them a rhythm and freedom of motion that stimulated new explorations in his other work – in watercolours, drawings, and gouaches especially. He incorporated the ideographs into his vocabulary of lettering forms.

Lettering was a vital element in his art in still another sense. Always an 'engaged' individual, always eager to express ideas and feelings, he spoke through letters and lettering. The letters might be painted forms moving with the rhythms of a painting or a print, they might be structural, or they might be used only as a small precise touch here and there (as in the serigraph *All That is Beautiful*). But they also spoke in words, saying directly just what he wanted to say – often a poem repeated, not infrequently a declaration of principle as in the Martin Luther painting *Credo* or the print of the same title.

In 1963 he wrote and published his book, *Love and Joy About Letters*, a verbal-visual celebration of his enjoyment of all lettering manifestations, from a laborious picture-with-words by his 10-year-old daughter about a cat, to an ancient Thai manuscript, a poem by William Carlos Williams written on Maillol paper, a Japanese wall covered with graffiti, and many examples of his own work. A piece of text that he relished greatly and once lettered out by hand came from the writings of the great medieval mystic Rabbi Abulafia who, in instructing the neophyte in the ways of gaining insight, said:

'If it be night, kindle many lights, until all be bright. Then take ink,

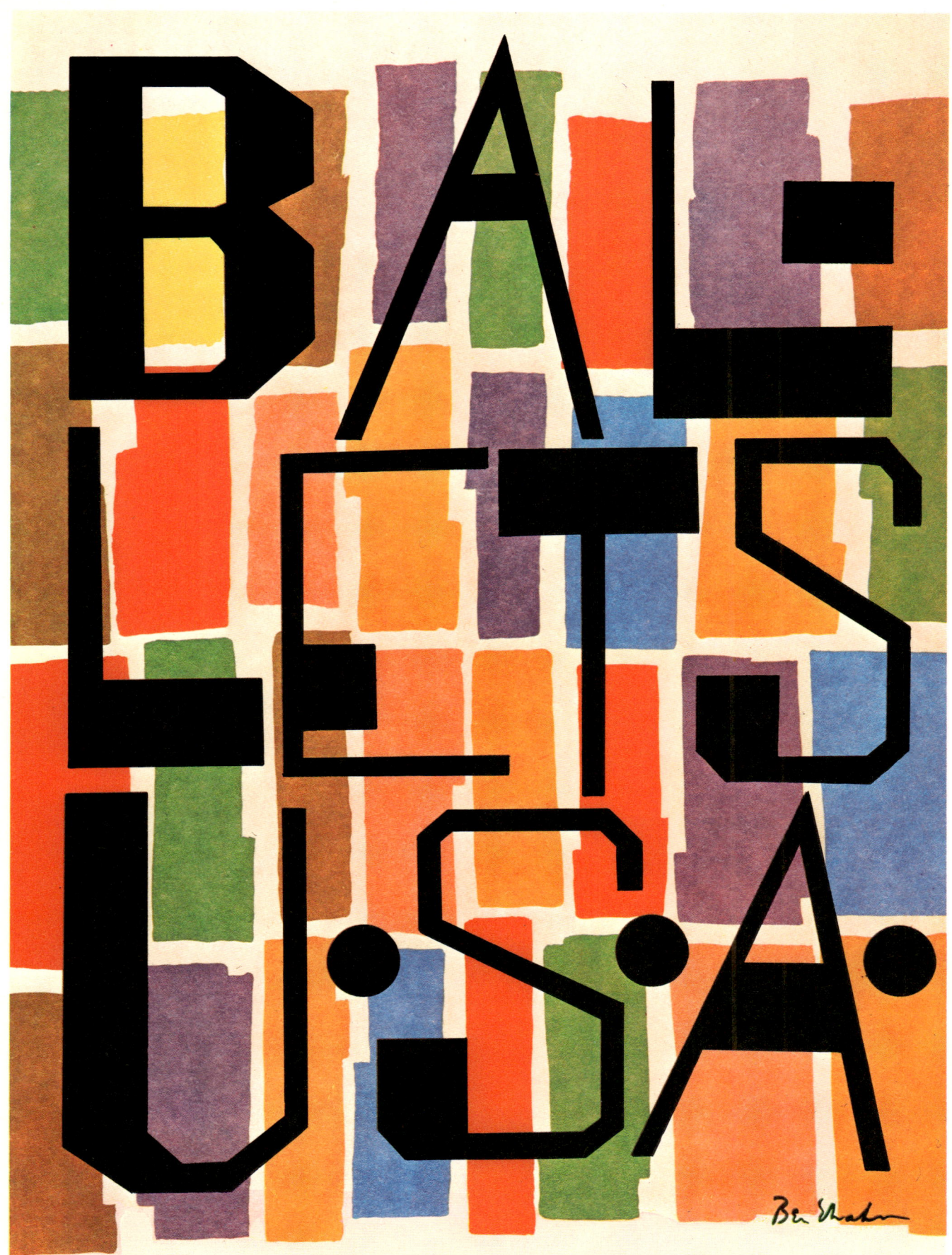

EXHIBIT-JEROME ROBBINS "BALLETS U.S.A."-U.S.I.S. GALLERY 41 GROSVENOR SQ. LONDON W.1. SEPT. 15-OCT. 23, 1959

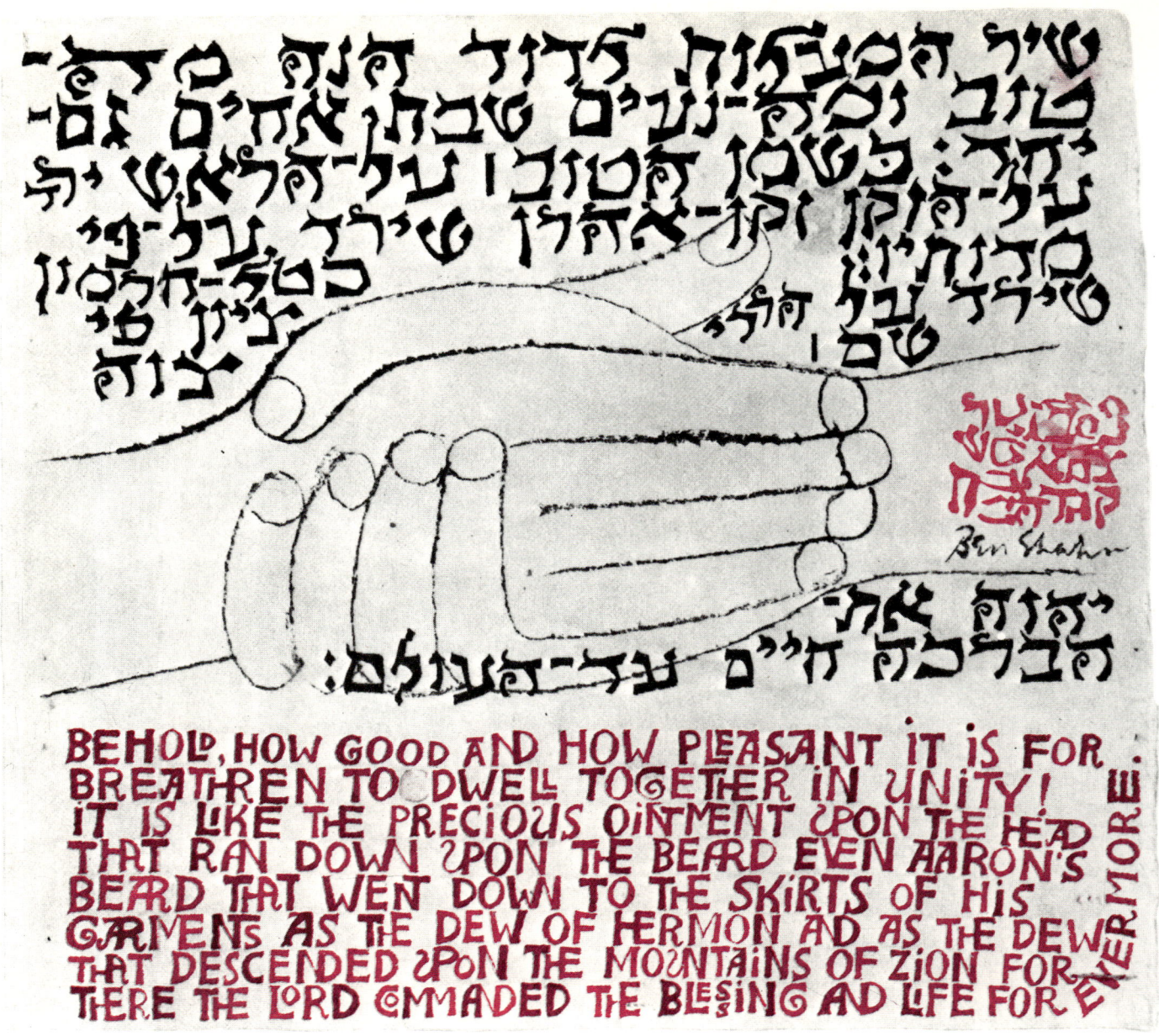

BEHOLD, HOW GOOD AND HOW PLEASANT IT IS FOR BREATHREN TO DWELL TOGETHER IN UNITY! IT IS LIKE THE PRECIOUS OINTMENT UPON THE HEAD THAT RAN DOWN UPON THE BEARD EVEN AARON'S BEARD THAT WENT DOWN TO THE SKIRTS OF HIS GARMENTS AS THE DEW OF HERMON AND AS THE DEW THAT DESCENDED UPON THE MOUNTAINS OF ZION FOR THERE THE LORD COMMADED THE BLESSING AND LIFE FOR EVERMORE.

A portion of Psalm 133, a subject often interpreted by Ben Shahn.

pen and a table to thy hand and remember that thou art about to serve God in joy of the gladness of heart. Now begin to combine a few or many letters, to permute and to combine them until thy heart be warm. Then be mindful of their movements and of what thou canst bring forth by moving them. And when thou feelest that thy heart is already warm and when thou seest that by combinations of letters thou canst grasp new things which by human tradition or by thyself thou wouldst not be able to know and when thou art thus prepared to receive the influx of divine power which flows into thee, then turn all thy true thought to imagine the Name and His exalted angels in thy heart as if they were human beings sitting or standing about thee. And feel thyself like an envoy whom the king and his ministers are to send on a mission, and he is waiting to hear something about his mission from their lips, be it from the king himself, be it from his servants. Having imagined this very vividly, turn thy whole mind to understand with thy thoughts the many things which will come into thy heart through the letters imagined. Ponder them as a whole and in all their detail . . .'

Walter Tracy, type designer

Allen Hutt

There is no end to the search for text types able to meet the changing technical circumstances of modern newspaper production and to stand up to rapid composition, stereotyping, and high-speed rotary printing. This article discusses the outstanding original contributions – Jubilee, Linotype Modern, and Times Europa are the milestones – made by Walter Tracy in this field. It traces his career from his early days as a qualified compositor and pays tribute to his many-sided typographic skills and deep erudition in all matters of printing practice and history.

The specimen settings on pages 102 to 105, 108 and 109 were provided by Linotype & Machinery Ltd. The blocks on pages 106, 107, 110 and 111 and the stereotypes on pages 112 and 114 were made by Gilchrist Bros. Ltd.

Of all type-forms, newspaper text has the greatest and most continuous impact on the greatest number of people. This applies to all advanced industrial countries with a highly developed daily and weekly newspaper press; more particularly to Britain, which heads the world league table for newspaper readership. The statistics show the immense influence of news-texts; after all, it is the text of the newspaper, not its headline display and make-up, which ultimately concerns the reader. Every morning over 16 million newspapers are sold throughout Britain, every evening over 8 million, every Sunday over 25 million; and every week the 'local rags' account for a further 13 million-plus.

This is why the type designs of Walter Tracy are so important; during the past score of years Tracy has designed for Linotype a whole series of newspaper text types, both for the editorial body of the paper and for the 'smalls', those advertisements which in the present generation have become a more essential anchor of newspaper economics than ever. News-texts have not been Tracy's sole concern since he joined Linotype & Machinery Ltd in 1947 and later became manager of the typographic department; reference is made below to his work in the sphere of non-Roman types, especially in Arabic and related fields; but here also the interest is mainly textual – and overall there can be no question that Tracy's Roman news-texts constitute his outstanding original contribution to type design.

His latest achievement, the new Times Europa text introduced by *The Times* last autumn in place of Stanley Morison's historic Times Roman, impressively underlines the point. Times Europa – destined to provide the text for all Times Newspapers, and discussed in detail later – is an enviable crown of a career.

Tracy's background is interesting and unusual, throwing a good deal of light on his work and its character. For him typography and type design did not begin with abstract academic training, though he had the advantage of two preliminary years at the Central School of Arts and Crafts (where the late J. H. Mason, one of the editors of *The Imprint*, responsible for its famous text type, was head of the printing department), but with the practical business of handling type as a compositor. He was apprenticed in the London house of the celebrated firm of Clowes, noted among other things for its Oriental and 'exotic' setting (including Greek and Russian). Tracy's apprenticeship was on the fringe of these esoteric exercises, though he recalls work on the British Museum Catalogue 'accession' slips – twenty-five copies of each pulled on a hand-press – which not infrequently involved non-Roman setting.

12 point Jubilee, roman, and italic.

THE graphic design of a newspaper is not a thing in itself. The good newspaperman does not assemble type in a page merely to make an agreeable pattern, or as an exercise in display for its own sake. Typography and make-up in a newspaper are only a vehicle for journalism; and it is journalism that is the most important. If it is poorly presented, however, good journalism loses much of its impact. First-class content, therefore, requires first-class form, and so the proper relationship of *form* and *content* is the central

8 point Jubilee, roman, italic, and bold.

THE graphic design of a newspaper is not a thing in itself. The good newspaperman does not assemble type in a page merely to make an agreeable pattern, or as an exercise in display for its own sake. Typography and make-up in a newspaper are only a vehicle for *journalism; and it is journalism that is the most important. If it is* poorly presented, however, good journalism loses much of its impact. First-class content, therefore, requires first-class form and thus the proper relationship of *form* and *content* is the central question of newspaper typography. Stanley Morison put the point admirably in the last sentence of his **famous book on the evolution of**

12 point Linotype Modern.

THE graphic design of a newspaper is not a thing in itself. The good newspaperman does not assemble type in a page merely to make an agreeable pattern, or as an exercise in display for its own sake. Typography and make-up in a newspaper are only a vehicle for journalism; and it is journalism that is the most important. If it is poorly presented, however, good journalism loses much of its impact. First-class content, therefore, requires first-class form.

8 point Linotype Modern, roman, italic, bold.

THE graphic design of a newspaper is not a thing in itself. The good newspaperman does not assemble type in a page merely to make an agreeable pattern, or as an exercise in display for its own sake. Typography and make-up in a newspaper are only a *vehicle for journalism; and it is journalism that is the most im-*portant. If it is poorly presented, however, good journalism loses much of its impact. First-class content, therefore, requires first-class form, and so the proper relationship of *form* and *content* is the central question of newspaper typography. Stanley Morison put the point admirably in **the last sentence of his famous**

ABCDEFGHIJKLMNOPQRSTU
VWXYZ 1234567890
abcdefghijklmnopqrstuvwxyz
ABCDEFGHIJKLMNOPQRSTU
VWXYZ 1234567890
abcdefghijklmnopqrstuvwxyz
ABCDEFGHIJKLMNOPQRSTU
VWXYZ1234567890
abcdefghijklmnopqrstuvwxyz

8 point Jubilee, roman, italic, and bold.

ABCDEFGHIJKLMNOPQRSTU
VWXYZ 1234567890
abcdefghijklmnopqrstuvwxyz
ABCDEFGHIJKLMNOPQRSTU
VWXYZ 1234567890
abcdefghijklmnopqrstuvwxyz
ABCDEFGHIJKLMNOPQRSTU
VWXYZ 1234567890
abcdefghijklmnopqrstuvwxyz

8 point Linotype Modern, roman, italic, bold.

Coming out of his time early in 1935, Tracy continued for several months at Clowes as a qualified compositor; at the end of the year he left to join the typographic studio of the Baynard Press in South London, an establishment then of high repute and handling much first-class work. In those days this was a fairly novel move for a young compositor and it was crucial for Tracy's own development. To practice, as it were, he was now able to add theory, though the two remained intimately connected; the Baynard studio was directly over the composing room, so that designer and compositor were in close contact and working together at every stage. The studio gave Tracy the chance to develop his skill as a typographic draughtsman; and he was also able to start acquiring his wide and deep erudition in all matters of typographic practice and history. As a sort of bonus the Baynard Press offered him the opportunity to become well acquainted with lithographic work, since it had a subsidiary litho plant nearby where Tracy recalls often seeing the late and great Barnett Freedman drawing direct on the stone.

At the end of 1938 Tracy moved to an advertising agency, where he spent about seven years, until he left the firm to freelance. In the autumn of 1946 the late James Shand of the Shenval Press offered Tracy a part-time job on a freelance basis, assisting with the Art and Technics publishing venture which Shand had just started, and which in addition to books was responsible for the later numbers of *Alphabet & Image*. In the spring of 1947 Shand – association with whom Tracy says he found '*very* rewarding' – secured him a complementary part-time post editing the revived *Linotype Matrix* for Linotype & Machinery Ltd. Vol.II, No.1 of the *Matrix* appeared in the spring of 1948 (Vol.I, edited by Shand, had only a few issues, just before the war). Appearing irregularly – it was described as an 'occasional publication' – it reached No.35 (1961) and was one of the most distinguished and informative house journals of the sort that the printing trade has known. After the first score of issues Tracy was relieved of the detailed work of editorship; he had become a full-time member of the Linotype & Machinery staff in 1949, and was now preoccupied with problems of type design.

These included Oriental forms, for Linotype, like all other composing-machine manufacturers, faced an insistent postwar demand from developing Eastern countries for mechanical composition of their non-Roman alphabets or scripts. With most of the Indian languages this presented no great problem; they had existed in movable type for

very many years and these types made suitable models for matrices.
Other languages required simplification before they could be
accommodated in matrix founts and on a Linotype keyboard; this was
the case with Amharic, the principal language of Ethiopia, which was
adapted for Linotype in 1955. The difficulties arose with the continuous-
script languages like Persian (adapted in 1958) and more particularly
with Arabic, whose calligraphic complexities hampered easy
mechanical composition. Here the story of the devising of Mrowa
Simplified Arabic – named after Kamel Mrowa, publisher of the
leading Lebanese daily *Dar Al-Hayat* – is characteristic. Mrowa
dramatically reduced the number of characters required, and Tracy
played a major part in the whole operation; not, as he is at pains to
explain, as a designer (this was done by Mrowa and his calligraphers)
but as supervisor of the translation of the design into matrix form. It is
typical of Tracy, nonetheless, that in the course of this work he
embarked on an intensive study of Arabic calligraphy, to the point at
which he can fairly claim to be able to form a sound aesthetic judgment
between one Arabic script and another.

The Oriental excursions were additional to Tracy's main concern,
which soon emerged as the provision of newspaper texts to meet the
changing production circumstances of the time. His first contribution
in this field was admirably described by himself when he addressed the
World Congress of A TYP I in London in 1971. I quote: 'In the early
1950s newspaper printers in Great Britain began to express
dissatisfaction at the inability of Times Roman to stand up to rapid
composition, stereotyping, and high-speed rotary printing. It seemed to
me that a new design of the same class should be attempted. This was
achieved by reducing the weight of the thick strokes and increasing the
thin strokes and serifs. This redistribution of weight enabled me to
increase the space between the letters, which improved the durability of
the matrices. In the course of designing, there developed in some
characters a strong echo of the Plantin type which was the general
model for Times Roman. The result was called Jubilee.'

This designation was of no more than house significance; the type
was completed in 1953, the Golden Jubilee of the incorporation of
Linotype & Machinery Ltd under that title (a merger of the original
Linotype Co. and the Machinery Trust). First installed by the *Glasgow
Herald* and its companion papers in 1954 (they still use it) Jubilee
scored substantial successes in the ensuing ten years. Adopted by a
string of provincial dailies and weeklies (the award-winning Beckett

THE GRAPHIC DESIGN of a newspaper is not a thing in itself. The good newspaperman does not assemble type in a page merely to make an agreeable pattern, or as an exercise in display for its own sake. Typography and make-up in a newspaper are only a vehicle for journalism; and it is journalism that is the most important. If it is poorly presented, however, good journalism loses much of its impact. First-class content, therefore, requires first-class form, and so the proper relationship of **form** and **content** is the central question of newspaper typography. Stanley Morison put the point admirably in the last sentence of his famous book on the evolution of English newspaper typography: 'The community would unquestionably benefit if **men of learning** would extend their interest to the end that the tranquillity, exactitude,

ABCDEFGHIJKLMNOPQRSTUVWXYZ
abcdefghijklmnopqrstuvwxyz 1234567890
ABCDEFGHIJKLMNOPQRSTUVWXYZ
abcdefghijklmnopqrstuvwxyz 1234567890

4¾ point Maximus.

Group of South Coast weeklies hastened to substitute it for Times Roman), by the *Morning Advertiser*, the *Daily Worker* (it continues, in the *Morning Star*, to show how well it works with web-offset, repro-proofed from hot metal), the *Parisien Libéré*, it reached the summit of Fleet Street approval when it was put in by the *Daily Telegraph* (1959) and the *Daily Mail* (1964). The fact that years later both the last-named papers had to change again, because of production problems with lightweight newsprint, was not relevant at the time. And it is noteworthy that Jubilee still ranks among Linotype & Machinery's top twenty-five matrix best-sellers.

As Tracy said, Jubilee was a news-text in the same class as Times Roman, namely a face that could broadly be described as Old Face (garalde) in its general design, its diagonal stress and its serif-structure: like Times, it could be described as 'a bit bookish', to quote a *Daily Worker* stonehand when it was introduced in that newspaper. In my contemporary estimate of Jubilee in THE PENROSE ANNUAL (1955) I wrote: 'In a sense it stands midway between Times and Excelsior. It meets the requirements of dry-flong stereotyping and high-speed rotary machining by being as open and sturdy as Excelsior and as big on its body. But in set-width it approximates to the economy of Times . . . Its serifs are blunt, as in Excelsior, but not left square; the simple device of chamfering the ends gives finish and sharpness without emulating the elegance of Times and its fine bracketed serifs.' I went on to note the 'delicacy of the design calculation' in the matter of shading, vital for retaining the open counters of the face and the stouter sidewalls of the matrices (the rapid breakdown of Times sidewalls presented all users of that face with a chronic and expensive problem). 'Taking an Old-Face thick-thin contrast in 10 pt', I remarked, 'Jubilee transfers approximately 0·001-inch of shading from the thick stroke to the thin; this transfer of shading is the means of achieving the open counters and the side-spacing.' To which it should be added that, as well as a strong related bold, Jubilee had an exceptionally good, close-fitting italic, one of the best and smoothest italics in any linecaster face.

Just as Jubilee's conception was motivated by the unsatisfactory performance of Times under common newspaper production conditions, so was Tracy's next venture. The post-war pressure on classified advertising space had led *The Times* in 1951 to introduce a 4¾ pt version of Times Roman, the celebrated Claritas, a typographic *tour de force*. This body size, yielding no fewer than fifteen lines to the column inch, proved an irresistible attraction to evening paper publishers in particular. But the delicacies of Times, which were making it unsatisfactory in the ordinary text sizes, proved even worse in this microsize. Thus Tracy had to solve the problem of producing a $4\frac{3}{4}$ pt type which would stand up to the production rush of mass-circulation evenings.

The classified advertising manager of the London *Evening News* had been much attracted by the sans style for 'smalls' common in American newspapers; this was the agate ($5\frac{1}{2}$ pt) size of Spartan Book with Heavy – a sans of German geometric style resembling Futura. But this face had never been made in $4\frac{3}{4}$ pt, which the *Evening News* man wanted, nor could it be automatically so reduced. Tracy therefore worked over the idea of a microsize, more of modernized Grot or Gothic style. The result was Adsans, first used in the *Evening News* in 1959; it was an instant success. Many daily and large weekly papers hastened to follow the example of the *Evening News*, including the *Sydney Morning Herald* in Australia. Not to be outdone by its rival, the Claritas-using London *Evening Standard* commissioned a $4\frac{3}{4}$ pt sans imitation from Intertype; but Standard Gothic proved an unsatisfactory imitation and had a short life.

Whatever arguments may go on about a sans for continuous text setting – and the 'smalls', where the reader is usually interested only in one section, are not really continuous text – there was no question that Adsans retained acceptable clarity under the roughest production conditions. Ingenious reduction of the descenders gave it a large face size (its $4\frac{3}{4}$ pt face was equal to that of some 5 pt or even $5\frac{1}{2}$ pt faces); the related bold amply contrasted with the normal weight; the all-important figures and fractions had been designed clear and wide.

Obviously a sans-serif was far from being the only, or the final, solution of the $4\frac{3}{4}$ pt 'smalls' problem. During the sixties demands for a

Enlargements of 8 point Jubilee (right) and 8 point Linotype Modern (below).

CM agsk
MR bcmt

new seriffed 4¾ pt grew; the most intense pressure came, naturally enough, from the *Daily Telegraph*, the national morning with by far the heaviest 'smalls' paging, which was finding its Claritas more and more unsatisfactory. Tracy's answer was Maximus, a 4¾ pt roman of novel design, duplexed either with a suitably strong related bold or a good, open Doric. It appeared in the *Telegraph* in mid-December 1967 and has since shown its capacity to adapt to the narrow measure of the ten-column make-up adopted by the *Telegraph* for its classified pages.

In design Maximus was what Tracy would call a 'hybrid'. Its serifs were sturdy and its sidewalls strong; but its main feature was its open appearance, far more open than any other microsize romans; this was secured by giving it greater width, its lower-case alphabet gauging 9 pts more than that of Claritas. At the same time unusual drawing of certain letters, like the lower-case 'g' (given an open-looped tail instead of the conventional bowl), helped to ensure the clarity of the face. While the greater width of Maximus might increase the linage of some 'smalls' (no disadvantage to the publishers, with all lines chargeable) its clear printing quality gave the *Telegraph*'s classified columns new impact. So much so, indeed, that Tracy's design was forthwith the victim of that imitation which can at any rate be reckoned the sincerest form of flattery; for the *Sunday Times*, Intertype proceeded to cut 4¾ pt Classad, an extraordinary copy of Maximus (open-tailed lower-case 'g' and all).

The setting of 'smalls' was not the only typographic worry of the *Telegraph* at this time. Advertising was steadily swelling the paper's paging, with thirty-two-page broadsheet issues a daily occurrence. This in turn had compelled the use of lighter newsprint, so light indeed that to avoid strike-through the pressmen were having to hold colour back to the point at which the Jubilee text printed far too grey and weak.

Enlargements of 4¾ point Adsans (right) and 4¾ point Maximus (below).

GR ae t3

ES htwc

THE graphic design of a newspaper is not a thing in itself. The good newspaperman does not assemble type in a page merely to make an agreeable pattern, or as an exercise in display for its own sake. Typography and make-up in a newspaper are only a vehicle for journalism; *and it is journalism that is the most important. If it is poorly presented,* however, good journalism loses much of its impact. First-class content, therefore, requires first-class form, and so the proper relationship of *form* and *content* is the central question of newspaper typography. Stanley Morison put the point admirably in the last sentence **of his famous book on the evolution of English newspaper design.**

7 point Times Europa.

THE graphic design of a newspaper is not a thing in itself. The good newspaperman does not assemble type in a page merely to make an agreeable pattern, or as an exercise in display for its own sake. Typography and make-up in a newspaper are only a *vehicle for journalism and it is journalism that is the most im-*portant. If it is poorly presented, however, good journalism loses much of its impact. First-class content, therefore, requires first-class form, and so the proper relationship of *form* and *content* is the central question of newspaper typography. Stanley Mori-**son put the point admirably in the last sentence of his famous**

8 point Times Europa.

THE graphic design of a newspaper is not a thing in itself. The good newspaperman does not assemble type in a page merely to make an agreeable pattern, or as an exercise in display for its own sake. Typography and make-up in a *newspaper are only a vehicle for journalism; and it is* journalism that is the most important. If it is poorly presented, however, good journalism loses much of its impact. First-class content, therefore, requires first-class form, and so the proper relationship of *form* and *content* is the cen-**tral question of newspaper typography. Stanley Morison**

9 point Times Europa

Maximus was still under way when Tracy began to turn his mind to this wider problem. More than once he has stressed that there are several ways of approaching the design of news-texts; in 1971 he told the A TYP I Congress that 'the designer should not attempt to produce a "universal" type. Instead he should design for a particular class of newspaper and satisfy *its* particular requirements'. Evidently the Old Face design of Jubilee did not satisfy the particular requirements of the *Telegraph*. What was to be the next step?

In the course of a provincial lecture-tour for the Linotype organization in 1966, Tracy and I had the opportunity to discuss this next step. We both agreed that the most fruitful move would probably be some adaptation of Modern (didone). The odd thing was that neither of us then recalled the highly relevant prophecy of Stanley Morison back in 1936. Writing (anonymously, as usual) on 'The Editorial Text' in the *Monotype Recorder* Vol.XXXV, No.1 of that year, Morison developed a detailed criticism of the Ionic news-text which concluded with these words: 'Certainly *Ionic* is materially better, technically, than most of the "modern" founts made available during the past forty years to line-composed newspapers. It is open and clear in design; it is well drawn and perfect in cut. But a similarly high degree of technical ability given to the old-fashioned "modern" would have transformed it into a very desirable face. It is more than probable that such a revised "modern" would be more readable than the admittedly readable American *Ionic*.'

Just this 'revision' or 'transformation' was what Tracy now undertook. For we had unitedly concluded that the basic Modern design offered the possibility of the necessary colour (to overcome thin inking on light newsprint) together with that crispness and contrast essential to a good news-text and notably lacking in the widely popular Corona (crowning achievement of the long 'Legibility Group' line begun by Ionic) and its Intertype version Royal. It is worth adding that we both had our eyes on the originators of Modern, the Didots.

Late in the 1930s, when James Shand asked whether I had any notions for a new newspaper text, I recall producing a Didot setting of 1838 which had attracted me. Tracy had delivered a lecture on the Didots in a St Bride London University series in 1955, using it as the basis for a similar lecture in a Paul A. Bennett Memorial series in New York in 1967; the curious may be referred to a two-page version of the 1955 lecture which appeared in *Linotype Matrix 24*. It is an impressive piece of erudition about a dynasty of type-designers and printers whom

ABCDEFGHIJKLMNOPQRSTU
VWXYZ 1234567890
abcdefghijklmnopqrstuvwxyz
ABCDEFGHIJKLMNOPQRSTU
VWXYZ 1234567890
abcdefghijklmnopqrstuvwxyz
ABCDEFGHIJKLMNOPQRSTU
VWXYZ 1234567890
abcdefghijklmnopqrstuvwxyz

8 point Times Europa, roman, italic, and bold.

it has too long been the custom to decry; with the self-effacement typical of Tracy it was presented in the *Matrix* with no by-line or other identification of the lecturer.

When the new face, Linotype Modern, finally emerged, to be successfully installed by the *Daily Telegraph* and its Sunday companion in May 1969, two things about it caught the eye. Tracy had re-worked the idiom of vertical stress, thick-thin contrast, unbracketed serifs in a quite new way; he had produced a very modern Modern. Further, his Didot inspiration was specific, not general; he had kept before him ('because I have always admired it', he later said) the father of all Moderns, the François Ambroise Didot face of 1784. 'Of course', to quote Tracy again, 'the spare elegance of this design, due to its very thin strokes and its fine serifs, has no place in a newspaper type. But some of the character shapes are echoed in the new design.' This was true, for example, of the lower-case 'a', as may readily be seen from the enlarged double-spread of the 1784 Didot which adorned my review of Linotype Modern in THE PENROSE ANNUAL (1970).

Perhaps I may repeat here the summary, in that review, of the principal design points of Linotype Modern: '(1) the x-height is generous, making it as big on its body as its "Legibility Group" predecessors; (2) all strokes are firmly and stoutly drawn, while retaining sufficient up-and-down contrast to avoid any monotone effect; (3) the flat, unbracketed serifs are sturdy, to come unscathed through moulding pressures; (4) letters are open in cut, to avoid ink fill-in. In letters like the cap "M" the crotches have been opened up – a special tool being devised for the purpose – so that ink accumulation will not blur the sharp appearing angle.'

As with Maximus, Tracy was generous in the set-width of Linotype Modern; and in so doing he exploded the myth, first propagated by Morison and long supported by myself among others, that a certain degree of condensation ('slenderness', Morison called it) is necessary in a news-text to save space. Tracy was able to demonstrate that, given the frequent paragraphing usual in modern newspaper presentation, the breaklines at the end of paragraphs were able to absorb the extra wordage arising from a wider text face. When a *Telegraph* page, set in Jubilee, was re-set in Linotype Modern, there were only three places in a page of eight 22-inch columns where the Modern made an extra line.

The success of Linotype Modern in the *Telegraph* led to its adoption by the *Evening Echo* (Southampton), by the *Cork Examiner* group (the Irish Republic's only dailies outside Dublin) and by a leading

EGMR

EGMR

CMRS

GKSW

These enlarged sample characters show
8 point Times Roman (top line) compared
with 8 point Times Europa, roman, italic,
and bold. The width of Times Europa
capitals is the same as Times Roman, but
the lower case has wider side-spacing,
giving stouter matrix sidewalls.

benstw

benstw

anpstw

gknry

Pastor Douglas Nichols, the first Aboriginal to receive a knighthood, and Mrs Nichols photograph[ed at] Palace for yesterday's investiture. Pastor Nichols is in charge of the Church of Christ, Melbourn[e]

Mr J. Scott
and Miss S. Ellison

The engagement is announced between Julian, son of Mrs Muriel Scott and the late Mr Alex Scott, of Ashington, Sussex, and Sally, daughter of Mrs Walter Salmon and stepdaughter of Mr Walter Salmon, of Angley Lake, Cranbrook, Kent.

Dr R. C. Tiptaft
and Miss H. G. Meadows

The engagement is announced between Richard, son of Mr and Mrs C. H. Tiptaft, of 26 Radinden Manor Road, Hove, and Gaye, younger daughter of Commander H. T. Meadows, DSC, RD, RNR (Retd), and Dr J. Meadows, of Dungeons Farm, Chorley Wood.

Marriages

The Marquess of Headfort
and Miss Virginia Nable

The marriage took place in London on November 11 of the Marquess of Headfort and Miss Virginia Nable.

Lord Bagot
and Mrs M. Hewitt

The marriage took place quietly in London on November 13 between Lord Bagot and Mrs Mary Hewitt.

Birthdays today

Sir Olaf Caroe, 80; Sir Hugh Greene, 62; Mr Averell Harriman, 81; Miss G. Ceris Jones, 66; Sir Richard Le Gallais, 56; Major-General J. K. Shepheard, 64; Sir Sacheverell Sitwell, 75; Air Vice-Marshal Sir John Weston, 64.

Dinners

Anglo-German Association

The annual dinner and dance of the Anglo-German Association took place yesterday at the Café Royal. Sir Christopher Steel, chairman of the association, presided and with Lady Steel received the guests. The other speaker was Mr A. L. Pope. Among those present were:

The German Chargé d'Affaires and Frau von Schmidt-Pauli, Mr T. Bradley, MP, and Mrs Bradley, Mr Walter A Brandt, Professor Sir George and Lady Catlin, Mr B J Hayhoe MP, and Mrs Hayhoe Lord and Lady Inglewood, Frau D. Krug, Air Chief Marshal Sir Christopher and Lady Foxley-Norris, Mrs A L Pope, Sir Frank and Lady Roberts Sir Eugene Melville, Herr Josef Stingl, Mr and Mrs George Turner and Professor and Frau Rudolf Wille

Tate Gallery

Sir Robert Sainsbury, chairman of the Tate Gallery Trustees, and Sir Norman Reid, director, were hosts at a dinner held at the Tate Gallery yesterday before a preview of the exhibition "The Age of Charles I". Those present included:

The Duke and Duchess of Gratton, the Duke and Duchess of Hamilton, the Duke and Duchess of Westminster, the Earl and Countess Beauchamp, the Earl and Countess of Bradford, the Earl and Countess of Dartmouth, the Earl and Countess of Radnor, Earl Spencer, Lord Brooke, Lord and Lady Ballantrae, Lady Lee of Asheridge, Lord and Lady Strabolgi, Lord Sackville, Lord and Lady Sandys, the Hon Alan and Mrs Clark, Sir Giles Isham, Sir Thomas and Lady Monnington, Sir John Pope-Hennessy, Sir Charles and Lady Wishaw, Mrs Humphrey Brand, Mr and Mrs Edmund Brudenell, Lieutenant-Colonel and Mrs H. R. Davies, Lieutenant-Colonel and the Hon Mrs John Johnston, Mr and Mrs L. G Stopford Sackville, Mr Edmund Verney, Mr and Mrs Simon Wingfield-Digby Dr and Mrs Roy Strong, Mr and Mrs Patrick Gibson, Mr and Mrs Oliver Millar, Mr and Mrs Alan Irvine and Mr and Mrs Anthony Lousada

United and Cecil Club

The United and Cecil Club dined last night at St Stephen's Club. Mr Edward Gardner, QC, MP (chairman) presided and the guest of honour was the Lord Chief Justice.

Wolfe Society

The annual dinner of the Wolfe Society was held last night at the Crown Hotel, Westerham. Mr J. St A. Warde presided and the guest of honour was Lord Tweedsmuir.

Windsor Castle

Peers learn how to lure tourists to [...]

From Christopher Warman
Beaulieu, Nov 14

The most select school in Britain opened its doors today to a group of pupils, including two peers of the realm, for a three-day course on a subject close to their bank balances.

Some 30 owners of historic homes and others associated with them gathered at the feet of their headmaster, Lord Montagu of Beaulieu, who during the past few years has practised what he preaches with such success that more than 500,000 people visit his Hampshire home annually and help to keep it in good repair.

For £100 a head the class will be told how to attract visitors, to run their homes as businesses, and to make them pay for themselves.

The course, "Leisure in the Countryside", has been arranged by Lord Montagu on behalf of the historic houses committee of the British Tourist Authority. He ran a similar course last year, when three peers joined it. This time Lord Bathurst, owner of Cirencester Park, Gloucestershire, and Lord Somerleyton, of Somerleyton Hall, Suffolk, head the list. Pupils include the administrator of Blenheim Palace, owners of historic homes in Scotland and the North of England, and members of the Historic Irish Tourist

Houses and Gardens Association, invitingly known as Hither.

Hither's organizing secretary, Mrs Brenda Weir, had to admit that tourism in Ireland was "not all that bright at the moment", but Irishmen had been persuaded to look at their own heritage, and figures for the top attractions had in the past two years risen from 250,000 to 500,000.

What Ireland has lost in tourists because of the troubles, Scotland appears to have gained. Mr A. J. Munro, assistant factor at Blair Castle, Perthshire, seat of the Duke of Atholl, said there had been noticeable increase this year in the number of Irish visitors, and in the number of tourists who had said that they would otherwise have gone to Ireland.

Mr Munro is here for his second consecutive course and is full of praise for the idea. "It was of great value to us last year, and we were pleased to see our numbers increase, and to be able to cope", he said.

Lord Bathurst has no aspirations to emulate the range provided at Beaulieu or Longleat or Woburn. "We are not in competition with any other stately home, except for our polo", he said. We had about 15,000 visitors during the season, and our aim is to provide good facilities for the people who want to come

"It is becoming a business but ours is low-key. What I want is to

be able to keep and mainta[in] Cirencester Park."

He enrolled for the course [be]cause "this is the centre of state home expertise. It is my humb[le] view that they have got it tape[d]. This is a very fine set-up".

He looked somewhat aghast [at] the new complex of buildings hou[s]ing the motor museum and thoug[ht] it looked like an atom bomb inst[al]lation. "But I am warming to [it] now", he added.

He and the other owners [of] historic homes have been surpris[ed] at the boom. It has come so quick[ly] that they have on occasions be[en] unable to cope with the numbe[r] of people arriving to view the[ir] treasures. This year, for examp[le] privately owned homes attract[ed] 500,000 more paying custome[rs] than last year, and the total w[as] more than seven million.

Lord Montagu faced the sa[me] trouble a year or two ago; he sa[id] that Beaulieu village was bei[ng] choked by the people coming [to] visit him, and he had to expand [his] operations. Now the staff [at] Beaulieu, with other gu[est] speakers, are handing on the[ir] skills. The subjects include pla[n]ning, taxation, architecture, so[u]venirs, catering, and publicity.

The difficulties can often [be] trivial. Warwick Castle, for e[x]ample, suddenly gained many mo[re] visitors by the simple measure [of] moving the pay kiosk from a poi[nt] where visitors could see only [...]

Luncheons

HM Government

Her Majesty's Government gave a luncheon yesterday at Admiralty House in honour of the Ambassador of Rwanda. Baroness Tweedsmuir of Belhelvie, Minister of State at the Foreign and Commonwealth Office, was hostess. The Cameroon Ambassador was among the guests

Sir Denys Lowson

Sir Denys Lowson, joint President of the British Section of the Council of European Municipalities, gave a luncheon at the Savoy Hotel to the officers and council members of the British section Those present included:

Mr Geoffrey Rippon, QC, MP, joint President, Mr Arthur Woodburn, joint President, Mr

John Hay MP, Chairman, Mr Charles Boreham, Secretary General, and officers and members of the council

IBM United Kingdom Limited

Mr W. McChesney Martin was the speaker at a luncheon held yesterday by IBM United Kingdom Limited at Grocers' Hall. Mr E. R. Nixon, managing director, was in the chair

Receptions

HM Government

Mr John Davies, Chancellor of the Duchy of Lancaster, and Mrs Davies were hosts at a reception held at Lancaster House last night in honour of delegates attending the Business International Round Table Conference.

British Council

Dr F. J. Llewellyn, Directo[r] General of the British Council, w[as] host at a reception held at t[he] council headquarters yesterday [in] honour of Mr George Rylan[ds]. Among those present were:

Lord and Lady Annan, Lady Barlow, Edward Lewis, Lady Redgrave, Mr Mich[ael] Hordern Mr and Mrs Richard Pasco [and] Professor T J B Spencer

Service reception

14th/20th King's Hussars

Princess Anne, Colonel in Chief [of] the regiment, was present at [an] informal reception of the 14th/20th King's Hussars held at the Caval[ry] Club last night before the office[rs'] annual dinner, at which Colon[el] R. P. D. F. Allen, colonel of t[he] regiment, presided.

Chinese vase fetches £50,000 among high prices for oriental ceramics

By Geraldine Norman
Sale Room Correspondent

Oriental taste again showed its power to confound Western experts when a green-ground Tz'u Chou vase of the eleventh or twelfth century was sold for £50,000 at Sotheby's yesterday. The purchaser was J. T. Tai, a Chinese dealer based in New York.

Imperial wares of the Sung dynasty, widely considered the greatest era of ceramic art, have reached this price level in the past but not the lesser Tz'u Chou wares

The vase is a considerable rarity Sotheby's had discovered only four other recorded examples. It is beautifully painted in dark [...]

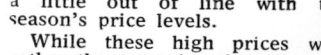

a little out of line with t[his] season's price levels.

While these high prices we[re] rather the exception than the rul[e] values overall were much above th[e] 1971-72 season. And 1971-72 w[as] the *annus mirabilis* for Chine[se] porcelain when Japanese biddi[ng] carried prices to undreamt-[of] levels. Again Japanese buyers an[d] almost more important, Japane[se] underbidders, were probably r[e]sponsible for the exceptional pric[es] at yesterday's sale.

Other major prices included [a] T'ang chestnut glazed wa[ter] figure of a Fereghan horse, [...] inches high, at £18,000 (Eskenaz[i]) a thousand or so above expect[ed]

Yorkshire weekly, the *Barnsley Chronicle*. As the *Chronicle* is photo-set on a Linotype V-I-P machine, Tracy re-drew the entire fount with a carefully calculated fractional increase in weight to allow for light web-offset inking when many half-tones are run.

We must now return to 1966 and *The Times*. It was a year of great change for the premier daily – news on the front page in May and acquisition by Lord Thomson in the autumn. Tracy had been retained as one of its technical advisers. It became progressively more apparent that the unsatisfactory text performance of Times Roman under common production conditions – which, as we have seen, led Tracy in the early fifties to design Jubilee – was being repeated in Printing House Square itself. The brilliance of Times Roman had always required careful presswork, possible with relatively slow running, on high-grade mechanical printing. When the run virtually doubled, and ordinary newsprint had to be used, the famous face went to pieces. By 1970 it was being appreciated that the day of Times Roman, as an effective and legible news-text under current production conditions, was over. A highly critical 're-assessment' of Times Roman which I contributed in the summer of that year to the *Journal of Typographic Research* (Vol.IV, No.3) was accepted as valid in leading circles of Times Newspapers. A committee of editorial men and other experts was set up, as it had been forty years before when Morison pressed the question of a new typography for *The Times*, with Tracy as consultant designer. In December 1970 I was asked to submit an exploratory memorandum to this committee; in this I argued first, that an entirely new text design was necessary, second, that it must be distinctive and appropriate in character for Times Newspapers as a group (i.e. for the *Sunday Times* as well as *The Times* and its supplements).

This view, which was also Tracy's own view, prevailed. Two designs emerged in the course of the committee's deliberations – one a re-drawing of Ionic, which need not concern us further, the other an original design by Tracy which the committee recommended to the board of Times Newspapers, and which the board accepted as the new text-type, in the autumn of 1971. Given the name Times Europa, this was the text, in 9, 8 and 7 pt, to which *The Times* changed over in October 1972, just forty years after the introduction of Morison's Times New Roman. The *Sunday Times* was expected to follow suit at an appropriate point not determinable as these lines were written.

In his third, and in many ways most remarkable, major news-text, Tracy has completed ringing the obvious changes. If Jubilee may be

Model Roger Law : Photograph Brian Morris

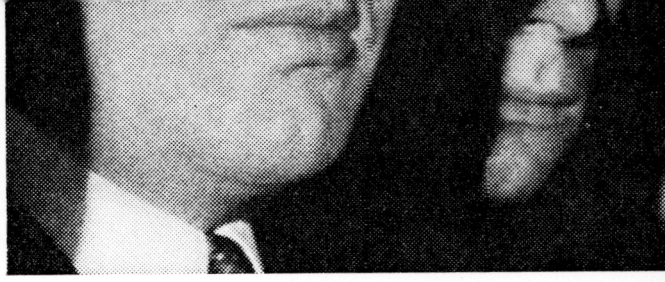

The Krays : A black side and a white side ?

The trial of Ronald and Reginald Kray was one of the longest in British judicial history. It revealed an extent of violence and organized crime previously unknown in this country. The activities which "The Firm", as the twins' criminal network was known, covered at its height ranged from murder and protection into fraud, crooked share dealing, gambling and beyond. Throughout, their main weapon was intimidation on a massive scale.

In the summer of 1967, perhaps sensing that after years of failure the police were beginning to close in, the Krays decided they would like a writer to chronicle their history. With characteristic flamboyance, they made contact with McGraw-Hill, one of America's largest publishing houses. In their turn, McGraw-Hill contacted John Pearson, a British author who had become a tax exile in Rome, as a result of the royalties earned from his best-selling account of the life of Ian Fleming.

A mild, a soft-spoken former journalist, Pearson looks anything but the part. Even today, he recounts his first meeting with his subjects in slightly disbelieving tones. "At the time I did not have the slightest idea what I would be involved in. I was merely told that a silver Mercedes would be waiting at the airport and that a suite had been booked at the Ritz."

Pearson readily admits to having strong initial doubts about the project. "I think it was genuine naivety that made me take it on—having been living abroad, I had no idea about these men's reputation."

For seven months, Pearson commuted improbably between Rome and a flat in Albert Family Dwellings, Bethnal Green, which had been leased to him by the twins. Referred to always as "the writer", and treated as something of a novelty, he was introduced to a small army of Cockney villains, the family and also given access to their psychiatrist and doctor. "The relationship was fine until they got hold of some letters written by my agent which

referred to their paranoia and also to a 'Scotland Yard scrambler'. After that, they never lost their suspicion of me."

Many friends and colleagues warned him of the risks he was taking, and one leading Oxford don accused him of making personal gain out of the Krays' criminal activities. "I had a few twinges in the early days", he admits, "but really it was a situation which no writer could resist."

Author of one novel and biographer of the speed ace Donald Campbell, Pearson had never been in contact with the underworld. "I found myself again and again trying to decide about the nature of evil and what I thought about the twins. I finally solved it to my own satisfaction by saying that they were split personalities with a white and a black side. On the one were two amiable people ; very good hosts who were easy to get on with, family loving men who did many good turns. There was also their criminal side, which was something quite different. Whether this is special pleading or another piece of naivety on my part, I don't know."

In his book, Pearson attempts to bring out a point which was deliberately underplayed at the trial—the strange and frightening power which the Krays gained from being identical twins. He also puts their criminal empire into the context of its East End background.

"They were an anachronism left over from the boozing, roistering world of nineteenth-century London. The more time I spent with them, the more became convinced that they

were throwbacks who had part in the modern East En

Today Mr Pearson is to found far from the nights frequented by the Krays their associates, living a dom cated life in a draughty Su rectory. Although he claim have received no real thr the uneasiness which came f such intimate knowledge o many hardened criminals left its mark: his teleph number remains ex-direct his address is rarely given a and when dining in Londo chooses his restaurant special care.

Pearson seems relieved have left the claustroph world of the Krays and retu to gentler literary pursuits. forgetting it completely wil be easy. Only last month, Ro sent a letter to his mo accusing Pearson of dou crossing and calling the l "a lot of rubbish and lies".

It is hard to imagine the brooding happily for the rem ing 26 years of their sent over his concluding paragra "What limited them was the law but their stupi They proved incapable exploiting the power they created and in the end bec self-indulgent and erratic, bored and often surprisi timid. Society was lucky: twins destroyed themse Another time, we may not b fortunate."

Christopher Wal

The Profession of Violence John Pearson will be publi by Weidenfeld and Nico (£3.00) on Thursday and wi reviewed in *The Times* by Gosling on the same day.

---

majority in favour of a realistic settlement with East Germany. But the polls also show that over 80 per cent of all West Germans regard price rises as the most urgent immediate problem facing their country.

Different issues bother different people in different ways. There are also party loyalties to consider, and they are very strong here.

My own belief as the campaign enters its last (but not its dying) days after truly coming to life only a week ago is that Willy Brandt will remain Chancellor, though quite narrowly. But I too am a foreign visitors, and the only logical support I have for my belief is the unanimity of the opinion polls.

Dr Barzel has only to confound the pollsters as Mr Heath did in 1970 to prove me wrong. And in such a finely balanced yet hectic struggle for power as this one, he is much better placed to do so.

Dan van der Vat

ce between The SPD record and mic issues d, being in is able to man treaty e.

away about ccuses the nt haste in reaty's text leadline in artificial n the fact ake up its w and War g and was hly foolish .

ys the two each other n the same ted to ask rmans will an question n inflation Brandt, or Dr Barzel. nion polls s a solid

---

present vice-chairmen, both of whom are lawyers, Antony Buck and Edward Gardner. Deedes will take over the vice-chairmanship vacated by the successful one, which is likely to be Buck, though he may at any moment be whisked away to the still-vacant position of Under-Secretary of State for the Navy.

A broader net, in any case, will have to be cast to find new secretaries; whoever is chosen will have to be a newcomer, because the Government has taken all the committee's activists.

Body blow

Hard on the heels of the pamphlet, *Memorial to the Prime Minister*, there comes from one of its authors the promise that he will vote against the Counter Inflation (Temporary Provision) Bill "all the way" unless the Government radically amends it.

Richard Body, MP for Holland-with-Boston, an apostle of Enoch Powell, sometimes described as a liberal, explained yesterday that he only voted for the bill on its second reading because "a defeat or near defeat

who share his deep concern about the Government's economic policies. Francis Pym, the Government Chief Whip, may be wishing that he had been appointed Minister of Agriculture after all. Whipping on this Bill, Body says, is going to be much tougher than anything in the past two years.

Whistler smother

The beautiful riverscapes of Walter Greaves, the nineteenth-century primitive painter, are going on exhibition for sale in London for the first time since Greaves' death 42 years ago. Greaves, a boatman on Chelsea Reach, taught Whistler to row in return for lessons in etching. Whistler was his arrogant, bullying, adored master. Now Greaves is gradually escaping from Whistler's shadow and coming into his own.

William Darby is exhibiting a collection of oils, watercolours and etchings in his new gallery in Bond Street from November 21 as his first show. Darby has been a keen collector of Greaves since he himself lived in Chelsea in Laurence Street.

Greaves's view of Cheyne Walk with the aged Carlyle.

oils have simply disintegrated, because he was so poor he used any paint he had, including boat paint which may have crumbled away. Some of the pictures have patches in the corners, where they were not supposed to show, because Greaves was too poor to buy whole canvasses and had

resident playwright, David nall, so impressed him that next project is to make a fil it.

The Phoenix and The Tu has no offscreen narration, uses on-the-spot sounds and logue: a highlight is a spee up sequence of the theatre b assembled for the night's formance. The Century The which has for the past 20 y been touring the theatre towns of the north-west of land, consists of a convoy vehicles, a latterday versio Elizabethan strolling player

Peking tube

Peking's new underground way seems likely to go into vice in the near future, acc ing to a western business who was one of a group sh round it last week. Trainl of Chinese sightseers as we foreigners are being taken to existing parts of the sys which is planned to cover eve ally a distance of about 16 m Five stations have been s placed relatively close toget and others are presumably b

---

y

King

") reached laxing on the King membered not in his middle of should not e were no ministerial ays King, ked with ook.

g ?

ty is much ons at the ere is a influential tee of the chairman, rhaps be d chances e elections of his

From *The Times* of 13 November 1972
showing 8 point Times Europa.

labelled Old Face, and Modern is what its name indicates, Times Europa may not unfairly be classed as Transitional ('though with some Old Face flavour' Tracy comments). Well-rounded, generous in width, with good stroke-contrast and crispness of cut, it certainly appears of the same order as the great Transitionals like Baskerville. In this way it amply possesses the requisite distinction, has a lively look lacking in the somewhat flat Royal long used in the *Sunday Times*, and exhibits the strength and colour needed for fast running on light newsprint. It has other technical virtues, like an x-height adjusted to provide the interlinear white essential for newspapers presenting long texts, and sturdy sidewalls which obviate matrix breakdown and the ugly hairlines which have latterly disfigured *The Times*.

At the A TYP I Congress Tracy spoke of 'the common requirement in *all* news text types, a well-developed physique'. Times Europa has that physique. It is a strong letter, 'hybrid' (as Tracy insists) if you like, but welding its various characteristics into a harmonious whole. It is plain and workmanlike, but distinctive and agreeable to the eye. The proof of the news-text is in the reading; and Tracy's Times Europa has now passed that test in *The Times* in exemplary fashion.

Graphic design in newspapers

Raymond Hawkey

A brief study of graphic design techniques as practised by some leading British newspapers. In the fifteen years since Arthur Christiansen first thought up the spectacular new trick of using graphic design in daily newspapers, it has provided the newspaper layout man with a wider variety of accents and intonations; but the métier is an exacting one demanding special skills, which are here described.

Blocks for the illustrations on pages 117 and 118 were made by Leeds Engraving Co. Ltd and those on pages 120 to 123 by Hislop & Day Ltd.

Opposite: A selection of eight-column heading blocks designed by Raymond Hawkey for the *Daily Express* between 1958 and 1964.

A newspaper is like a city. A city which, like London, is an amalgam of districts, each with its own character but all unmistakably part of the whole. A city packed with shops and theatres competing with one another to sell us news, opinion, and entertainment. A city crowded with advertisement hoardings. A city where every day is made to seem like the last shopping day before Christmas.

It is this frenetic competition within themselves which gives newspapers, like cities, their vigour and excitement. Without it, they would seem like ghost towns. All newspapers employ basically the same technique to create this effect, a technique which, in all essential respects, can be traced back to the turn of the century. Headlines and pictures to excite our attention; straplines and standfirsts to win our confidence; crossheads to coax us, like a succession of carrots held before a donkey, to the end of the story.

In 1958, however, a spectacular new trick was added to the traditional repertoire of newspaper presentation techniques: graphic design. It was thought up, like so many of the best journalistic tricks, by Arthur Christiansen for the *Daily Express*. Its function: to introduce a feeling of modernity into the paper while retaining the robustness of traditional methods of presentation.

The form and content of a newspaper are so closely linked that they can rarely be separated. They are, therefore, mostly laid out by a journalist who happens to be a bit of a designer, rather than by a designer who happens to be a bit of a journalist. At the time of Christiansen's innovation, the five men responsible for the appearance of the *Daily Express* were the features editor, the assistant features editor, the so-called page one layout man, the chief sub-editor (responsible for the inside news pages), and the sports editor. They became, in effect, the clients of the newspaper's newly-founded graphic design department and it is a tribute to their initiative, and to the adventurousness of the then editor, Edward Pickering, and, above all his associate editor, Harold Keeble, that modern graphic design techniques have come to be so widely used in newspapers.

Perhaps the best known Fleet Street aphorism is that the news is as big as the headlines. One of the most important advantages gained by the introduction of graphic design techniques (and not foreseen by Arthur Christiansen) is that one can create a feeeling of bigness and a sense of occasion in a fraction of the space demanded by traditional methods.

Graphic design techniques also offer the enterprising newspaper

FAIL SAFE

The book so hot the White House had to clear it

AN EXPRESS PULL-OUT ON THE SECRETS OF A SUCCESSFUL HOLIDAY

SPYING FOR SUMMER

THEY PLAYED THE DEADLIEST GAME OF ALL... ...WITH A WHISPER!

THE INFORMERS

HAUNTING DREAMS
THE STORY OF SIGMUND FREUD

William Hickey AT THE White Rose Wedding

SAFARI TO SOUTHERN RHODESIA

The day the DAILY EXPRESS EARTH CAUGHT FIRE

BOND YOU ONLY LIVE TWICE

阪垣源藏正堅

應需 一筆亀誌

117

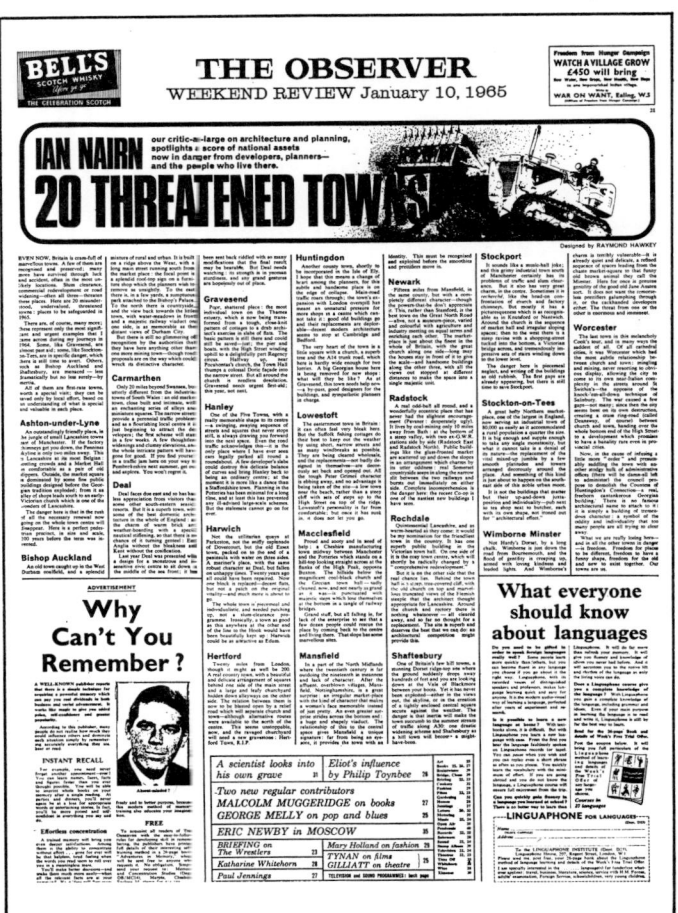

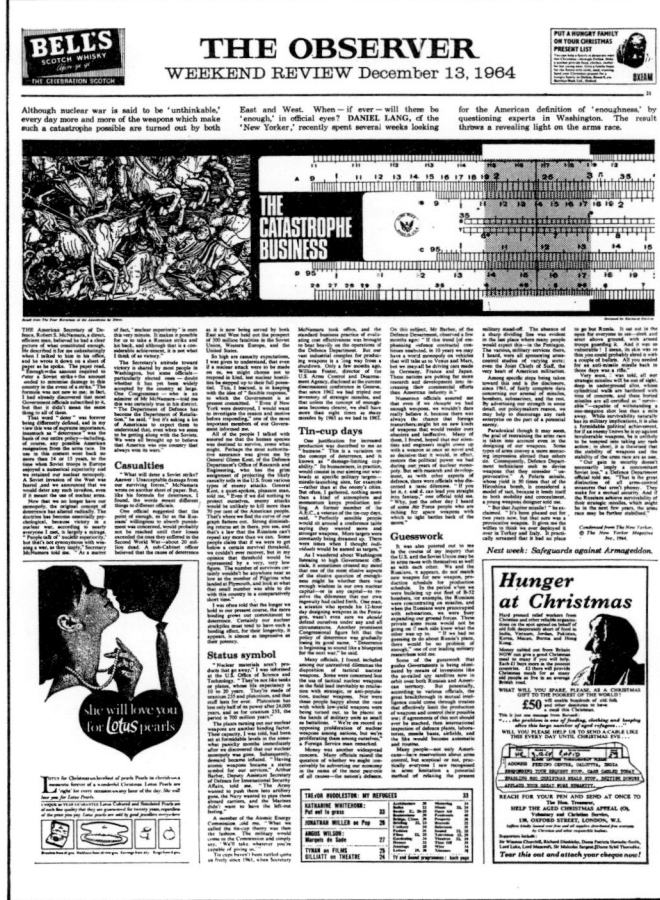

BELL'S SCOTCH WHISKY
THE CELEBRATION SCOTCH
THE OBSERVER
WEEKEND REVIEW January 10, 1965
WATCH A VILLAGE GROW
£450 will bring
WAR ON WANT, Ealing, W.5
IAN NAIRN
20 THREATENED TOWNS
our critic-at-large on architecture and planning, spotlights a score of national assets now in danger from developers, planners—and the people who live there.
Designed by RAYMOND HAWKEY
Ashton-under-Lyne
Bishop Auckland
Carmarthen
Deal
Gravesend
Hanley
Harwich
Hertford
Huntingdon
Lowestoft
Macclesfield
Mansfield
Newark
Radstock
Rochdale
Shaftesbury
Stockport
Stockton-on-Tees
Wimborne Minster
Worcester
Why Can't You Remember?
What everyone should know about languages
LINGUAPHONE
A scientist looks into his own grave
Eliot's influence by Philip Toynbee
Two new regular contributors
MALCOLM MUGGERIDGE on books
GEORGE MELLY on pop and blues
ERIC NEWBY in MOSCOW
BRIEFING on The Wrestlers
Mary Holland on fashion
TYNAN on films
GILLIATT on theatre
Katharine Whitehorn
Paul Jennings

BELL'S SCOTCH WHISKY
THE CELEBRATION SCOTCH
THE OBSERVER
WEEKEND REVIEW December 13, 1964
PUT A HUNGRY FAMILY ON YOUR CHRISTMAS PRESENT LIST
OXFAM
Although nuclear war is said to be 'unthinkable,' every day more and more of the weapons which make such a catastrophe possible are turned out by both East and West. When—if ever—will there be 'enough,' in official eyes? DANIEL LANG, of the 'New Yorker,' recently spent several weeks looking for the American definition of 'enoughness,' by questioning experts in Washington. The result throws a revealing light on the arms race.
THE CATASTROPHE BUSINESS
Casualties
Tin-cup days
Status symbol
Guesswork
she will love you for Lotus pearls
Hunger at Christmas
£50
Next week: Safeguards against Armageddon.

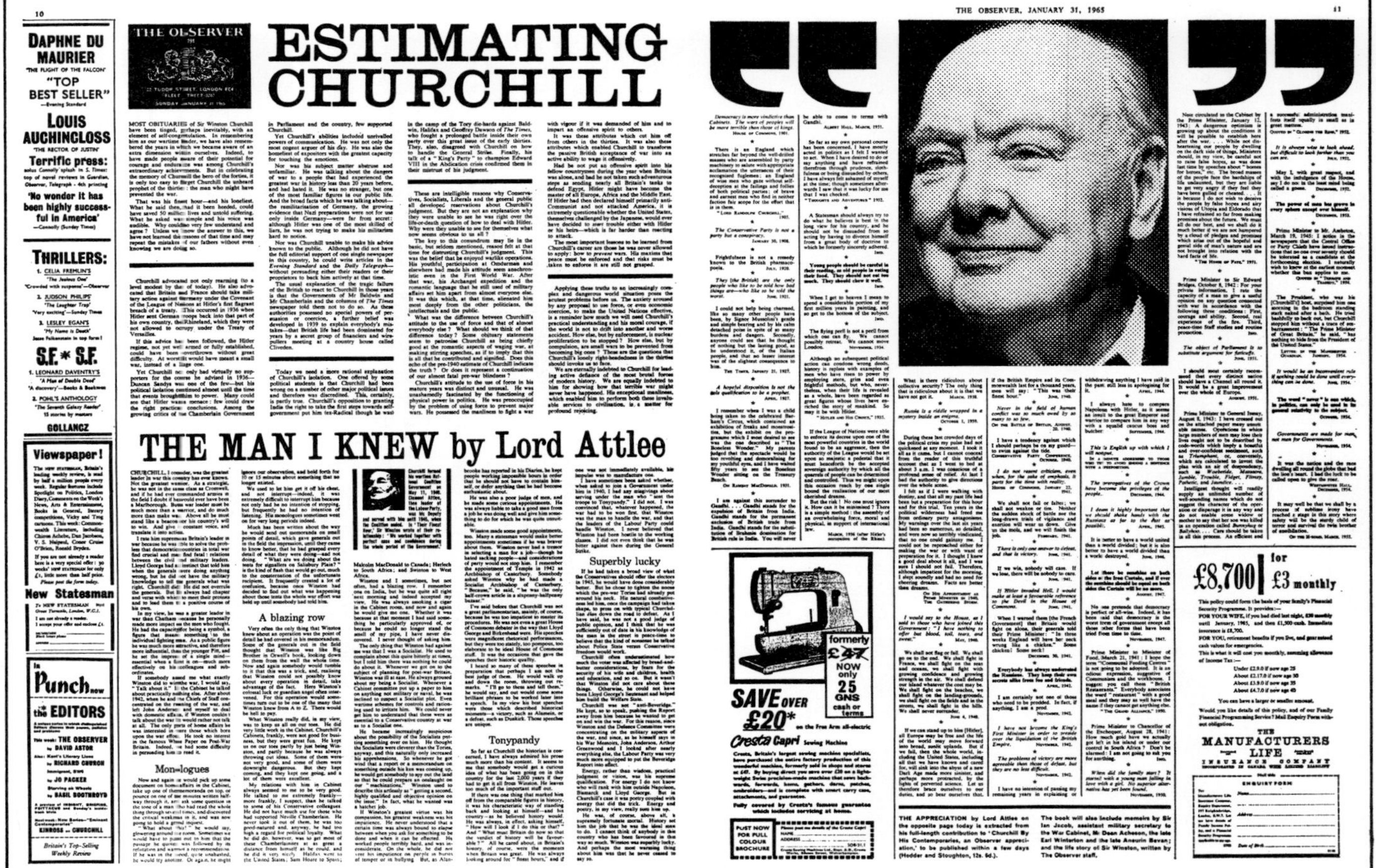
THE OBSERVER, JANUARY 31, 1965
DAPHNE DU MAURIER
"TOP BEST SELLER"
LOUIS AUCHINCLOSS
Terrific press:
'No wonder it has been highly successful in America'
THRILLERS:
S.F. * S.F.
GOLLANCZ
Viewspaper!
New Statesman
Punch
the EDITORS
ESTIMATING CHURCHILL
THE MAN I KNEW by Lord Attlee
A blazing row
Mon-logues
Tonypandy
Superbly lucky
SAVE OVER £20*
Cresta Capri
£8,700 for £3 monthly
THE MANUFACTURERS LIFE INSURANCE COMPANY

Raymond Hawkey: Graphic design in newspapers

Two pages and a double page spread
designed and illustrated by Raymond
Hawkey for *The Observer*, 1964 and 1965.

layout man the means with which to achieve a subtlety of expression
that was not in the past available to him. Until 1958 his visual
vocabulary was extremely limited. He could thunder, shout, whisper –
and very little else. With graphics he was not only able to do all these
things in an almost endless variety of accents and intonations, he was
suddenly able, when he wished, to sing! And to sing anything from
grand opera to the blues.

Among the journalists I regard as having been particularly adept in
their use of these new techniques are Harold Evans of *The Sunday
Times*, Michael Molloy of the *Daily Mirror*, and Ken Obank of *The
Observer*. And this is not to forget the pioneers at the *Express* – men
like Peter Baker, Clive Irving, and John Macdonald.

Of the graphic designers themselves, Michael Rand is undoubtedly
one of the most important and influential. Echoes of what Rand did for
the *Express* during the early sixties are still clearly discernible in much
of the newspaper graphics of today. Now art director and managing
editor of *The Sunday Times* magazine section, Rand possesses all the
skills and attributes necessary to succeed in a business where very little
quarter is expected or given.

The newspaper graphic designer has to be able to understand and
respect the essential journalistic function of what he is asked to do –
whether it is to design a diagram explaining how a bank was robbed or
a heading block for a book which is being serialized. He has to be able
to think on his feet at all times, for he will frequently be asked to give
substance to impossible concepts. An example of this (and there have
been many like it) occurred when I was asked to design a single column
heading block for a compilation of stories from foreign correspondents
to be called 'Dialling the World'. The brief was, and I quote: 'Can you
knock up a little white-on-black of the title surrounded by drawings of
reporters on the telephone. Maybe they could have typewriters in front
of them . . . one could be wearing a sun helmet, another a fur hat and so
on. And can you let me have it in half-hour.'

The challenge in such a situation is to understand what lies behind
the concept, and to produce an acceptable, workable alternative, not in
ten minutes' time but immediately. The newspaper graphic designer has
to be able to start a job before all the facts are available and change it
radically, if necessary, when they become available. He has to be able to
tolerate having a job rejected at the last minute because the story it was
to accompany has either been supplanted by another, or drastically
reduced in status – even though that job may have stretched his

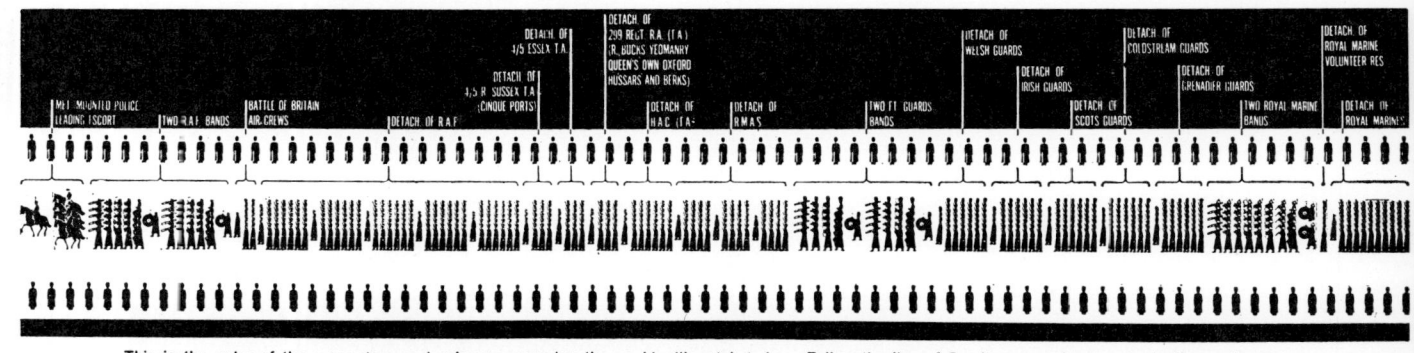

THE PAGEANTRY...Your guide

This is the order of the momentous and solemn procession the world will watch today. Follow the line of Servicemen and mourners to the next page. .

Top: Diagram designed by Malcolm Topp, drawn by Roy Castle. 16 columns. *Daily Express*, 1965.
Heading blocks designed by John Hill, 1961 (above, left) and by Malcolm Topp, 1962 (above, right.) 1 column. *Daily Express*.

Right, from head to foot:
Diagram designed by Raymond Hawkey and Michael Rand, drawn by Michael Rand, Roy Castle and John Hill. 8 columns. *Daily Express*, 1962.
Logo for series about horse doping, designed by John Hill. 3 columns. *Daily Express*, 1962.
Title-piece drawn by Richard Leadbetter. Banner designed by Leslie Jessup. 8 columns. *The Observer*, 1972.
Diagram designed by Leslie Jessup, drawn by David Jefferies. 4 columns. *The Observer*, 1970.

Opposite page:
Map designed by John Castle. 3 columns. *The Observer*, 1964.
Logo for series about first American manned space flight, designed by Raymond Hawkey. For adaptation and use at various sizes *Daily Express*, 1961.
Logo for feature, 'Recipe for a Royal Party', designed by Michael Rand. 1 column. *Daily Express*, 1963.

Opposite page, extreme right:
Two heading blocks designed by John Hill. 3 columns. *Daily Mirror*, 1971.
Two diagrams designed by Michael Rand. 3 columns and 8 columns. *Daily Express*, 1960 and 1962.

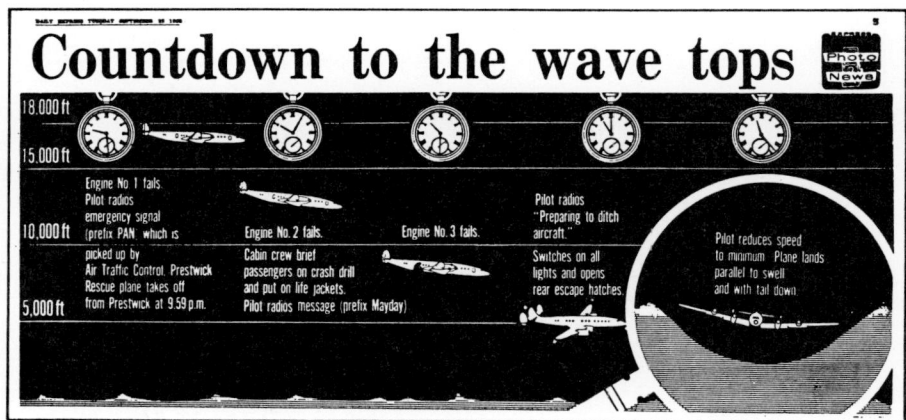

Countdown to the wave tops

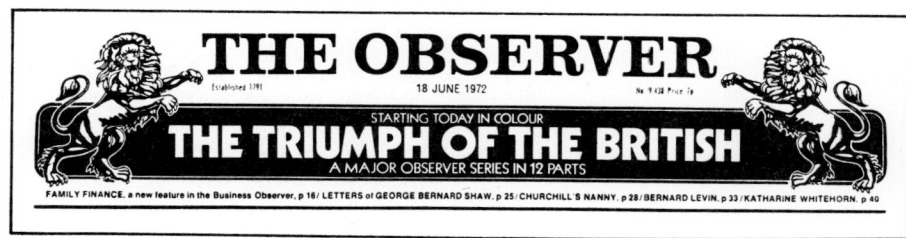

THE OBSERVER

18 JUNE 1972

STARTING TODAY IN COLOUR
THE TRIUMPH OF THE BRITISH
A MAJOR OBSERVER SERIES IN 12 PARTS

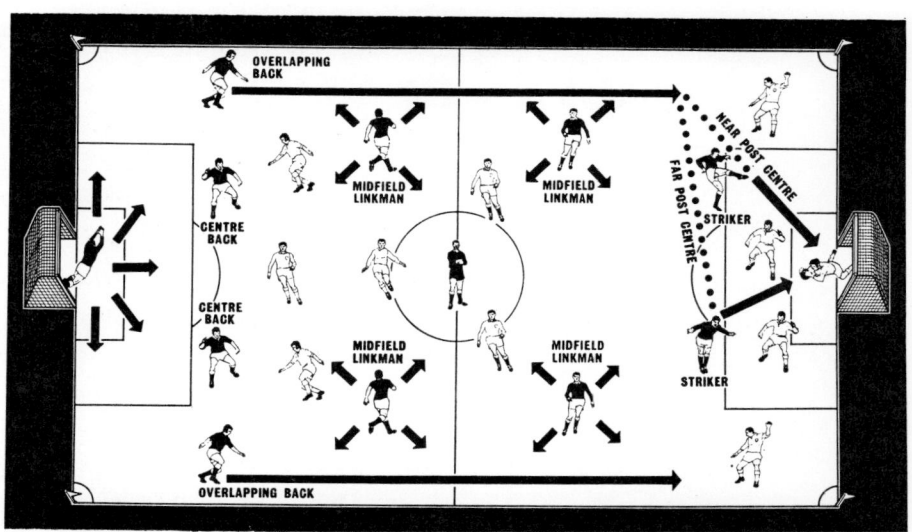

–whether you're there–or watching on TV

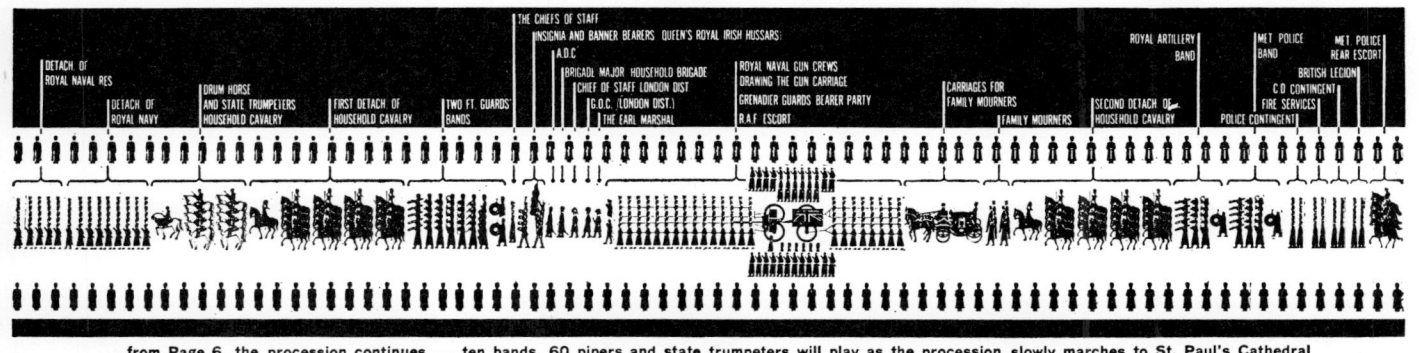

THE CHIEFS OF STAFF
INSIGNIA AND BANNER BEARERS · QUEEN'S ROYAL IRISH HUSSARS
A.D.C.
BRIGADE MAJOR HOUSEHOLD BRIGADE
CHIEF OF STAFF LONDON DIST
G.O.C. (LONDON DIST.)
THE EARL MARSHAL

DETACH OF ROYAL NAVAL RES

DETACH OF ROYAL NAVY

DRUM HORSE AND STATE TRUMPETERS HOUSEHOLD CAVALRY

FIRST DETACH OF HOUSEHOLD CAVALRY

TWO FT. GUARDS BANDS

ROYAL NAVAL GUN CREWS DRAWING THE GUN CARRIAGE
GRENADIER GUARDS BEARER PARTY
R.A.F. ESCORT

CARRIAGES FOR FAMILY MOURNERS

FAMILY MOURNERS

SECOND DETACH OF HOUSEHOLD CAVALRY

ROYAL ARTILLERY BAND

MET POLICE BAND

C.D CONTINGENT
FIRE SERVICES CONTINGENT
POLICE CONTINGENT

MET POLICE REAR ESCORT
BRITISH LEGION

... from Page 6, the procession continues ... ten bands, 60 pipers and state trumpeters will play as the procession slowly marches to St. Paul's Cathedral

DE GAULLE'S SOUTH AMERICAN ENDURANCE TEST

START

COLOMBIA Bogota Altitude 8500'

Caracas VENEZUELA
Bogota COLOMBIA
Quito ECUADOR
PERU Lima
BOLIVIA Cochabamba
ECUADOR Quito Altitude 9000'
BOLIVIA Cochabamba Altitude 8000'
Arica
CHILE
PARAGUAY Asuncion
ARGENTINA Cordoba
URUGUAY
Valparaiso
Santiago
Buenos Aires
Montevideo

ARGENTINA OAS refugees Threat of assassination

BRAZIL
Brasilia
Sao Paulo
Rio de Janeiro
FINISH

VENEZUELA Pro-Castro terrorists

EQUATOR
CAPRICORN

BRAZIL OAS refugees Threat of assassination

4 3 2 1 ! ZERO

WEEKEND TV & RADIO

This Way for Murder BBC2 tonight. 10.5

Espionage · Espion · How RUSSIA & AMERICA run their Intelligence networks

The shoot-out seat that saved Johnny Squier

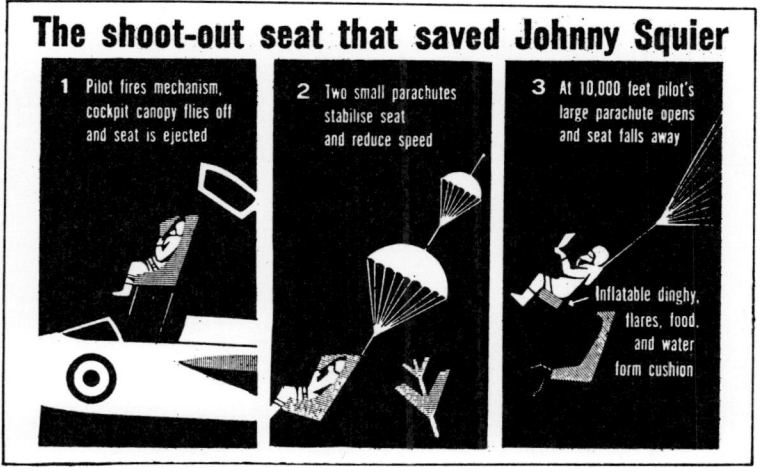

1 Pilot fires mechanism, cockpit canopy flies off and seat is ejected

2 Two small parachutes stabilise seat and reduce speed

3 At 10,000 feet pilot's large parachute opens and seat falls away

Inflatable dinghy, flares, food, and water form cushion

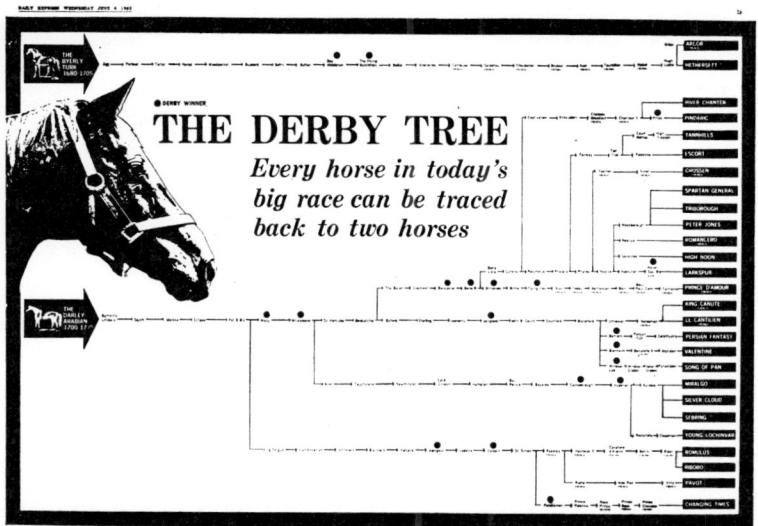

DAILY EXPRESS WEDNESDAY JUNE 4 1965

THE DERBY TREE

Every horse in today's big race can be traced back to two horses

THE DARLEY TURK 1600-1705
THE DARLEY ARABIAN 1700-17..

121

THE SUNDAY TIMES
WEEKLY REVIEW

CHARLES CHAPLIN
MY AUTOBIOGRAPHY
Part 1: The Workhouse Boy

| EARTH | JULY 16 14.42hrs LIFT OFF | 17 hours TRANS LUNAR INJECTION | 18.42hrs SPACECRAFT FREE OF THIRD STAGE | JULY 19 18.26hrs TRANS-LUNAR INSERTION | 22.41hrs ORBIT CIRCULARISED | JULY 20 20.14hrs LUNAR MODULE DESCENDS | 21.23hrs TOUCHDOWN | JULY 21 07.17hrs FIRST MAN ON THE MOON | 07.44hrs SECOND MAN ON THE MOON | MOON | 18.50hrs LUNAR LIFT OFF | 22.32hrs DOCK WITH MOTHERSHIP | JULY 22 05.56hrs TRANS-EARTH INJECTION | JULY 24 17.49hrs SPLASH DOWN | EARTH |

07.17 BST, JULY 21, 1969 : FOOTSTEPS ON THE MOON

FROM start to finish, the period which Neil Alden Armstrong and Edwin E. Aldrin will spend on the surface of the Moon will be 21 hours 27 minutes.

With his first tentative step Neil Armstrong will enter an era of exploration of which men have dreamed for centuries.

Lunar Module 5 will be under the astronauts' control in the last dozen minutes of the flight. Touchdown will be within an elliptical area of the Sea of Tranquillity, seven miles by three. They will be able to fly LM-5 forwards, sideways and backwards, like a helicopter, during the last few minutes. This will enable Armstrong to choose a smooth, level landing site free of craters or boulders. Five-feet-long probes suspended from the footpads will give him the cue to cut the engine when they strike the surface.

Many checks will be carried out after touchdown, then the astronauts will eat a meal and have a long rest. When they wake they will eat breakfast and spend two more hours preparing for their Moon walk. At 7.7 a.m. on Monday, July 21, they will release a valve to allow their cabin oxygen to escape and open the hatch. Ten minutes later Armstrong steps on the Moon.

On the Moon the astronauts will be protected by £40,000 multi-layered Spacesuits. On their backs will be P.L.S.S. - Portable Life Support Systems, which will give them oxygen and cooling water.

1 AT 7.11 a.m. Armstrong will go down on all fours to the centre of the Lunar Module's floor, with his feet out of the hatch, and crawl backwards on to the little platform outside. As his feet, shrouded in heavy boots, feel for the first rung of the ladder, he will reach over with his left hand and pull a D-ring on the side of the LM. This will open a door in the descent stage and out will swing a TV camera which will transmit pictures back to an estimated audience of 1,000,000,000 viewers on Earth.

3 When he steps on the Moon Armstrong will be in a gravitational field one sixth as strong so that on the Earth's surface. Surprisingly he will find walking difficult and probably tiring for we depend on the force of gravity to tell us to "lilt" forward with each stride.

2 AFTER his first tentative step, Armstrong will scoop up a "contingency sample" of lunar rocks—just in case a hurried departure from the surface of the Moon is necessary before the full sample is gathered. As the pressurised Spacesuit will make it difficult for him to bend, he will be equipped with a long-handled scoop to pick up the sample.

3 ONLY after the sample has been safely stored in a plastic bag and winched up to the "upper floor" of the LM will Aldrin emerge from the hatch. He will back down the flimsy ladder while his comrade records the event on film and with a cine camera. Aldrin will be doing more of the hard work on the Moon's surface than Armstrong. The mission planners have decided that they must...

4 FOR the next 15 minutes the two men will be busy deploying the experiments in the EASEP - the Early Apollo Scientific Experiments Package. EASEP is a masterpiece of compactness and is designed to gain a maximum of scientific information for a minimum of effort. A layer of aluminium foil will be unrolled to catch particles ejected by the Sun in the so-called solar wind. A device powered by solar cells will be left a few yards from the Spacecraft to record future 'quakes' on the Moon. Aldrin will spend an hour and thirty-three minutes out on the surface and will go back into the LM at 9.11 a.m. Armstrong will stay out a further twenty minutes and will return at 9.15 a.m. The hatch will be opened once...

5 THERE is one camera which will be operated for Armstrong and Aldrin and that is the one on a collapsible arm close to the LM. This may be necessary if TV voice and data communications are bad between the LM and the Earth. ARMSTRONG and Aldrin will spend half their time collecting samples of Moon rocks and smaller particles. They will be carefully wrapped in plastic bags and placed in a hermetically sealed box which will not be opened again until it is inside a vacuum chamber in the Lunar Receiving Laboratory at Houston. Scientists of many nations including partners in Britain will spend years studying these first samples.

...more at about 10.54 a.m. to jettison unneeded equipment such as cameras and doors.

7 FOR the two men one "activity" will be more important than anything else. The plan tells them to sleep for minutes during their stay on the Moon. There are no beds in the LM and one astronaut will have to lie down on the floor in front of the hatch, while the other slumps on the cover of the ascent engine.

8 IT WILL be at 6.50 p.m., after a sleep and two meals, that the astronauts will fly the LM ascent stage off the Moon, using the descent stage as the launch pad. After 3½ hours of complicated manoeuvres their strange-looking craft will rendezvous and dock with the command module at 10.32 p.m. The most hazardous part of the epoch-making voyage will then be over.

ALL TIMES ARE B.S.T. AND ARE SUBJECT TO ALTERATION

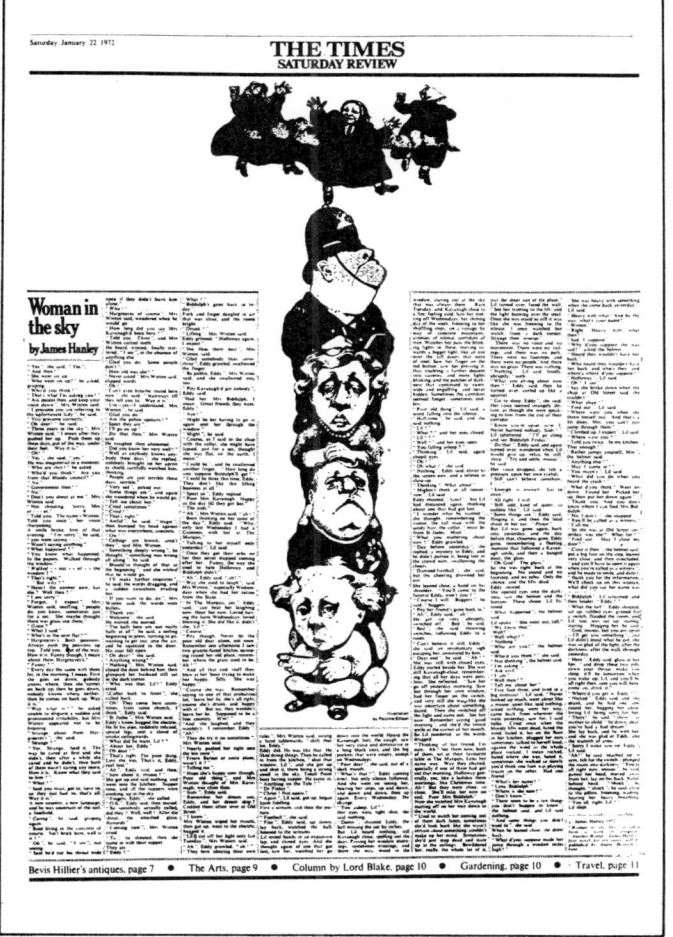

ingenuity, technical resources, and nerves to near breaking point. And he must also be able to tolerate being given a job to do in two hours that should have had – and often could have had, if only someone had thought about it – two days allocated to it. He has to be able to jigsaw a big, urgent job between several assistants and pace their output so that all the pieces come together correctly and to the minute.

He must make do with technical facilities which are geared more for speed than finesse. The ink on repro pulls sent up from the case-room will, as likely as not, still be wet when they arrive and the type seen to be damaged. Copy prints will be damp, blocks over-etched. He has to be able to bear, from time to time, the imposition of bizarre restrictions by one or other of the mechanical unions as to what they will, or will not, accept from him. He must live with the knowledge that his work will not, unlike that of his counterpart on a magazine, be enshrined on a coffee table. At the end of it all it will appear on poor-quality paper, under-inked in the early editions and scummed-up in the final edition. Twenty-four hours later people will be eating fish and chips out of it.

Scientific and technical illustration

Romek Marber

Modern industry, marketing, publicity and education create an ever growing demand for the services of the scientific and technical illustrator, but only a few art colleges in Britain offer diploma courses in this strict and precise field of graphic design. With examples taken from the course at London's Hornsey College of Art, the needs and problems involved in educating people for this métier – against the unfavourable background of the fashionable emphasis on individuality and an undisciplined breadth of approach – are here examined.

The illustrations in this article were reproduced by
The City Engraving Co. (Hull) Ltd
and the whole printed offset-litho by
Lund Humphries.

Scientific and technical illustration is the objective visual interpretation and representation of scientific and technical data. The illustrator is involved in an investigation of the nature and structure of his subject and his work must reflect a rational approach to visual organization. To conceive and produce successful work, the student must be able to analyse and visually clarify complex information beyond the confines of purely mechanical drawing, and be sensitive to detail and capable of precise skills. He must be interested in science and technology and have an aptitude for drawing. In recent years, the emphasis in art and design education has been placed more and more on broadening the areas of study to give students the widest possible understanding of design involvement. To a great extent, this emphasis has worked to the detriment of design subjects which demand particular specialist application. The word 'specialized' itself now carries certain emotive overtones and precisely defined design studies are often considered inferior to broader and less specific courses. This holds true especially for graphic design studies. The term graphic design loosely covers many related aspects of design and of visual expression, one of which is technical and scientific illustration. In so diverse a subject a degree of specialization ought to denote depth of involvement rather than superficiality. The specific knowledge and skills necessary for executing the very exacting work of scientific and technical illustration are outside the scope and experience of most graphic design courses today.

Most scientific and technical illustrators went into this field accidentally. Traditionally they studied painting or book illustration, subjects whose foundations lay in objective drawing. The situation is not unlike that which prevailed in typographic design twenty years ago. But over the years the completely changed approach to the study of painting and illustration has made the transition to objective and analytical work difficult. Fine Art courses today concern themselves mainly with creativeness rather than with specific disciplines capable of leading to freedom of creative expression. Students adopt from the start a personalized and subjective attitude to work. Little interest is shown in objective observation and drawing, and little importance attached to supplying the necessary facilities to this purpose. The result is that few students at graduation can draw objectively.

Graphic design courses are in the main broadly based. Clear definition of the frontiers or limits of the subject is impossible. Students on a three-year course work on many disciplines. This is an exciting and valuable experience, but it can also be too large an undertaking for the

125

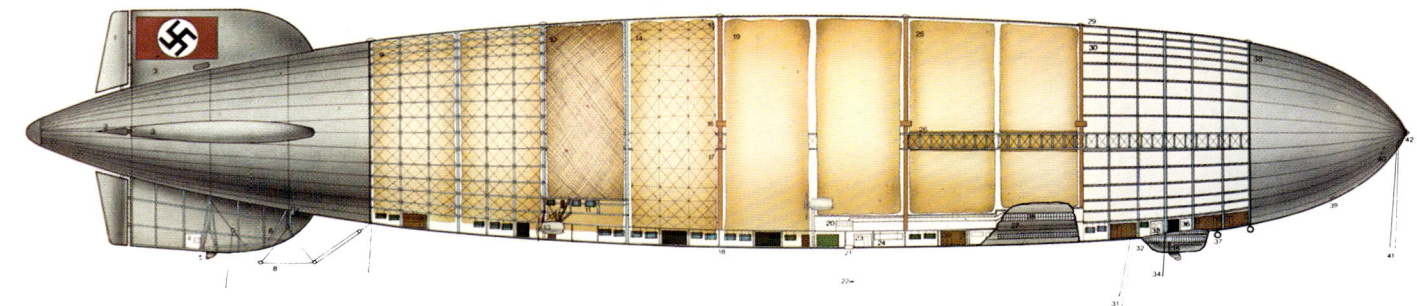

period of study. The students have little opportunity to exercise and test in depth their sensitivity, intellect, and skills. The result is a superficial experience in the attitude to resolving design problems.

The book illustrator's approach to visual communication differs from that of the scientific or technical illustrator. The book illustrator is mainly concerned with the interpretation or amplification of narrative, facts and ideas. His approach can be either emotive or intuitive, with the stress on individuality, and need have little or no reference to objectivity. This emphasis on individuality or an undisciplined breadth of approach is introduced into primary and secondary education by art graduate teachers and finds its way back into higher art and design education. It is becoming progressively more difficult to find artists interested in objective drawing or capable of teaching the subject. Photography as part of scientific and technical illustration is a visual aid but it is no substitute for drawing. It adds to the realism of a subject – drawing can *interpret* an idea or a theory.

At London's Hornsey College of Art students enter at the age of 18 for the diploma course in scientific illustration or technical illustration. The course, which was started at advanced level in 1967, functions within the graphic design department and uses all the available facilities. In their first year students of technical and scientific illustration and students of graphic design follow a common broad programme. In the next two years they enter a specialized area of design work according to their interests and ability. The emphasis is on fluent and imaginative visual interpretation and the development of a rational and aesthetic judgment to enable students to translate given data into clear and precise visual statements. The programme covers the following areas: drawing from live subjects, museum specimens and natural form with reference to anatomy, structure, and movement; investigation of small specimens in detail with emphasis on accurate rendering of scale and colour; drawing with the aid of the binocular microscope; study of perspective, three-point perspective grid construction and the use of perspective grids in illustration from orthographic drawings, reference sketches and notes; basic principles of engineering practice and principles of mechanics; basic knowledge of photography, microphotography, and recording of specimens.

Left: Hindenburg airship
(general configuration).
Drawn by Bill Easter.
Below: Design study of steam locomotion
versus diesel and electric power.
Drawn by Lyn Brooks.

This is complemented by typographic design, study of production procedure and printing processes, analysis and conversion of scientific and technical data into charts, diagrams and three-dimensional models, organization of editorial material and research, classification and filing of information, exercise in film animation related to the animation of drawings, charts, and diagrams, and lectures and seminars in related studies. Students who wish to specialize in medical illustration apply to St Bartholomew's Hospital to continue the course at advanced level in liaison with the college.

Only a few colleges now offer courses in scientific and technical illustration. Experience at Hornsey College of Art indicates, however, that students who have the interest and aptitude find the work rewarding and have no difficulty in finding a satisfying occupation after they graduate. There is an increasing demand for design in scientific and technical illustration. The growth of communication technology and the increase in leisure time have stimulated interest in all types of activities. The public demands to be better informed and instructed. To fulfil the design requirements for creative and clear communication it is essential to be attentive to every detail and to draw on specialist co-operation. So scientific and technical illustrators are making an increasing contribution to the work of presenting information. They enhance both the clarity and the visual excitement of a message on a

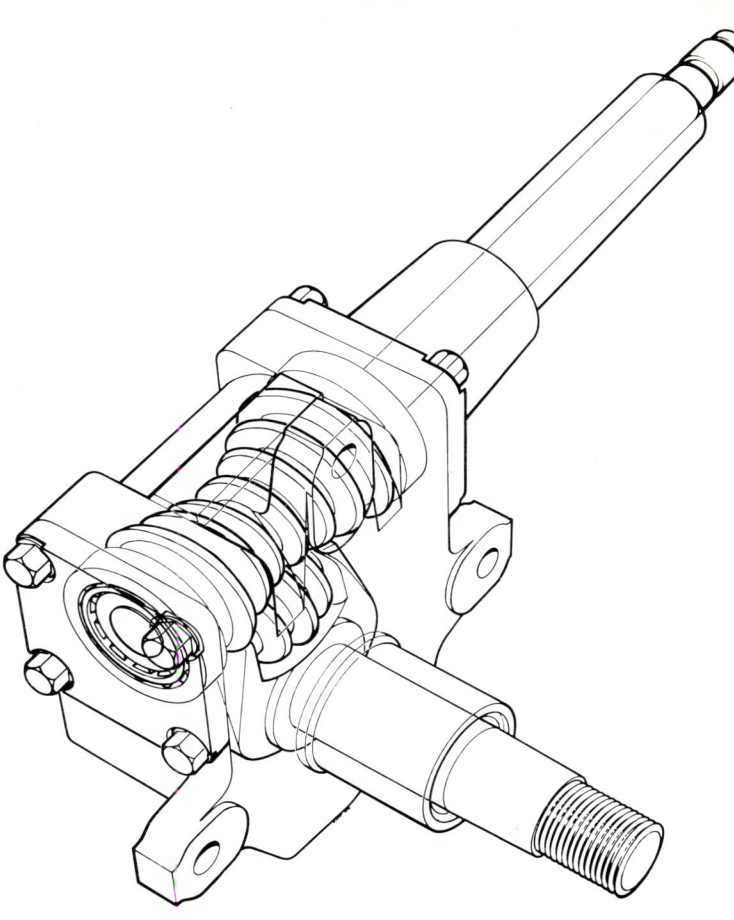

Study of steering box.
Drawn in line and halftone by Colin Rose.

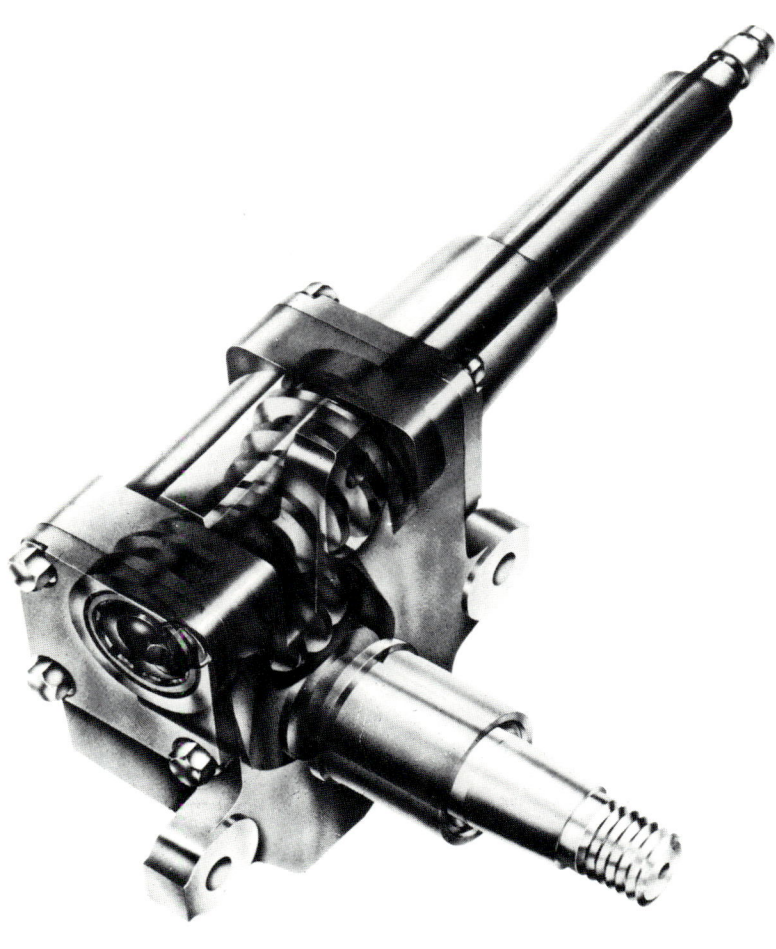

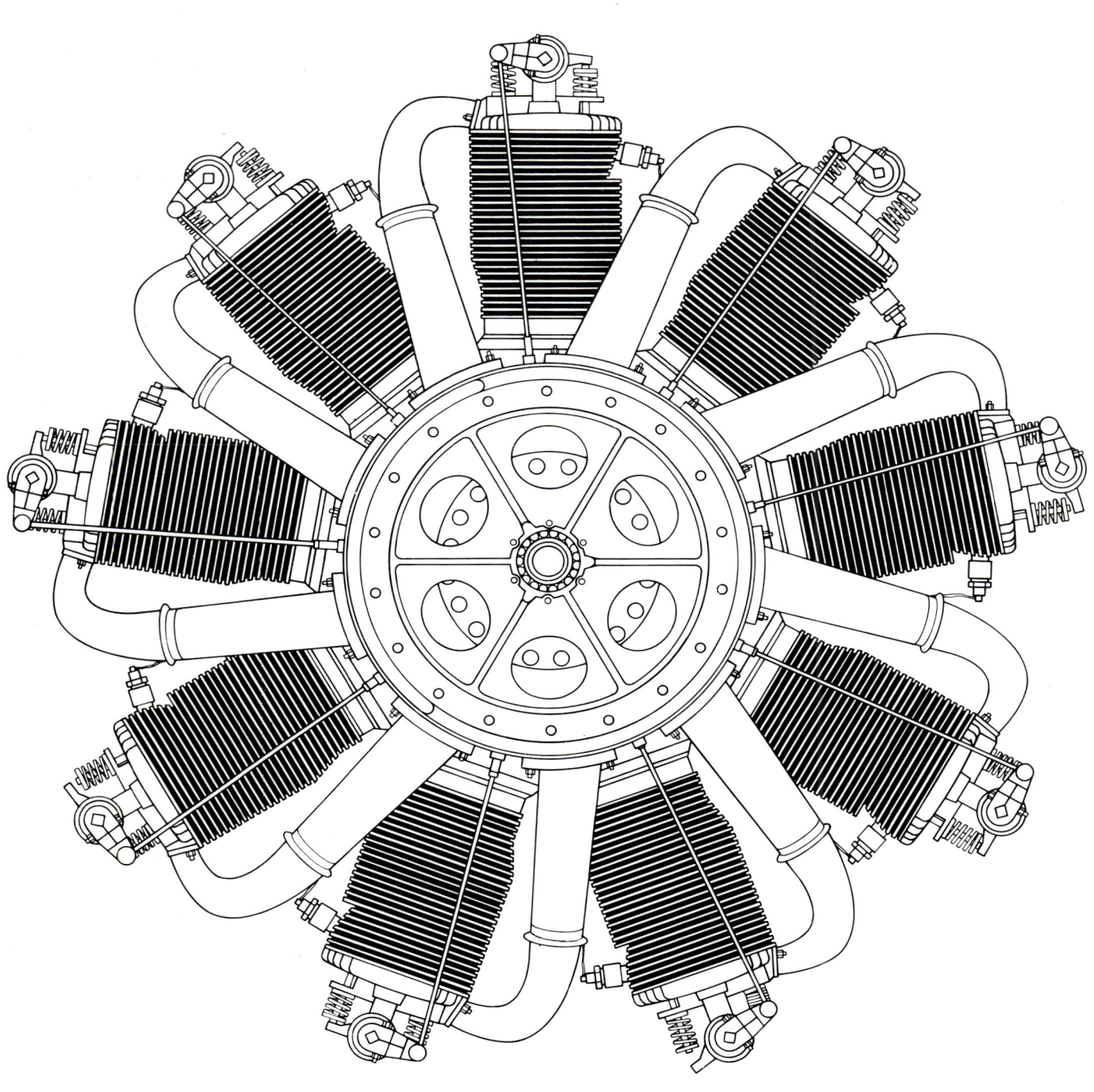

Radial engine.
Drawn by David Penney.

American and European bison, above.
Drawn by Annabel Milne.
European porcupine, below.
Drawn by Annabel Milne.

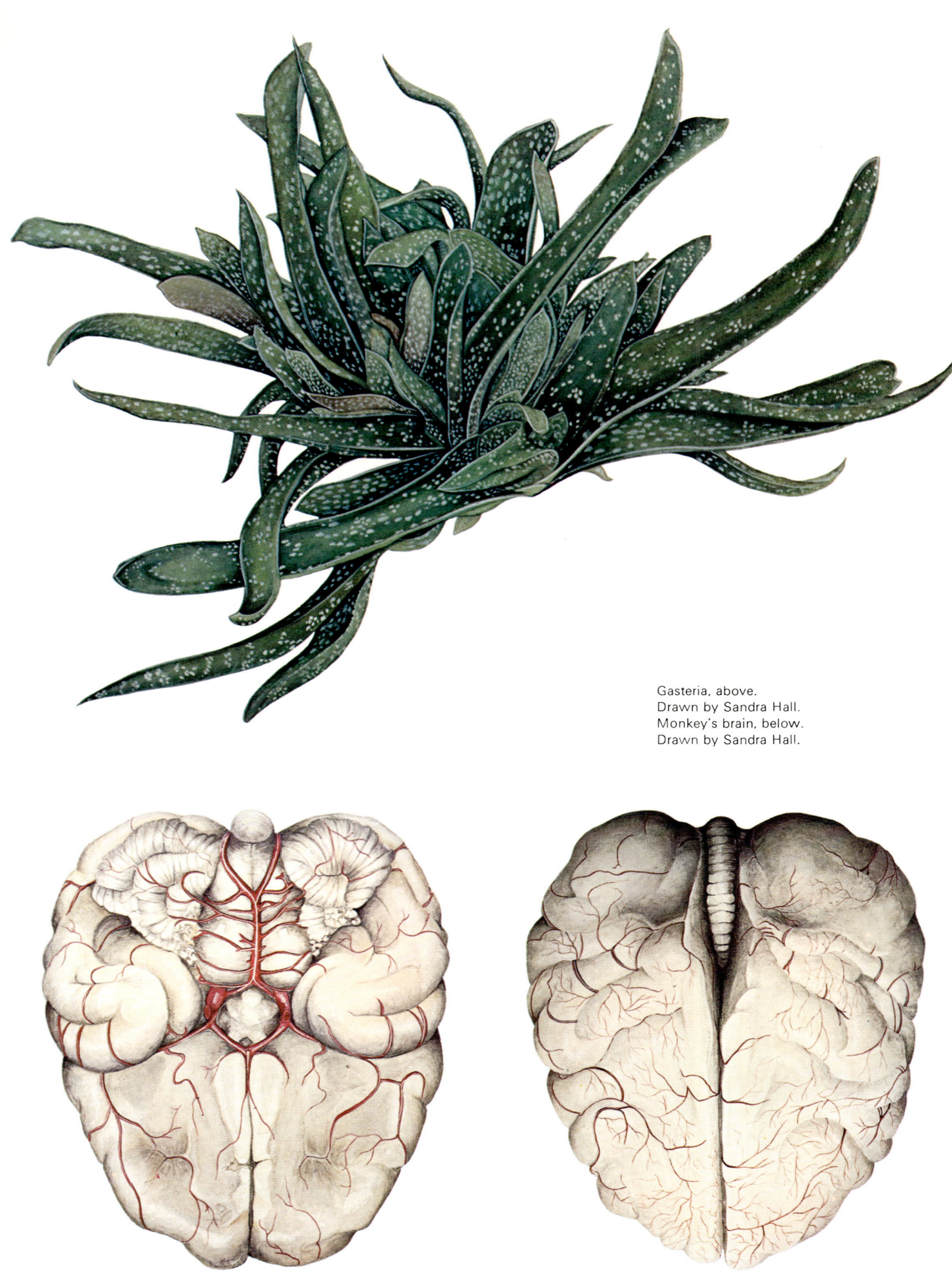

Gasteria, above.
Drawn by Sandra Hall.
Monkey's brain, below.
Drawn by Sandra Hall.

printed page or on audio-visual media. Within a co-ordinated design concept, they give an invaluable help to successful production in many varied fields of information. Every year, Government, education, industry, and commerce issue a mass of informative and instructional material. In hospitals, slide and film programmes, charts and leaflets are prepared for doctors, nurses, and students, for information or as teaching aids, and they are designed to be viewed in groups or individually. Schools, colleges, and universities employ visual and audio-visual aids in teaching programmes. Social services instruct the public on health, hygiene, physical fitness, road safety, and so on, using the whole technology of communication. Books, magazines, and partworks dealing with medicine, science, hobbies, home management, history and natural history are published, and both the clarity of the information and the visual appeal depend greatly on their visual content and overall design. Industry and commerce require illustration through the development and production stages of products and later in publicity and marketing. With almost every item of equipment bought by the consumer come instructions or manuals on its installation and operation.

Most social, educational, industrial, and commercial establishments have access to up-to-date communication technology. The scientific and technical illustrator who is not only a capable draughtsman but also has a design awareness and a knowledge of communication technology can make an imaginative contribution to the production of programmes to feed a variety of technological hardware.

Tools for schools

Michael Shayer

An examination of modern methods used to 'humanize' science teaching, in the light of the work sponsored by the Nuffield Foundation in Britain and some of the text-books produced by CRM Books in the United States. The respective roles of 'prose' graphics and the 'poetry' of art in the work of communicating scientific ideas in secondary schools are analysed.

The blocks in this article were contributed by Philipson & Son Ltd.

What kind of a tool ought the science book for schools to be? What are the operations which it will have to aid? What needs to be known about its users? These were among the questions discussed at a conference on 'The Art of Designing Science Courses for Publication', held at the University of Leicester in July 1972. In the late fifties there was a widespread feeling that science teaching was in a rut. It was in response to this feeling that a chemistry course for British secondary school pupils taking the O-level examination was produced, under the sponsorship of the Nuffield Foundation. Later science courses for schools were sponsored by the Schools Council. When, in the early sixties, a group of experienced teachers came together and in all seriousness planned a five-year course for secondary schools without any text-book, that was a plain indication that something very wrong must have happened to the science text-book in the previous forty years; it had become the visible part of an iceberg in which science teaching had been turned into a routine surprisingly like North and Hillard's Latin text-book. Doing without a course-book altogether proved, however, to be too extreme a step, and in the revision commissioned in 1971 this omission was the feature most often criticized by teachers. A pupil's book is now being written. What kind of book should it be? The committee entrusted with the matter was confronted with all the obvious questions about *how* a book communicates. It emerged that science, as an activity, was closer to the visual than to the verbal arts. A scientific theory is nearly always an image of some kind applied to a situation and tested for its consequences, and it is communicated in this shape when it is first used; a science text-book should try, therefore, to communicate the image as directly as possible to the reader. The trial edition of the revised Nuffield chemistry course pupil's book contains some interesting applications of this principle. To show how an idea is translated into an apparatus that embodies it, a plan-view, a photograph of the apparatus, and a three-dimensional simplified line-drawing of the same apparatus are all shown on the page together with the verbal explanations. Colour is used functionally, for example in showing how the three-dimensional packing of two ions of different sizes in sodium chloride leads to the cubical shape of the salt crystal. And where chemists use images of different levels of abstraction for the same thing – in this case molecules – these are tabulated together so that the reader can bear them all in mind when subsequently he meets any of them.

The relationship of the book to the course was also questioned, and

133

4.5 MORE ABOUT X-RAY ANALYSIS

Sir Lawrence Bragg found that it was usually very difficult to decipher von Laue's photographs. Had this been the only method available, progress in determining the structure of substances would have been very slow and laborious. However, his father, Sir William Bragg, had invented an instrument known as an X-ray spectrometer in order to study X-rays. Photographs of one of the original instruments which he used are shown here. The apparatus permitted a narrow beam of X-rays to be directed into the crystal at a glancing angle θ. The intensity of the beam was found by measuring the charge produced in the ionization chamber. The intensity of the reflected beam was found to depend on the glancing angle. For example, with one particular face of a crystal of sodium chloride the graph shown here was obtained.

The Braggs were able to derive a simple law, known as Bragg's Law, which expresses the relation between the wavelength, λ, the spacing of the planes, d, and the glancing angle, θ, which is $n\underline{d}\, 2d \sin \theta$, where $\underline{n}$ is a whole number. Applying this equation, they were able to use the X-ray spectrometer to work out the structure of numerous substances much more rapidly than they would have been able to do from the von Laue photographs.

The study of X-ray crystallography has today grown into an important science. New methods of determining structure have been developed, but methods based on von Laue's original one are still used, often in conjunction with other methods of analysis (see pages 22-23).

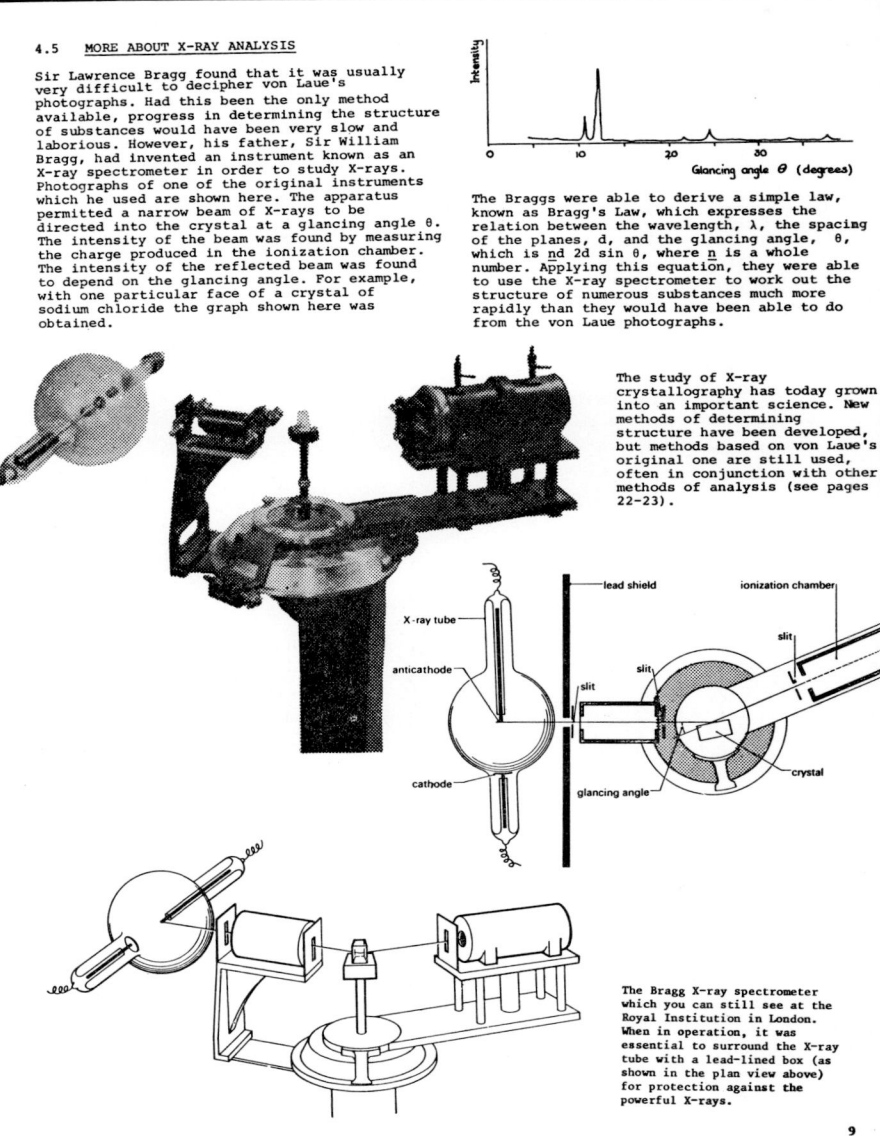

The Bragg X-ray spectrometer which you can still see at the Royal Institution in London. When in operation, it was essential to surround the X-ray tube with a lead-lined box (as shown in the plan view above) for protection against the powerful X-rays.

9

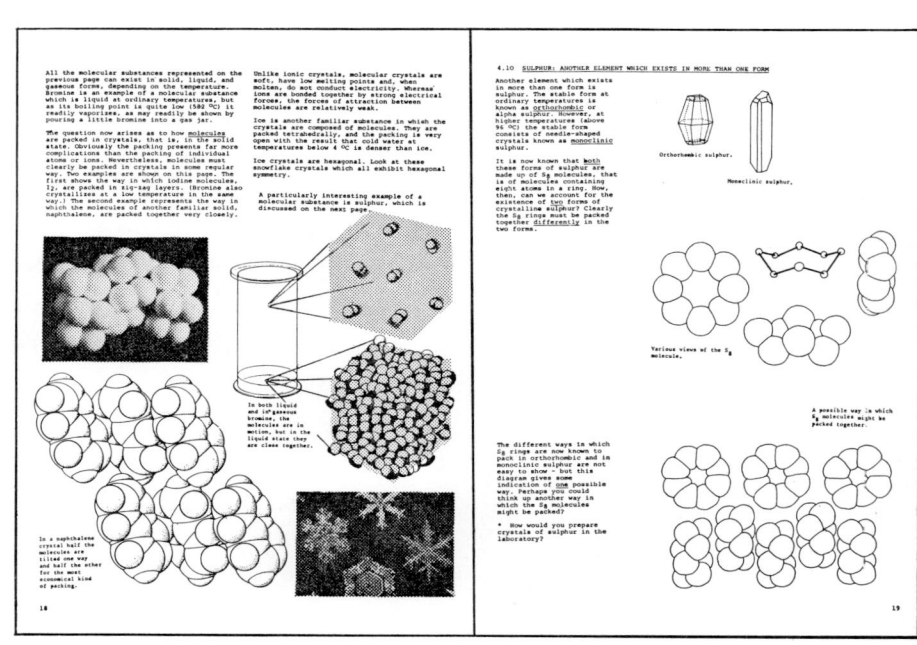

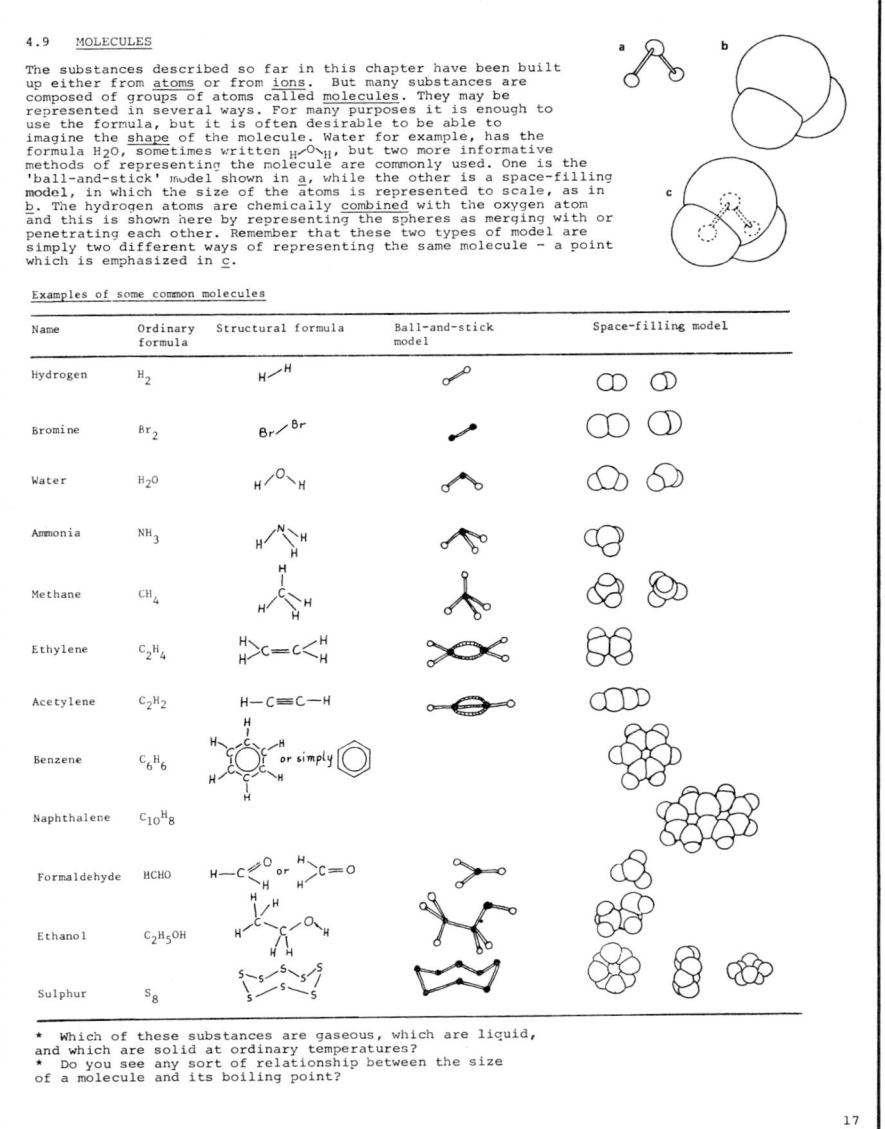

4.9 MOLECULES

The substances described so far in this chapter have been built up either from <u>atoms</u> or from <u>ions</u>. But many substances are composed of groups of atoms called <u>molecules</u>. They may be represented in several ways. For many purposes it is enough to use the formula, but it is often desirable to be able to imagine the <u>shape</u> of the molecule. Water for example, has the formula H_2O, sometimes written H–O–H, but two more informative methods of representing the molecule are commonly used. One is the 'ball-and-stick' model shown in <u>a</u>, while the other is a space-filling model, in which the size of the atoms is represented to scale, as in <u>b</u>. The hydrogen atoms are chemically <u>combined</u> with the oxygen atom and this is shown here by representing the spheres as merging with or penetrating each other. Remember that these two types of model are simply two different ways of representing the same molecule – a point which is emphasized in <u>c</u>.

Examples of some common molecules

Name	Ordinary formula	Structural formula	Ball-and-stick model	Space-filling model
Hydrogen	H_2			
Bromine	Br_2			
Water	H_2O			
Ammonia	NH_3			
Methane	CH_4			
Ethylene	C_2H_4			
Acetylene	C_2H_2			
Benzene	C_6H_6			
Naphthalene	$C_{10}H_8$			
Formaldehyde	HCHO			
Ethanol	C_2H_5OH			
Sulphur	S_8			

* Which of these substances are gaseous, which are liquid, and which are solid at ordinary temperatures?
* Do you see any sort of relationship between the size of a molecule and its boiling point?

17

to preserve continuity with the original spirit of the course, a rare, if not altogether new, editorial brief was decided upon. This was that the book must in no way constitute a teaching programme, but should rather outline the fundamental principles, and show in unusual explanatory detail the essential interconnexions of ideas used in the course, so as to serve as illuminatory reading for pupils following *any* programme based on the Nuffield experimental work.

It has still to be seen how teacher and pupil will manage to use a pupil's book written to such a brief. Already the Nuffield courses have diverged from the aim of traditional science courses, which was to provide an apprenticeship in the tools and matter of the science. They have done so by attempting to impart the style of scientific investigation. The use of images in the chemistry book obviously promotes this aim, by bringing the reader closer to the use of images by the scientists who originally developed these fields.

The Leicester conference crystallized another, more fundamental aim: that of 'humanizing' the sciences. This aim requires thought and sensibility. I take gratefully the phrase used by Germano Facetti, in an

135

article on the Visual Books in THE PENROSE ANNUAL 1964, where he wrote that the artist can complement the prose text of the scientist by 'an intuitive, analogical method'. The years since that brave article, and the fine editorial vision of Frédéric Ditis which lay behind its subject matter, have made it possible to see a little more clearly the distinctions which need to be drawn between the contributions that the graphic and the fine artist respectively can make to the science text-book. In the Visual Books it was not made clear whether it was the artist's role to communicate the scientist's insight more succinctly and with more clarity than a verbal text can do, or to do something which the scientist himself had not even thought of doing; that is, in words used by Ditis, to 'transform abstract intellectual science into a living and expressive reality, which could be integrated into our consciousness and into our daily lives'. The suggestion is that the imagery of science can suffer a sea-change in the sensibility of the artist, and come out capable of being assimilated as a poem rather than as analytical prose.

Figure 7.1 (below). The microscope Robert Hooke used to observe the microscopic structure of cork.

Figure 7.2 Anton van Leeuwenhoek (far right) ground hundreds of fine lenses in order to observe sperm cells, yeasts, and bacteria. One of his early microscopes is shown at right.

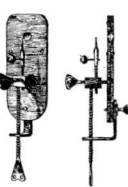

Figure 7.3 (left). Lorenz Oken was among the first theorists to set forth an early version of the cell theory.

Figure 7.4 (middle). Matthias Jacob Schleiden, a German botanist whose ideas were instrumental in the development of the cell theory.

Figure 7.5 (right). Theodor Schwann, a German zoologist and a colleague of Schleiden's.

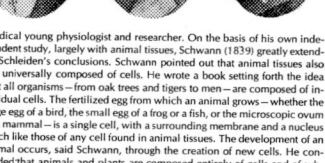

About the same time, microscopists were discovering that the interior of the cell is not the simple fluid originally described. Leeuwenhoek had described small dark objects within some cells, and other investigators began to report a confusing array of "inclusions" in various kinds of cells.

Among the biological writings of the early nineteenth century, there are precursors of the cell theory. The German natural philosopher Lorenz Oken elaborated a complex theory in which all of nature was regarded as reflecting the ideal characteristics of man. His extensive writings include one passage that seems to be a brilliant forecast of the cell theory. He states that "all organic beings originate from and consist of vesicles or cells."

Another early cell theory was set forth in 1824 by the French physiologist René Joachim Henri Dutrochet. He concluded from his microscopic studies that plants are composed entirely of cells and that plant growth occurs both through increase in the volume of cells and through the addition of new cells. Dutrochet then turned to the study of animal tissues and concluded that they too are composed of fluid-filled cells. He theorized that various plant and animal tissues are of different natures only because they contain different fluids in their cells.

With the benefit of hindsight, it is easy to see that Oken and Dutrochet were on the right track. However, as Canadian physician William Osler once commented, "In science, the credit goes to the man who convinces the world, not to the man to whom the idea first occurs." Neither Oken nor Dutrochet convinced the scientific world of the importance or the universality of cells.

That task was successfully accomplished by two young biologists—the botanist Matthias Jakob Schleiden and the zoologist Theodor Schwann, who in 1839 joined forces to become the "public relations" men for the cell theory. Schleiden had begun his career as a lawyer but became so depressed over his lack of success in that profession that he attempted suicide. Upon his recovery, Schleiden turned to the study of plants. He denounced the systematic collections of various species made by most botanists as so much "hay" and devoted his own efforts to careful microscopic analysis of plant structures. Schleiden (1838) argued that all higher plants "are aggregates of fully individualized, independent, separate beings, namely the cells themselves."

During a visit to the University of Berlin, Schleiden enthusiastically described plant cells and their nuclei to his friend Theodor Schwann, a me-

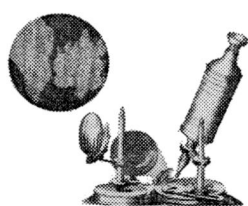

thodical young physiologist and researcher. On the basis of his own independent study, largely with animal tissues, Schwann (1839) greatly extended Schleiden's conclusions. Schwann pointed out that animal tissues also are universally composed of cells. He wrote a book setting forth the idea that all organisms—from oak trees and tigers to men—are composed of individual cells. The fertilized egg from which an animal grows—whether the large egg of a bird, the small egg of a frog or a fish, or the microscopic ovum of a mammal—is a single cell, with a surrounding membrane and a nucleus much like those of any cell found in animal tissues. The development of an animal occurs, said Schwann, through the creation of new cells. He concluded that animals and plants are composed of cells and of substances produced by cells and that the cells, to some extent, are independent living units, although they are subordinate to the entire organism.

By the fortieth anniversary of the publication of Schwann's book, the cell theory was so well established that an international ceremony was held in Schwann's honor. Tribute was also given to Schleiden for his important contribution to the recognition of the universal importance of cells in plants. Thus, by the late nineteenth century, Schleiden and Schwann were being credited as the "fathers" of the cell theory. The publications of Schleiden and Schwann were followed by rapid progress in the understanding of plant and animal organization.

The cell is recognized today as the basic subunit of any living system. A single cell is a clearly defined unit, bounded by a membrane that separates it from other cells or from the outside environment. The definition of the cell as a biological unit, however, has more basis than merely the existence of a physical boundary. A cell contains all of the genetic information, all of the translational molecules, and all of the enzymes that are essential to the life of that cell. In short, a cell is the simplest unit that can exist as an independent living system.

THE STRUCTURE OF CELLS

To most of the early investigators—particularly those specializing in the study of plant tissues—the cell appeared to be a fluid-filled wall or bladder with a granular or dense nucleus in the fluid. In later studies, attention shifted from the cell wall to the material inside the cell.

Gradually, biologists found that most animal cells are filled largely with protoplasm, a viscous, granular, constantly moving fluid inside the cell.

Both tasks are worth doing, but one must clearly decide which of the two is being attempted. *Anxiety*, perhaps the most successful of the Visual Books – and they are all classics of the art – concentrates on the latter task. In graphic work, there appears to be a direct parallel between two types of art, as there is in language between the work of the poet and the work of the prose writer. Much graphic work on signs and images and communication is prose activity. Much of the work both of *Scientific American*, and of the artists responsible for the Life Science books, is excellent and sophisticated prose. So are the examples quoted above from the revised Nuffield chemistry book. The sensibility of the artist is involved certainly, but it is a formal sensibility, concerned with economy and elegance of image, and has its parallel in the prose writer with his ear for avoidance of repetition, and neatness of sentence-construction.

Thus when Ditis, analysing the cause of the 'failure' of the Visual Books, says that 'the price that man has paid for his intellectual

Below and opposite:
Double-page spreads from
Biology Today, CRM Books.

Opposite : Double-page
spreads from two CRM
books : *Abnormal psychology,*
and *Biology Today.*
The originals are in colour,

evolution has been the loss of his visual perception', and that 'as soon as a child learns to read words it seems that he forgets how to interpret images', he is getting very near to the truth, but still has not quite defined the inherent skill. This skill is contemplative rather than active, and is found in the poem (when the medium is that of words), or in the poetic use of images. It is not that the public refuses to 'read' images, but rather that it will not slow down enough to read a poem, whether it be written in words or images. The reader is accustomed to texts whose vacuous words exactly parallel the 'speedreading' techniques evolved to promote them, and it is no wonder that he forgets what live words are like.

Thus in the task of humanizing science there is work for both the artist and the user of words. It is Ditis' achievement to have guided at least six artists (and those who have written the accompanying text) to use their art poetically, in a way that helps pupils to digest the scientific material on which they have worked. His intuition was certainly right in having sought such people to attempt this task; almost all scientists have allowed their poetic functions to wither – if these were ever even awakened.

The need to humanize science faces us in all fields, but in the sphere of teaching it will clearly have to be tackled as a major operation in the sixties and seventies. Only about five children in every hundred are able at the age of 13 to make the conceptual leaps required for picking up the scientific method. There is certainly a need for the graphic 'prose' referred to earlier; it would appear, however, to be more suited to the needs of the over-16's at school and for the undergraduate who requires an efficient but formal introduction to the methods of a science in which he might later work.

Yet all boys and girls between 12 and 16 (with boys rather more toward the latter part of this period) face the problem of defining their personalities in terms of what and whom they value, and their relationship both to people and to the physical world. This problem is tackled much better by the holistic approach of the poet than by the analytic or logical methods of the academic; there is an open market here for publishers imaginative enough to see what needs to be done in digesting and integrating the imagery of science and possessing the art to do it.

A Californian firm, CRM Books, has produced a remarkable series of books on the Life Sciences, under the guidance of its director of design, Tom Suzuki. These are books for the intelligent adult or the markedly different manner; under ordinary circumstances American culture does not consensually subscribe to beliefs such as bodily deterioration in physically healthy persons, the imminent demise of man, or divinely inspired missions.

Combining the common dimensions of these three cases, psychotic behavior patterns might be defined as extreme deviations from expected social behavior that do not appear to be a product of deliberate control and that may appear to reflect deviant ways of construing reality. In this definition, cautious phrases such as "appear" and "may appear to reflect" are used because the degree of control that the psychotic individual has over his behavior and the extent to which statements of belief portray his actual beliefs are matters of theoretical dispute. Irrespective of the ultimate control or belief, behavior is labeled psychotic if it is socially deviant and if there is no evidence of intentional control; in many cases the individual also appears to perceive or interpret reality in a deviant manner.

Psychotic behavior may also involve bizarre postures and motor behaviors, for example, prolonged immobility or prolonged excitation; extreme emotional states, such as intense elation or depression, or prolonged absence of emotional responsiveness; and severely disrupted social relations, including social withdrawal or depression and subsequent failure to fulfill familial and occupational obligations. In addition, psychotic behavior often appears to reflect cognitive distortion and confusion, which involves inability to maintain a logical thought sequence or confusion concerning the meanings of words and verbal messages, and disturbance of reality contact, as indicated by statements about delusions and hallucinations.

Persons behaving psychotically may manifest an almost infinite combination of the above types of behaviors, which creates a significant diagnostic problem. Furthermore, psychotic functioning often prevents the individual from harmonious coexistence with his environment either because he is dangerous to others, fails to care for himself, or is incapable of functioning within the limits tolerated by

society. His behavior constitutes a nuisance, burden, or danger to those around him and also possibly to himself. In any case, eruption of psychotic behavior usually leads to psychiatric hospitalization, and a large number of persons in such institutions are diagnosed as being psychotic.

Some psychotic patterns fit the popular stereotype of "madness." For example, the person whose complex delusional system involves the belief that invisible creatures control his thoughts and invest him with magical powers to read and destroy minds; the individual whose euphoria, energy, and good spirits are so extreme that he rushes frantically from one activity to the next, interrupts himself repeatedly in conversation, and responds with verbal and physical violence to any attempts to restrain him; and the stuporous, depressed individual whose only energy appears to be invested in declaring that the world is coming to an end and that he is responsible for its demise are "classic" syndromes that are common in psychiatric texts. Most psychotics, however, do not fit neatly into these or other stereotypes and, in addition, such "madness" characterizes only a minority of persons labeled psychotic. This seeming paradox can be resolved if a differentiation is made between *acute psychotic episodes* and *long-term psychotic adjustments*.

Acute psychotic episodes are behavioral reactions that may involve intense anxiety, disorientation, cognitive confusion, marked extremes of mood, and severe delusional beliefs or hallucinatory experiences. These episodes usually have a rapid onset and constitute a marked departure from the person's previous functioning, although they are often recognizable as intensifications of trends in the individual's previous adjustment. There is often an identifiable situational stress to which the psychosis is an extreme reaction, and the episode is generally of limited duration. Among the diagnoses discussed in this unit, acute psychotic episodes are included in the discussion of acute schizophrenic episodes, schizo-affective schizophrenia, and most of the subtypes of affective psychosis (see Chapters 13 and 14). It should be noted that most of the stereotypes and assumptions about psychosis

derive from observation of the behavior of acutely psychotic individuals. Such persons often create dangerous or threatening situations and sometimes fit the popular conception of "madness."

Long-term psychotic adjustments are life styles or personality patterns that may include marginal social adjustment, some degree of cognitive impairment, and low emotional responsiveness. Most individuals who manifest a long-term psychotic adjustment function reasonably well most of the time, with minimal disruption of their own and society's routines. Socially, they may be viewed as "eccentric," "weird," or "different," but they are not usually considered to be in need of hospitalization. On close psychological examination there may be indications of loose or confused thought processes and, possibly, delusional beliefs. Under stress they may experience acute psychotic episodes of limited duration, with a subsequent return to their usual level of functioning. Diagnostically, persons with long-term psychotic adjustments may fit into many categories of schizophrenia, particularly the paranoid, chronic, and latent subtypes.

The demarcation between acute psychotic behavior and long-term psychotic adjustment is not clear-cut. In some individuals, acute psychotic episodes may become so frequent that their social and personal functioning progressively deteriorates to the point where they require continuous care. Although these cases blur the distinction, most individuals who are diagnosed as psychotic can be characterized as being of primarily the acute type or the long-term type.

DISTINCTIONS BETWEEN NEUROSES AND PSYCHOSES

Although psychotic behavior differs greatly from neurotic behavior, specifying the characteristics of the distinction is difficult unless numerous qualifications and exceptions are made. In general, there are three dimensions on which neuroses and psychoses are considered to differ: *danger, social functioning,* and *reality contact.*

Psychotics are often said to be a greater danger to themselves and to other people than are neurotics (Coleman, 1964; Buss, 1966). Although it is true that acutely psychotic individuals present a considerably

Figure 12.2. An early-nineteenth-century writer referred to William Blake (right, self-portrait) as "an unfortunate lunatic whose personal inoffensiveness secures him from confinement." A retrospective diagnosis of Blake would probably label him a paranoid schizophrenic, for he made no secret of the fact that he was ". . . under the direction of Messengers from Heaven, Daily and Nightly." Blake's first hallucination involving divine personages occurred at the age of four, and succeeding "visions" probably provided much of the material for his illustrations of works such as Milton's PARADISE LOST, which includes SATAN COMES TO THE GATES OF HELL, shown above. This watercolor illustration depicts Satan advancing from the left, preparing to confront Death, right. In the center, thrusting them apart, is Sin. Flames writhe in the background, and to the right is Hell's latticed gate.

Figure 38.28a. Representative reptiles. Mangrove snake (upper left). Box turtle (lower left). Chameleon (right).

Figure 38.28b (below). Reptilian anatomy as represented by a schematic cut-away diagram of a lizard.

Figure 38.29a (right). White mynah bird (India).

Figure 38.29b (left). General internal anatomy of the pigeon.

is covered with leathery or calcareous substances that protect the embryo from desiccation, and a body of food for the early development of the embryo is stored in the yolk of the egg. Copulation is a well-developed mechanism of fertilization, so a body of water is unnecessary for reproduction. The young hatch from the eggs as tiny replicas of the adults, ready to feed and avoid danger. Although they grow and in most cases change in proportions after hatching, they do not pass through a larval stage. The reptiles possess more highly developed respiratory systems, mechanisms of locomotion, circulatory systems, and means of preserving body water while eliminating waste products than do the amphibians. Primitive reptiles appear in the fossil record about 290 million years ago and probably evolved from primitive amphibians. During the period from about 250 million to about 70 million years ago, the reptiles were the dominant large animals on the land, in the oceans, and in the air. Today, birds and mammals occupy many of the niches in the biosphere once occupied by reptiles, and many groups of reptiles such as the dinosaurs have become extinct.

Class Aves, the birds, includes animals characterized by wings, feathers forming protective coverings and wing surfaces, very efficient systems of lungs and air chambers for external respiration, and highly developed sensory and nervous systems. Fossils of primitive birds are found in rocks formed about 150 million years ago. Except for their feathers, these early birds are reptilelike in body organization, and in that respect, so are modern birds. There are more than 8,500 species of living birds, with a great variety of forms and ways of life. Like mammals, birds maintain a constant temperature within the body and a high rate of metabolism, regardless of external conditions.

The class Mammalia is thought to have evolved from a group of reptiles different from those that gave rise to birds. Like birds, the mammals developed an efficient circulatory system and a complex nervous system, as well as the ability to maintain a steady internal temperature. Hair protects mammals in the same manner that feathers protect birds. In most mammals, the embryo is nourished within the mother's body rather than being

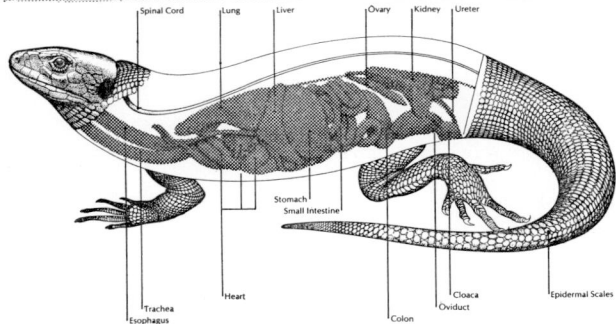

Spinal Cord | Lung | Liver | Ovary | Kidney | Ureter
Trachea | Esophagus | Heart | Stomach | Small Intestine | Colon | Cloaca | Oviduct | Epidermal Scales

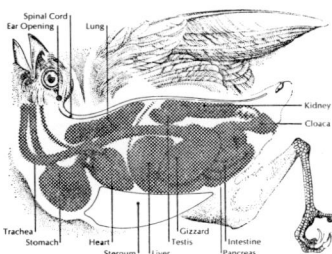

Spinal Cord | Ear Opening | Lung | Kidney | Cloaca
Trachea | Stomach | Heart | Sternum | Liver | Gizzard | Testis | Intestine | Pancreas

university student, but they do point the way to what might be done for schools. Images from Munch, Hathe, Kollwitz, Moore, Blake, and Van Gogh, introduced in a natural manner among the pages of this firm's *Abnormal Psychology* text-book, will help the next generation of doctors and psychologists to identify with the matter of the text rather than taking the verbal cue of the language and remaining – 'objectively' – outside the matter. A Blake watercolour in this text-book, because of the supremely healthy normalizing message conveyed by the images, must slowly bring the reader to realize the shallow inhumanity of the accompanying text.

The firm's *Biology Today* is full of excellent 'prose' graphics. It also has something of the humanizing intent found in the psychology text-book. The tone is set by Szent-Györgyi's introduction. An image chosen to represent man, in a photographic survey showing the variety of life, reminds one of how many medical books do as great an insult to the human image as a 'wanted' notice in a police station. Particularly noteworthy is the art used in presenting images of scientists of previous ages.

For editors, artists, and science-writers a ten-year collaborative task of transforming the role of science in education lies ahead.

Literacy for what?

Theo H. Oltheten

This article is based on UNESCO experiences in the developing countries. It develops the thesis that communications – with print, radio, education, journalism, and all the media operating in network – supply a form of energy indispensable to the growth of production and social and cultural progress. Information as power, the 'knowledge industry', is usually out of balance in these countries, the author finds, and shows how it could be made more effective as a development impulse.

Information is a form of energy. It makes the 'brain-motor' work in the same way as electricity energizes an electric motor; neither will work if it is not fed with energy. Electric motors provide the power without which manufacturing industries could not operate. The human 'brain-motor' performs the same function in the 'knowledge industry'.

All activities undertaken with a view to collecting, processing, and transmitting knowledge may be grouped together under the heading 'knowledge industry'. One of its foundations is education and another is journalism. Newspaper editors, television producers, and graphic designers are part of this industry in the same way as school teachers and university professors are. The 'knowledge industry' supplies the software that humanity requires to make the hardware. The hardware is the capital component of the manufacturing and services industries, the software the human component in the form of organized knowledge.

It is this division of labour and responsibilities and the mutual adaptation inherent therein that have made the economic development of what are called the industrial nations possible. But the moment we think of the non-industrialized countries, we realize that they lack both hardware and software. Between these two there is an often forgotten interdependence. Electricity is transmitted in the form of pulses and information energy is transmitted in the form of codes, of which the alphabet is the most important. The ability to encode and decode information in alphabetical characters is the basis upon which a 'knowledge industry' can be built up. Unfortunately, a large proportion of the people of the world are illiterate; their inability to read and write prevents them from tapping vast sources of energy. Thirty-four per cent of the adult population of the world – one-third of all human beings over the age of 13 – are illiterate. But illiteracy is not evenly distributed. In the industrial nations it is less than 5 %, in Africa about 80 %, and in southern Asia over 60 %. Putting the matter another way, 800 million 'brain-motors' are working on far too low a voltage. In the last twenty years much has been done to remedy this, but the world's total of illiterates has still risen by 80 million.

There has also been a spectacular change in education. The number of children attending primary schools in the emerging countries has trebled in fifteen years. Quantitatively, there has been a marked improvement in primary education and in the steps being taken to eradicate illiteracy. The Pearson Report, however, sounds a pessimistic note. This report of the commission on international development expresses concern at the fact that only 30 % of the children at primary schools in emerging countries complete the course. This is indeed a very serious matter. I think it is odd, however, that this commission did not raise, in this connexion, the question: literacy for what? The answer would perhaps explain the low percentage of non-finishers. Even those in the emerging countries who can read and have some schooling often cannot maintain or extend the knowledge they have acquired because of the chronic shortage of information media. Seventy per cent of the world's population do not have access to the accepted minimum of media – ten copies of a newspaper, five radio receivers, and two cinema seats per hundred inhabitants.

Written information is not a monopoly of newspapers. Other periodicals and books are also important information media, and it is regrettable that they are not better developed. From the more than half a million book titles published in the world yearly – twice the output of twenty years ago – Europe alone publishes almost half. And Europe together with the United States, the Soviet Union, and Japan accounts for 80 % of each year's titles. Per million inhabitants, Europe produces 490 titles, Africa 23, Asia 50, and Latin America 64. Consumption of 'cultural paper' in the developing countries has been rising steadily during the last few years, but the gap between the informed and the uninformed peoples is widening rapidly. The eradication of illiteracy and the development of information media in the emerging countries are out of balance.

It is rightly said that one 'learns to read in order to read to learn'. Learning to read is not one of the human rights, but man has a right to be informed. Reading must be functionally linked with activity which is of some significance to the reader in his daily existence or which springs from a social or cultural need. Lack of printed information largely nullifies efforts to educate. Many of these efforts avail little because of the appalling shortage of teaching aids.

If we may look upon information as energy for the 'knowledge industry', we shall obviously require some form of infrastructure for the transmission of that energy. In broadcasting, we are quite clear about the position; an infrastructure for telecommunications must be built, because information by radio and television could not be given without a network of transmitters, relay stations, and antennae. But publishers and printers of newspapers, magazines and books are also part of an infrastructure. They really are the mainstays of the information infrastructure, the substations in the transmission system, although they are not easily seen in that light. Paper, of course, is indispensable to the transmission of information; it is the powerline along which information energy is transmitted from source to user. A powerline is useless without a generator to feed it. There has to be a system of generators to energize the network of powerlines, that is, to provide the information energy for transmission to the receiving end.

Every country needs a network of agencies for the transmission of information, with publishers and printers serving as the sub-stations through which the transmission lines run. There is no such infrastructure in the developing countries. All newspapers are concentrated in capital cities but most of the people live in the country. In India 80 % of the people live in over half a million small towns and villages, and newspapers do not reach them; 40 % of the newspaper press is concentrated in four cities, New Delhi, Calcutta, Bombay, and Madras. In Indonesia, with a population of 125 million, 20 % of all daily newspapers are published in the capital Jakarta. Together they account for half the national circulation. The situation in Latin America does not differ fundamentally. In Europe in the last century many new newspapers sprang up in a very short time. But before that, Europe already had an information infrastructure in the form of a widespread network of printing production plants. Technically there was no difference between the production of books and newspapers; the same hand composing, the same letterpress printing machines, the same materials and methods. In developing countries, where newspapers could start to play a vital role in the changing society and could give an important impulse to development, there exists no such infrastructure, arising as in Europe from the development of the written cultures on which the whole European development was based. The scarcity of production centres hampers the development of regional and local rural newspapers and a book production industry.

It is of course difficult to set up an infrastructure of the kind required. We cannot expect things to evolve naturally with the rapidity we desire. Developing countries cannot afford to take the time that people in Europe took to grow to their present state. But now Europeans have the knowledge and can help developing countries to achieve their objectives with much less delay. Obviously, very little information can be imported by the developing countries and what is imported must be presented in a form which the receivers can digest. A newspaper is tied to the language and culture in which it appears. You can import newsprint; you cannot import newspapers. And even books printed in national languages cannot be imported on a large scale.

With the great advances made by radio and television the question now arises: why should not preference be given to these media? In developing countries radio communication is already growing at a faster rate than printed communication. The Philippines has 349 broadcasting stations with 4 million radio receivers. On a visit to Colombia I found a network of 243 radio transmitters and 2·8 million radio receivers, serving a population of 21 million. Of all families in Colombia, 95·2 % are linked to the information network of radio broadcasting, in the less developed rural areas as well as the big cities. In Latin America radio is a universal mass medium.

In this area of the world various non-profit organizations are active in popular education and in promoting rural social development through radiophonic schools. But the results are not satisfactory. Although educational broadcasting stimulates personal initiative to improve living conditions in rural areas it has not succeeded in changing the old-fashioned economic and social structures. Transmitting general education to raise the socio-cultural level is of the utmost importance, but the income per head cannot be raised without solving specific social and economic problems in specific rural areas. Radio communication is a mass medium in a one-way channel of communication. But this limitation would not matter greatly if radio could be used as one component of a complete communication system including a network of book publishers and urban and rural newspapers. It is the absence of these that holds up progress in Colombia and so many other developing countries. The development of information media in this part of the world is out of balance, in the same way as it is in south Asia. Consumption of newsprint in Latin America and Asia has increased during the last decade, but it is less per literate adult than it was ten years ago.

In all circumstances, print is irreplaceable as a medium of communication. It has exceptional advantages. Communication by printed matter provides the greatest possibility of differentiation. The other media either do not offer this possibility, or do so to a much smaller extent; they are pre-eminently mass media. Printed communications can, of course, be distributed in very many copies, and in that sense acquire a mass medium character, but this is not necessarily the case. Another advantage of print is that it can also be produced and distributed economically in small quantities. As a medium it is therefore particularly well suited to serve the cultural needs of smaller communities. And mass media should be as local as possible to promote economic and social development effectively.

I ask again: literacy for what? Writing and reading belong together. Without a written culture one cannot achieve a social and economic development; nor can one create a climate in which democracy can flourish. In the industrialized world, too, the press is not a by-product of democracy; democracy arose from its written culture.

In a report on the role of mass media in development, the Director of Mass Communications of UNESCO speaks about the activities of the newly established schools of journalism in Africa. Education in journalism is a basic condition to develop a network of communicators. The report says: 'In the rural economies such networks should be based upon the fundamental needs of the rural population for relevant information and subtle motivation. The amount of new knowledge to be passed on, the potential capacity among the rural people for adaptation of new learning and their eagerness to participate individually in any prospective improvement of life and preparations for change should be regarded as assets and met by the authorities with a considerate, determined policy to make available any means of communication in the mobilization of rural resources. The technology is available, the methods have since long been tested in various projects, but the determination, the manpower, the devotion or the continuity in implementing the techniques and know-how have been lacking.' The observation is correct. But 'information', in the eyes of economists, is not a missing component of economic development in the under-developed countries. In recent years, economists have turned their attention toward education as an 'investment in human capital'. They have failed, however, to recognize and follow up the implications of mobilizing the brainpower. In otherwise well-conceived economic development plans one very rarely finds any indication that investments in information will yield quantitatively measurable rates of return. In most development plans, education and communication, which ought to be considered as components of a single entity, are considered separately. The different forms of printed media do not represent a 'development impulse' in themselves – they form an integral part of the communication pattern of society.

We have, therefore, to convince the economists. The problem, however, is how to convince policy-makers and planners of the earning capacity of investments in mass media when these investments are not only aiming – as radio does – at reaching the national population on all levels as cheaply as possible. They have to be convinced that the necessary mass media structure must also include an infrastructure of graphic media, giving the additional forms of communication which can be used for an effective 'two-way' flow of information.

Success in winning this conviction will depend on success in proving the point. An important way to do so is to participate in the new international programme of communication research formulated by UNESCO and recently presented to all member states. We need the knowledge that only research can provide before we can develop adequate communication policies. And this research – according to the UNESCO proposals – 'can play a vital role in showing the ways in which communication can be activated in those sectors of the society which are in the greatest need of the "developing impulse" but are precisely those which barely participate in matters of public interest. This is the case with rural people in so many countries.'

After experiences with two mobile printing units in Iran and Indonesia a programme of communication research will be started in Colombia in the middle of 1973 and another in Kenya in 1974. They will be focused partly on the function of the smallest rural newspapers in areas with radio communication only, and partly on visual perception, i.e. the function of illustrations and the visual instruments of design in printed forms of information. The mobile printing units are installed in containers, transported by a truck. An off-loaded container with typewriters, photographic headliner, direct photoplate camera, and an offset press can be employed as a self-supporting small graphic communication laboratory.

Much communication research has been carried out in industrialized countries, but the question immediately arises about the relevance of the findings to the situations in developing countries. Can we transfer research findings from one culture to another and are there important differences in adaptation of written material, illustrations or other forms of visualized information? Our research programmes in Asia, Latin America, and Africa will be linked by a joint evaluation programme, using the same evaluation techniques.

Specialists in written communication are already convinced of the importance of the written culture, the basis upon which the development of Western society was achieved. We know that the gap between the haves and the have-nots is really the gap between the informed and not-informed. Our experience equips us to help to create the intellectual and material conditions necessary for closing this gap, and to bring the societies living outside the written world inside.

Graphic design in Poland

Szymon Bojko

The highly specific and national
graphic design for which Poland has
won world recognition is deeply linked
to the country's history and general
cultural heritage. Artists working in
this field ranked with writers and
painters as exponents of the national
spirit and culture during the long years
when Poland was partitioned.
The author explains these still living
traditions and examines the creative
interplay between them and *avant-
garde* influences from the wider
spheres of world art.

Blocks illustrating this article were made by
Siviter Smith Engravers (Process) Ltd.

There is a widely prevalent notion that Poles are born with artistic
talent and a liking for the free and picturesque shaping of forms. Polish
folk art, which fascinates foreigners by its authenticity, is usually cited
in support of this. True, it is more abundant and filled with fresh
fantasy than the folk art of other European nations. Not yet destroyed
by stylization, it has the enchantment of youth. It possesses a beauty
that reflects both a natural and noble human raw material, and a coarse
and rough matter. The values originating from the cultural traditions
of the Polish people, which the professional artists have absorbed,
adopted, and developed, have helped to prevent Polish art from being
dispersed among other, more influential cultures, and also from being
shut away in an out-of-the way locale. Extremely susceptible and eager
for innovation, Polish art goes to meet the whole of human culture and
is open to the world. It possesses two elements which overlap: tradition,
representing cultural continuity and specifically Polish attitudes of
mind, and a modern artistic consciousness.

The unity of the two elements is perhaps most evident in textile
design and graphic art. These disciplines for a long time developed
against the background of Poland's own artistic heritage. But the more
strongly textile design and graphic art are rooted in the national soil,
and the more traces they contain of naïve folk imagination, the more
the artists show their attachment to the twentieth century. At the end
of the 1950s, art criticism launched the notion of a 'Polish poster
school'. Later there was talk of a 'Polish school of weaving' – but after
its innovations had already been generally accepted outside the country.

Graphic design as an independent branch of art emerged from the
'Young Poland' movement which arose at the turn of the century. It
was kin to the attempts all over Europe to bring about a renaissance in
literature, the theatre, and the arts. The ideas of Ruskin, Morris, Crane,
and Grasset, and in Poland the work of Stanisław Wyspiański, a
reformer of the theatre and of book design, formed the intellectual
superstructure of the movement. In a country deprived of its
independence until 1918, where culture and education developed
contrary to the will of the partitioning powers, or at least without their
help, the programme of reviving art acquired a greater ideological
import than in other countries. Books, posters, printed advertisements,
illustrations in periodicals, typography, our own characters,
bore irrefutable witness to the fact that Polish culture was a living
thing and a presence among the world's civilized nations.

In its most ambitious works, graphic design manifested the nation's

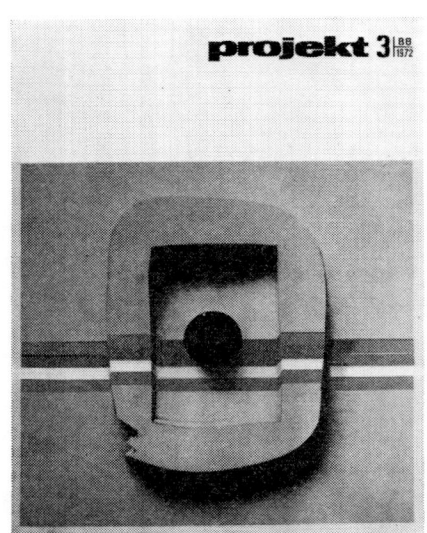

Józef Mroszczak: Magazine cover design, 1972, incorporating an interpretation of Warsaw's International Poster Biennale symbol designed by Wojciech Zamecznik.

spiritual sovereignty by the mere fact of its accessibility to all, its presentation to the public, almost apart from the textual content of the works. Artists gave their graphic work additional meanings, not conveyed in the text. A decorative motif shaped in a familiar way, an allegorical figure, or some special object releasing emotions of a patriotic nature, could all become *symbols*. If folk ornaments or historical souvenirs were transformed into symbols it was because they were supposed to be understood metaphorically: their contents were supposed to be guessed at.

A style in graphic design grew out of the specific soil of Polish poetry and romantic imagination: a spirit that is youthful, sceptical, free from commercial glibness. This spirit survived down the generations in its general stylistic tendencies, in spite of history and fluctuating artistic trends. In highly developed countries in the West, applied graphic art, harnessed to the mechanisms of the market, fulfils practical, economically justified, functions which belong only indirectly to the area of culture. In Poland, however, the programme promulgated from the very beginning sought to serve many purposes, above all in the sphere of education. The practical function seemed to be a peripheral one, and it was overshadowed by social considerations. Deep in the social consciousness there existed a belief in the educational mission of art and artistic activity, in its great moral prestige. The priority of non-commercial, indeed educational, motivation – a characteristic of successive social and political structures in Poland – forms the closest link between graphic design and artistic culture as a whole.

If one looks from this point of view at the twenty years between the wars, one is astounded by the wide discrepancy between the scale of the creative initiatives displayed – and Polish graphic design did not lag behind the world *avant-garde* – and the poor economic and technological basis. During this period Poland was one of the most economically retarded countries in Europe: what social and individual energies had, therefore, to be set into motion if the creative potentials were not to drain away!

The 'market' for this art was obviously limited to the intellectual élite and the wealthier groups. However its role as *animator* was extremely important, starting with the improvement of popular taste with regard to the daily environment. This was pioneering work, and astonishing results were achieved particularly in areas to do with the education of the young. A group of writers, poets, painters, and

Jan Bokiewicz: Cover design for
Franz Kafka's book *The Trial*. 1971.
Art director: Jolanta Barącz.

Miron Białoszewski

Pamiętnik
z powstania warszawskiego

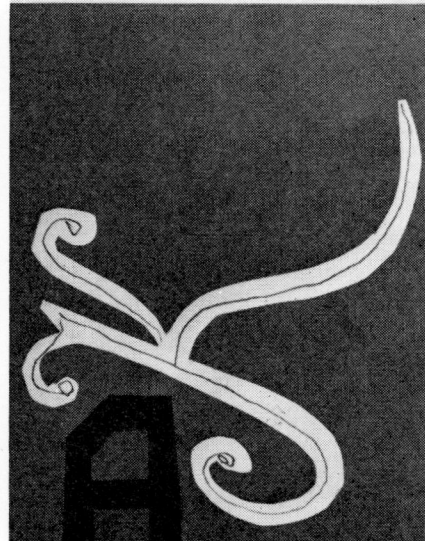

Andrzej Kuśniewicz

Król
Obojga Sycylii

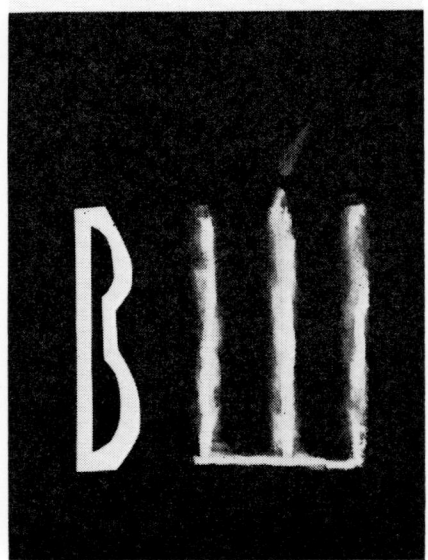

Bogdan Wojdowski

Chleb
rzucony umarłym

Above : Henryk Tomaszewski : three
jackets in a series. Each design contains a
graphic interpretation of the author's initials.
Polish Publishing Institute, 1972.
Art director : Jolanta Barącz.

Right : Janusz Bruchnalski : cover design for
book by Tadeusz Peiper, 1972.
Art director : Janusz Bruchnalski.

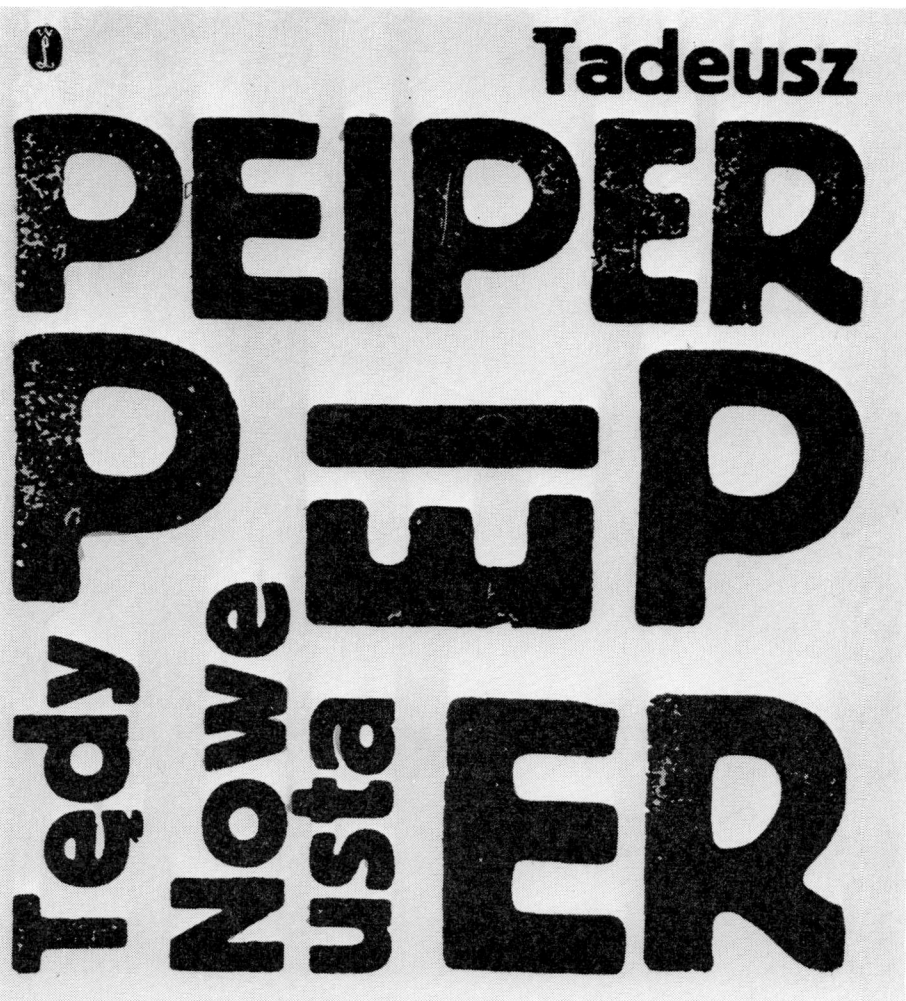

150

WZROKU NIC NIE ZASTĄPI

This industrial accidents poster by Maciej Urbaniec won third prize at the IV Biennale of Graphic Design, Brno, in 1970.

graphic artists who were associated in the twenties and thirties with Nasza Księgarnia – publishers for the teachers' union – helped to produce modern manuals, books, and periodicals for young readers. The tradition of separating the illustrations from the text was abandoned, dynamic methods of visual narration were attempted, and value was placed on original ideas and on wit. Books were produced which taught children to deal with intelligent illustrations. They were designed by such artists as Lewitt and Him as well as Franciszka Themerson who has been in London for many years. Another proof of the engagement of graphic artists in educational problems was provided in the field of safety at work. Poland in the thirties suffered from severe unemployment and the tradition of labour legislation that the rich countries in the West could boast of had no place there. Yet posters warning workers against professional hazards were designed on so high an artistic level and with such originality that when they were shown at the World Fair in Paris in 1937 they all won the Grand Prix.

Graphic design of the inter-war period is also remembered for its experiments in typography. Since they may be known to the British reader from the book *Pioneers of Modern Typography* by Herbert Spencer, I will mention only a few facts not recorded in that work. The first work designed according to the new rules of typography was a catalogue of the New Art Exhibition (Vilna, 1923). The typographic layout was designed by the individual participants in the exhibition, but Witold Kajruksztis and Władysław Strzemiński, members of the *Blok* group, played the most significant role. This inconspicuous brochure, printed on poor quality newsprint, is an example of the application of Suprematist aesthetics and Constructivism in printing. We must remember that the conceptions of functional typography stemmed from the environment of Polish constructivists, on the basis of their theory of art and experience of printing. Hence, even very unimpressive typographic works can pass as a manifestation of the designers' attitude toward the function of the composition of print. We find this above all in the work of Strzemiński, whose profound interest in typography was an expression of his attempts to find a wide front along which the new art could have social influence. His aim was to establish optical laws governing a flat area of print. 'A page of print' he wrote, 'is an order of spatial units (of the printed space) following one another (as the contents are being read) and this is why it should be regulated by measurements and numbers.' The proposed modular and numerical rules were observed by Strzemiński in the volume of poetry by Julian Przyboś, entitled *From Above* (1930). The undeniable merit of the Polish *avant-garde* in this field was its success in linking the artistic with the utilitarian purpose in such a way that the creative process and the technical-productive process became inseparable. It would be a mistake, however, to think that a rationalized, functional graphic art, which was also guided by its own theory, reached great heights in Poland. Constructivist ideas followed a roundabout path, mixed with other, more moderate trends. The geometrical style, with a whole range of variations, was a compromise between the *avant-garde* and the colourism then dominant in Polish painting.

After the war a new situation emerged. As a result of the changes in the political system, the educational and enlightening functions of art became even more pronounced, and were elevated to become part of the country's cultural programme. The weight of political propaganda,

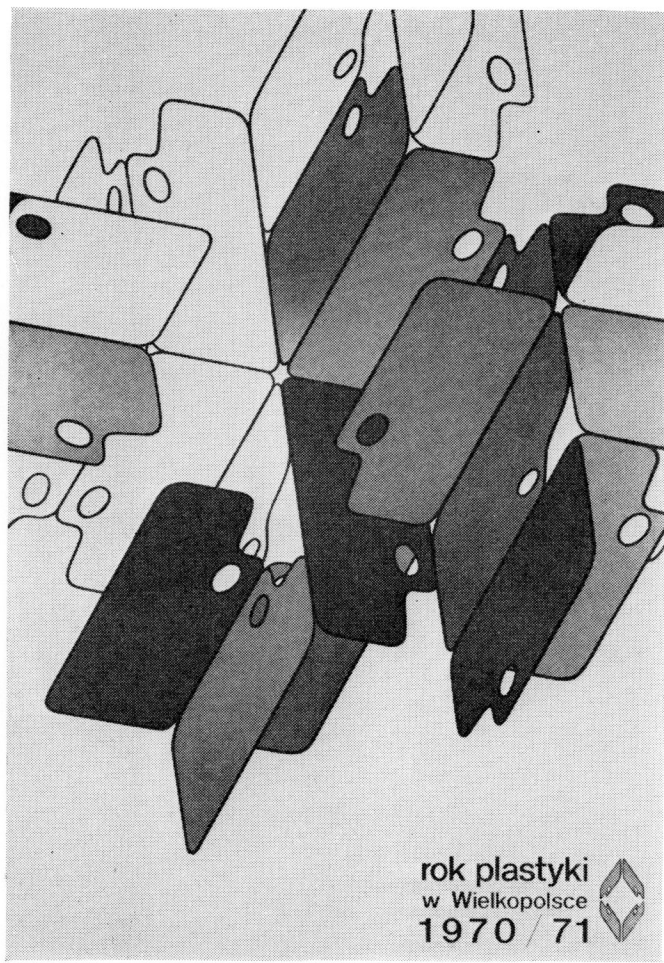

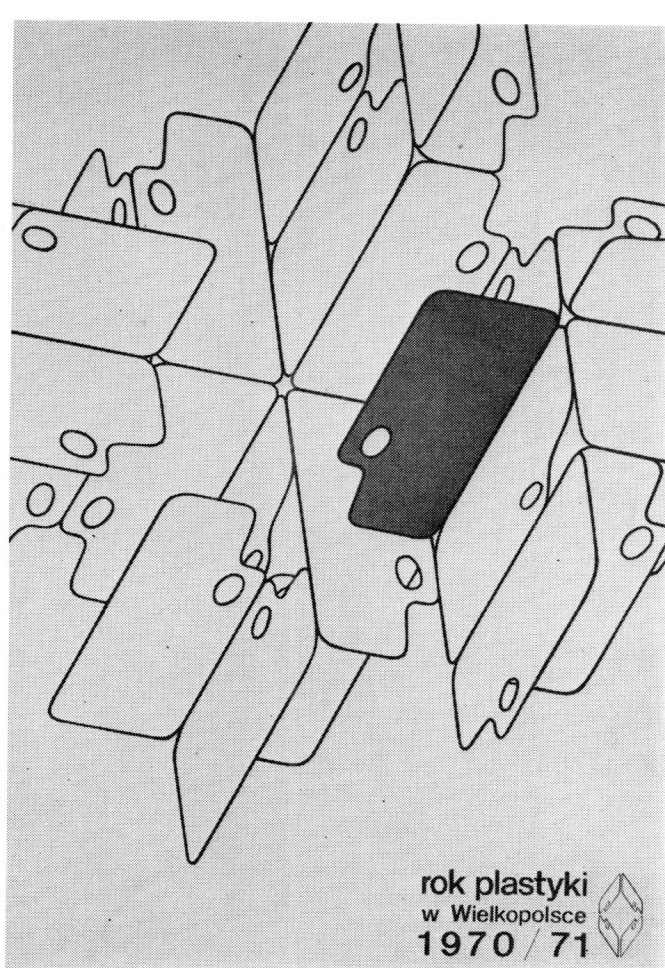

Jerzy Bak: Two sections of a poster in eight parts produced in 1970 to commemorate the Polish 'Year of Art'.

of educational and representational tasks, lay heavy on graphic design. The amount of problems connected with the graphic shaping of prints, books, periodicals, and other mass communication media increased immensely. Gradually new fields where graphic solutions were called for came into existence. Poland's graphic designers today form a coherent professional group. There are many of them, there is no concentration of designers in the capital, and they are quite independent economically. Within the group, the members formulate their own ambitions and conceptions of success. Something like an accepted social code exists and it even includes models for the artist's appearance and behaviour. But although the professional status of Polish designers is certainly unlike that of designers elsewhere, the 'graphic designers republic' is preoccupied with the same artistic problems as those preoccupying artistic *milieux* in general – but fortunately Poland is without the narrow professional barriers found in other countries. The work of a talented graphic designer is ranked as high as that of a well esteemed painter. The prestige of this discipline increased especially in the early fifties; this was because poster designers had considerable reservations about the conventional aesthetic approach which was leading to uniformity and monotony. Bombastic paintings with naïve messages were being exhibited and given prizes at exhibitions. The designers of posters and exhibitions, however, rejected many taboos and used the language of modern art. The

153

Right: Theatre poster by Waldemar
Swierzy, 1968.

Below: part of a theatre programme for
Mrozek's play 'Magic Night' designed by
Franciszek Starowieyski in 1966.

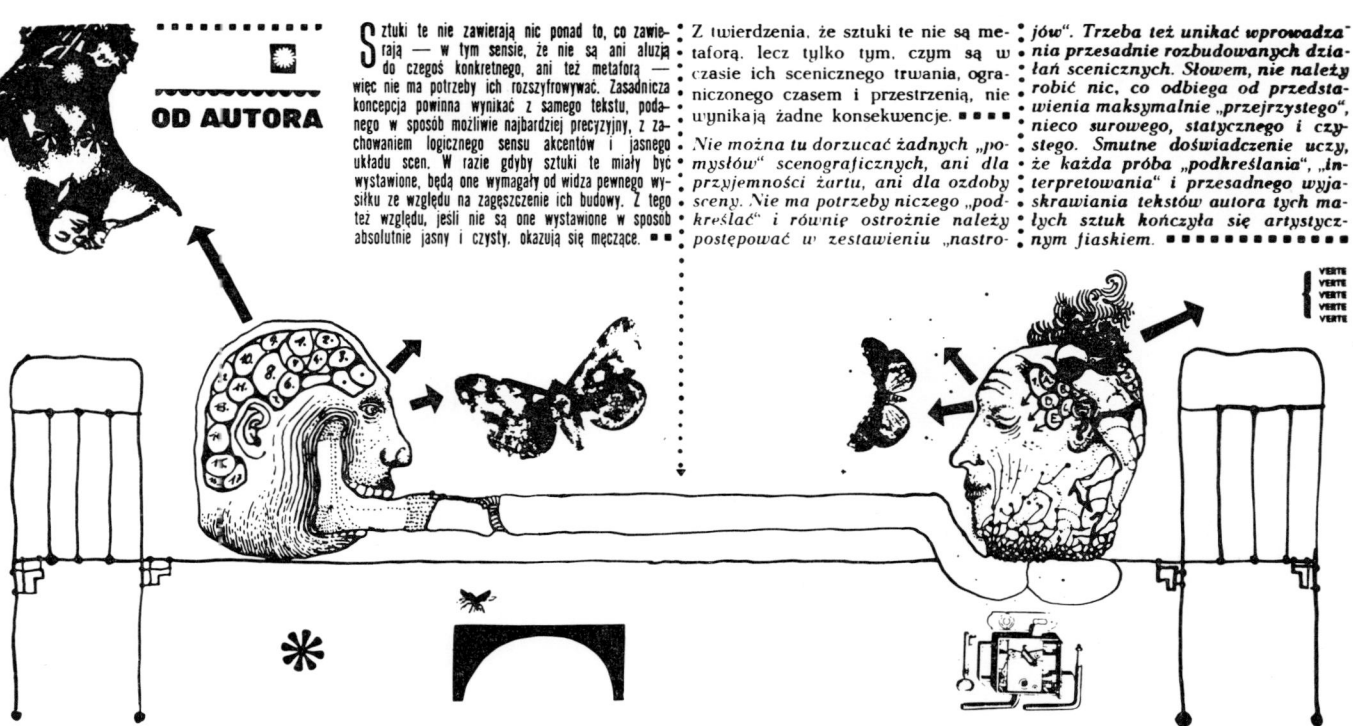

OD AUTORA

Sztuki te nie zawierają nic ponad to, co zawierają — w tym sensie, że nie są ani aluzją do czegoś konkretnego, ani też metaforą — więc nie ma potrzeby ich rozszyfrowywać. Zasadnicza koncepcja powinna wynikać z samego tekstu, podanego w sposób możliwie najbardziej precyzyjny, z zachowaniem logicznego sensu akcentów i jasnego układu scen. W razie gdyby sztuki te miały być wystawione, będą one wymagały od widza pewnego wysiłku ze względu na zagęszczenie ich budowy. Z tego też względu, jeśli nie są one wystawione w sposób absolutnie jasny i czysty, okazują się męczące. ■ ■

Z twierdzenia, że sztuki te nie są metaforą, lecz tylko tym, czym są w czasie ich scenicznego trwania, ograniczonego czasem i przestrzenią, nie wynikają żadne konsekwencje. ■ ■ ■ ■

Nie można tu dorzucać żadnych „pomysłów" scenograficznych, ani dla przyjemności żartu, ani dla ozdoby sceny. Nie ma potrzeby niczego „podkreślać" i równie ostrożnie należy postępować w zestawieniu „nastro-

jów". Trzeba też unikać wprowadzania przesadnie rozbudowanych działań scenicznych. Słowem, nie należy robić nic, co odbiega od przedstawienia maksymalnie „przejrzystego", nieco surowego, statycznego i czystego. Smutne doświadczenie uczy, że każda próba „podkreślania", „interpretowania" i przesadnego wyjaskrawiania tekstów autora tych małych sztuk kończyła się artystycznym fiaskiem. ■ ■ ■ ■ ■ ■ ■

This political poster by Julian Pałka 'Let's defend the idea' won a Gold Medal at the International Printing Exhibition (IBA) at Leipzig in 1965.

traditions of the graphic art of the inter-war years were continued, and enriched with experiences from new branches of art – the geometrical abstract, surrealism, and action painting.

The years between 1953 and 1960 were truly 'golden years' for graphic design, particularly for posters. Displayed almost all over the world, the graphic design of this period aroused enthusiastic reactions both in art circles and among a wider public. Foreign critics, disappointed by the feeble results that came from the boisterously propagated socialist realism, saw in Polish poster designs a way forward for commmunicative art, for an art that would not relinquish richness of expression or any formal means capable of stirring the imagination. The success of the poster designers brought vigour to their co-operation with publishers as well as with other public bodies and graphic designers. The effort made to raise the aesthetic standard of books was not inspired merely by market considerations. After the war there was a considerable increase in the amount of reading and books were sold out at once, even if their physical appearance was mediocre. Publishers followed the lead given by the monthly and yearly competitions for the best poster held in Warsaw without a break from 1961. They awarded a prize for the year's best published book, thus creating a basis for professional rivalry. Leading publishing houses, such as Czytelnik, the Polish Publishing Institute, Nasza Księgarnia, Silesian Publishers, Literary Publishers, were ambitious to have the best artists work with them. Firms began to employ artists having a good standing among their colleagues as artistic directors supervising their house style. This move by publishing houses to create for themselves a unified style encountered some obstacles. One problem arose from the strongly developed individuality of graphic designers and their free attitude toward the subject. So far only some publishing series have been able to achieve really original and interesting graphic solutions. Covers and jackets sometimes achieve a markedly intelligent pictorial interpretation of the contents, but the typographical side leaves much room for improvement. The general increase in the number of titles published, compared with the pre-war period, has not been accompanied by a quality of print satisfying modern aesthetic and legibility requirements. The divorce of the design from the final product began to menace the very foundations of the profession of a graphic designer, of a *Buchgestalter*, conceiving the book as a well defined optical entity. This situation gives importance to the graphic designers' individual results. These do not submit to the dictates of industry, which is concerned with quantitative results; they create enclaves of sound typography. And if from time to time there appear scientific publications, albums, volumes of poetry, and outstanding prints which continue the 'beautiful book' traditions, this arises out of the struggle for artistic recognition generated by the graphic *métier* itself. Small prints produced for a particular occasion are ephemeral and often do not remain on record. but they do reflect the culture of everyday life and *mores* to some degree. Theatre programmes provide one example. These ceased long ago to count as an art subject in graphic art circles. But some of the more ambitious theatres in Warsaw, Cracow, and Gdansk treat the printing of the programme as part of the mystery of the performance. When Polish artists are provoked to 'stage design' a performance with graphic means, they find here an outlet for their considerable and exuberant ingenuity. Because all kinds of tricks are acceptable, mini-works of great piquancy are created in this

Book illustration by Emilia Piekarska-Freudenreich, 1972.

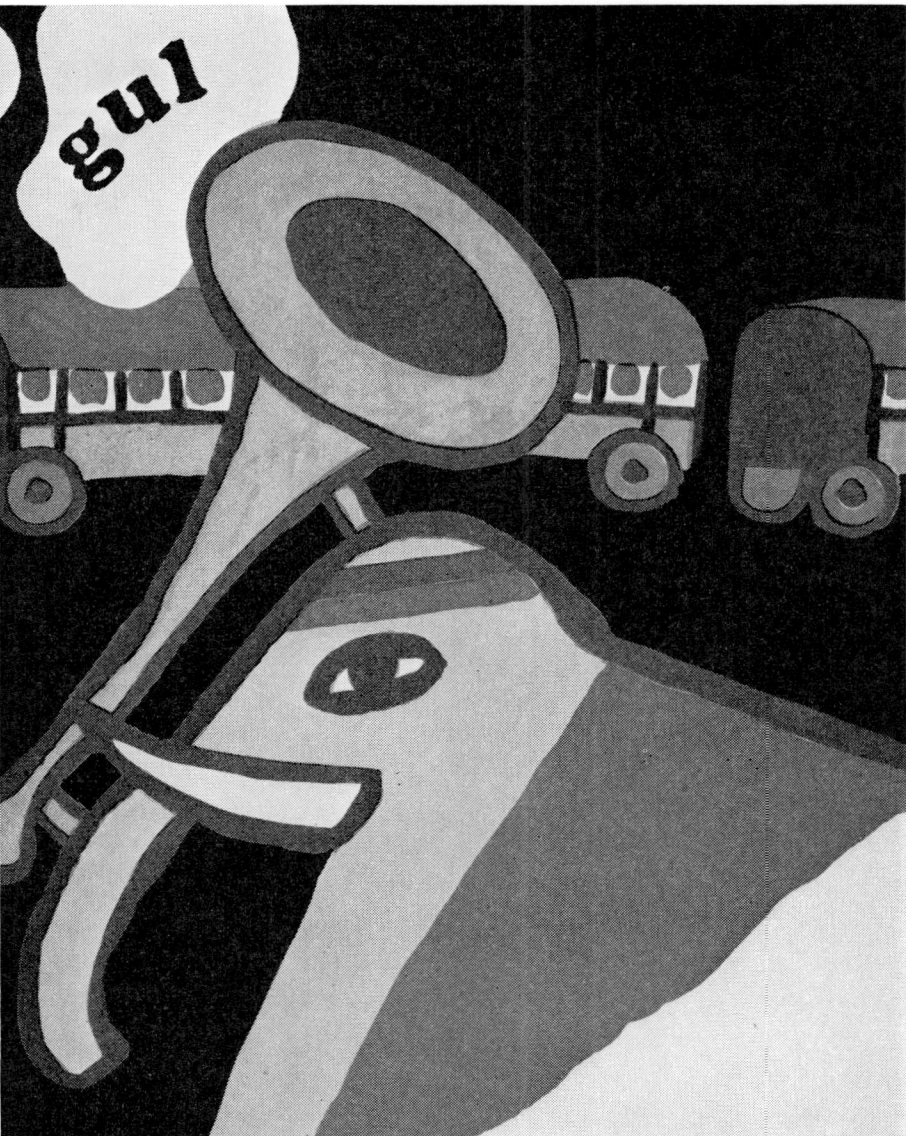

atmosphere of art free from inhibitions. The information given in the text of the programme becomes an enjoyable visual game for the spectator. The motif of a fair is a familiar one in graphic design and those who employ it in Poland have some excellent antecedents. One may mention only the history of the literary-artistic cabaret, *Zielony Balonik* (The Green Balloon), born from the spirit of 'Young Poland', from which so much sharp wit and satire flowed. Here fun was poked at smugness, a pseudo-patriotic slogan was exposed, philistines were jeered at. Humour flourished on the lithographic pages of the programmes and the invitations to Bohemian gatherings. These were designed by the best painters and graphic artists, with a feeling for style and an aggressive force. And all this took place, let us not forget, in Cracow, long before the Dadaists had established their own cabaret.

Links between literature, poetry, and the theatre on the one hand and graphic art on the other, have always existed and are very typical of our times. It is no coincidence that such writers as Witkiewicz, Gombrowicz, Schulz, Gałczyński, and Lec, and from abroad Joyce, Gogol, Kafka, and Ionesco are popular at least among some graphic artists. These artists, of course, do not turn to these authors to find subjects for illustration but rather because their interest is provoked by these writers' critical way of thinking, characterized by a spirit of opposition and contrariness which finds a sympathetic partner in graphic art. These inspirations flow so strongly and have so regenerative an influence that they are immune to the restlessly changing art fashions of the second half of this century. This can explain the meagre and derivative career both of pop art and of the neo-Art Nouveau style, despite the fact that many graphic artists placed great hope in these trends. Much more interesting are the numerous attempts at an ironic, even grotesque interpretation of pop art, attempts which produced something like a coarse anti-pop. And in the work of the younger generation of graphic artists – those who entered professional life in the mid-sixties – new interests are becoming evident, an apparent reaction against the excess of emotional motivation in the work of their older colleagues. A mechanized and urbanized reality influences young people's imagination and reactions; the world has become more closely-knit and uniform; mass communication media assault the eye with an avalanche of images; theoreticians give us a menacing picture of visual pollution and call for order to be introduced into the visual environment. Thus young people are susceptible more than ever before to proposals to objectify the creative process. They consciously bridle their emotions with the discipline of thought; they look for solutions which are closer to the method of rationalistic design. This goes hand in hand with a greater concern to master modern reproduction techniques, involving photography as well as typography, which present new problems. The technical innovations are undoubtedly valuable, particularly now when the design of informational material for industry and commerce is at last growing out of its swaddling clothes.

What future for plastics papers?

N. K. Bridge

Dr Bridge, of PIRA, examines the advantages and disadvantages of plastics papers, for which the Japanese papermaking industry has big production and world marketing plans. Previous cost estimates, the author notes, have assumed no breakthrough in plastics technology: such a breakthrough, however, he believes to have now occurred in the form of synthetic pulp, which is likely to be recognized as by far the most important development in papermaking for many years.

An area of activity likely, sooner or later, to make a big impact on the printing scene is that of plastics paper and synthetic pulp. The plastics paper considered in this article is the kind that might prove suitable for printings and writings only. There are three main kinds – plastics films with paperlike properties, foamed plastics papers, and synthetic fibre papers (including non-woven fabrics and spun bonded structures). We are concerned here only with the first kind; foamed plastics papers have not proved suitable for high-class printing, though techniques have been investigated for improving their printability; and synthetic fibre papers seem unlikely to compete with paper on a large scale because of high raw material and production costs.

It is well known that plastics papers production technology has been carried furthest in Japan. The basic reason for this was Japan's vast increase in gross national product and hence in demand for paper. This increased 2·3 times between 1960 and 1969 – an average of 10 % a year – and Japanese imports of pulp and wood rose from 12 % to 50 % of requirements. (The comparative British figure is now about 60 %.) The Japanese consequently felt the need for an alternative source of raw materials. Plastics papers were developed and in 1968 the forecast was that it ought to be possible to raise annual production to 3·5 million tonnes by 1978. (Recently, however, the Japanese have revised the estimate downward to 2·2 million tonnes a year by 1985.) Four or five years after the original development, two companies are attempting seriously to market large tonnages of plastics paper in Japan and agencies have been set up throughout the world. The speed of development is impressive. Will plastics take over the bulk of conventional printings and writings papers? Will they exist marginally side by side? Or will the whole development fail because of either the high price, or serious product deficiencies compared with cellulosic papers, or other factors?

To answer these questions, information is needed on the future markets and costs of printings and writings papers and of the new plastics papers, and we must also have some idea of the present and future technical acceptability of the product. The question of technical acceptability is much the easiest one. Most of the references to plastics papers in the literature over the last two or three years have stated or suggested at least some of their technical advantages and disadvantages. The advantages with which plastics papers are generally credited are: good appearance, good print quality, high water resistance, high grease resistance, good hygro stability, high wet strength, high dry strength, absence of linting, and good pick resistance. Some definite disadvantages that have been stated are: slow drying of ink, lack of ink key, low opacity, low stiffness, static problems, poor heat stability.

The list is probably far from complete and will, of course, be modified by the type of plastics paper. Papers with a clay coating like Q-kote will have ink drying properties similar to those of conventional papers but linting and picking may be defects. Many of the advantages and disadvantages of individual types of plastics papers can be inferred from the numerical test data. Although some data of this kind have been published, the results have been determined and expressed in different ways, and comparison is also made difficult by the variety of grammages used. Some discrepancies, possibly due to batch-to-batch variation, have also been noted.

Table 1 represents an attempt, based on available published data, supplemented by some PIRA data, to compare the properties of a number of plastics papers. All the results except folding endurance have been converted to those for a hypothetical 100 g/m² material. Of course, except possibly for homogeneous materials such as Polyart, this procedure is not strictly valid. The table should consequently only be used to compare orders of magnitude of results. It should also be stressed that for some materials there are several grades differing, for instance, in surface finish. The results are strictly correct only for the grade tested, which is not always known with certainty.

The test data available confirm that plastics papers have many of the advantages and disadvantages claimed. There is evidence, however, that the high strength of plastics papers has been over-stressed. As a generalization based on the available information, bonded plastics papers such as Tyvek do have a very high bursting strength, tearing resistance, and folding endurance compared with conventional paper of the same grammage, but the tensile strength will be only slightly greater than that of such papers. Filled polyolefine sheets, such as Polyart, will also have greater bursting strength and internal tearing resistance than paper, although the difference is less pronounced. Against this, the stiffness of all plastics papers except the Tyvek type is low in comparison with paper and for many purposes this will mean that a significantly higher grammage material must be used to obtain the necessary handling characteristics. Under these circumstances, the better strength characteristics of a plastics paper may be wasted, since for most of its bulk usage applications paper already has adequate strength.

Table 1: comparative properties of some plastics papers (converted to grammage 100 g/m²)

Property		Proprietary material					Comparison papers	
		Polyart	Printel S	Q-Kote	Q-Per, QM grade	Tyvek	Typical coated	High quality uncoated
Apparent density, g/cm³		1·10	1·14	1·22	0·57	0·48	1·19	0·83
Thickness, μm		91	88	82	174	210	84	120
Tensile strength, N/15 mm	MD	96	20	42	37	100	70	95
	CD	80	18	37	31	85	40	45
Stretch, %	MD	100	1·2	30	35	35	2	2
	CD	100	1·8	30	10	35	4	5
Internal tearing resistance, mN	MD	410	180	220	160	2900	400	220
	CD	480	230	260	150	5000	410	250
Folding endurance, no. of folds	MD	≫10K	900	2600	720	≫10K	80	1000
Stiffness, mN	MD	1·9	1·4	1·3	4·2	10·4	7·0	10·0
	CD	1·6	1·4	1·2	3·2	9·0	4·0	5·5
Roughness (Bendtsen), ml/min		<5	20	<5	200	600	20	150
Opacity, %		95	88	94	75	98	95	94
Oil absorption (SORT), (s or h)		>48h	—	>48h	<3s	<3s	24s	3s
Approximate cost,	£/t	700	760	715	2000	1550	280	220
new pence/m²		7·0	7·6	7·2	20·0	15·5	2·8	2·2

Table 2: properties of plastics and conventional papers*

Property		Polyart	Q-Kote	Q-Per	Ambassador Art
Grammage, g/m²		118 (8)	137 (3)	54 (3)	134 (1)
Apparent density, g/cm³		1·11	1·18	0·57	1·19
Thickness, μm		104 (8)	116 (2)	94 (1)	112 (1)
Tensile strength, N/15 mm	MD	116 (5)	70 (3)	21 (8)	79 (2)
	CD	85 (9)	70 (3)	18 (7)	41 (8)
Stretch, %	MD	129 (4)	56 (60)	36 (34)	2·2 (6)
	CD	175 (8)	48 (39)	10 (32)	5·6 (16)
Internal tearing resistance, mN	MD	355 (18)	510 (7)	94 (20)	563 (5)
Folding endurance, No. of folds	MD	41000 (20)	2600 (10)	680 (10)	84 (15)
Stiffness, mN	MD	3·6 (3)	5·3 (10)	0·53 (17)	10·2 (3)
	CD	3·4 (2)	5·0 (7)	0·74 (16)	7·1 (7)
Roughness (Printsurf), μm		0·93 (13)	0·87 (10)	4·90 (3)	0·64 (7)
Opacity, %		95	95	75	98
Oil absorption (SORT), s or h		>48h	>48h	<2s	24s (18)
Approximate cost, £/t		700	715	2000	280
new pence/m²		8·3	9·8	10·8	3·7

* Values given are mean values: figures in brackets are coefficients of variation.

The really exceptional physical property of plastics paper is its folding endurance. To this should perhaps be added initial tearing resistance for which, unfortunately, there is no standard test method. These two properties confirm the very high durability of plastics papers and for some special uses, for example charts and maps, they have some very considerable advantages over conventional papers. The tests carried out at PIRA have also shown that at least some plastics are dimensionally sensitive to organic fluids, for example oils and alcohols used in the dampening solution. Furthermore, even relatively small temperature rises have a marked effect on the dimensions and properties of plastics papers.

Although physical test data can go some way toward comparing plastics and other papers, they cannot provide the complete answer. The printability and runnability of printing papers, as we all know, can only be determined with certainty on a printing press. To illustrate potential quality, three plastics papers, Polyart, Q-Kote, and Q-Per, and also a coated art paper, have been printed at PIRA in black, and in four colours, by offset-litho using the same inks throughout. Space does not permit a full discussion of results obtained but one or two comments can be made.

The quality of the prints on the plastics papers was considered to be good in view of the short lengths of run possible and the lack of experience with these papers. No feeding difficulties were experienced with Polyart or Q-Kote, but with Q-Per considerable problems arose as expected both in feeding and delivery, particularly on the second run through the press. The difficulties were attributable to the high level of static and low stiffness of the material. Static was very slow to clear. No register problems arose with any of the materials. Ink requirements for Q-Kote and Q-Per were similar to those for coated paper but Polyart required a lower ink weight. Great care was needed with the ink/water balance on all three plastics papers.

There is no doubt that plastics papers can be used for many other purposes for which conventional papers are at present used and, because of their special characteristics, new areas of use may be found for which conventional papers are less suitable. However, two aspects of the use of these papers should be stressed. First, it has been claimed that the high strength of plastics papers makes it possible to use a material of much less grammage than would be necessary with conventional paper. This is not in fact true of printings papers. If plastics papers were twice as 'strong', a reduction of 50 % in grammage would give adequate strength but would reduce the already low stiffness level by over 80 % and would also have a big effect on opacity. To achieve the required levels of stiffness and opacity, there is some evidence that existing plastics papers would need to be used at higher grammage level than are conventional coated papers, giving a lower yield per tonne. Compared with uncoated papers, this tendency would be even more pronounced. It might therefore be concluded that the plastics papers at present available could not be expected to replace conventional papers in most applications unless the price of plastics papers per tonne was reduced to rather less than that of conventional papers.

Secondly, it might be thought that plastics papers, being manufactured on small machines from more consistent raw materials, should be less variable than conventional papers. The second table based on measurements also made by PIRA indicates that this is not necessarily so. Most of the properties of the plastics papers are at least as variable as those of conventional papers. The Polyart sample examined showed considerable variations in grammage and thickness. These no doubt were reflected in the variability of the other properties. Q-Kote and Q-Per showed high variation in stretch, in folding endurance and (particularly Q-Per) in stiffness.

Plastics papers capable of being used in place of papers for some printing applications are already available. Examples are maps and wall charts, guides, maintenance manuals, handbooks, outdoor posters, labels for car batteries, car licence discs, file indices. They are, however, very expensive. Table 2 shows that the UK price of some of the plastics papers varies between £700 and £1,500–£2,000 per tonne whereas the price of a typical coated paper is about £280 per tonne, a ratio of at least 2·5 to 1. Even when the price is based on the cost per unit area, the ratio is not improved. Coated paper prices, on the other hand, have not even kept pace with the general inflation in prices over the last few years. Some increase in price in real money terms is obviously inevitable in the next few years to provide the papermakers with a reasonable return on capital. Plastics manufacturers, however, face very similar pressures.

A recent PIRA report forecast that the price of the basic plastics raw materials will grow by 2–3 % to the end of the decade, and that the actual price of the plastics papers in 1975 is likely to be between £300 and £450 per tonne. In 1980 it is likely to be between £300 and £500 per tonne. On the basis of these figures, it was forecast that by 1975 there could be a market of between 50,000 and 100,000 tonnes per annum for plastics papers in the UK, made up of approximately 12,000 tonnes of cast-coated and 60,000 tonnes of brush-coated and high quality art papers. This appears at first sight to be a large tonnage. However, by papermaking standards it is very small, as it represents the annual output of only one large paper machine. A year or so ago when PIRA was carrying out the work on which those forecasts were based, it was carefully pointed out that projected costs and markets assumed no breakthrough in plastics technology. I believe that such a breakthrough has now in fact occurred in the form of synthetic pulp.

Two companies have recently announced that they have developed such a material – Crown Zellerbach in the United States and Solvay & Co. in Italy. Basically, they have overcome the slow rate determining step of conventional plastics extrusion by producing fibres very similar to wood fibres directly from the polymerization reactor. Crown Zellerbach has already quoted prices for the pulp – for trial amounts – of between £130 and £155 per short ton. This is about double the price of a conventional bleached pulp but there seems little doubt that the price will be reduced in the future. Crown Zellerbach started to investigate synthetic woodpulp about five years ago and began collaboration with the Japanese Mitsui company in February 1971. Two pilot plants have been constructed to manufacture the pulp, one in Japan and another which recently started up in Camas in Washington. A semi-commercial plant capable of manufacturing 6,000 tonnes per year was due to begin running in July 1972. Market development will be carried out in Japan. It is possible to disperse the fibres in just the same way as woodpulp and to use them, alone or in combination with woodpulp, to form paper on a conventional paper machine. Heat treatment of the fibres can be used to change the properties of the paper. The fibres melt between 130 and 135°C and soften at a lower temperature. It is therefore possible to provide wet strengthening at the paper-machine calenders. Pronounced opacifying and brightening effects can also be produced. Plans have very recently been announced for developing the material in Europe, where Crown Zellerbach will co-operate with Hoechst in Germany. I believe that this development will be looked back upon as by far the most important in papermaking for a number of years, and one which is likely to be of considerable benefit both to the papermaker and to the printer.

The evolution of
Times New Roman

John Dreyfus, with drawings by Matthew Carter

Ring in Times Europa and ring out Times New Roman – at least in *The Times* newspaper for which both types were created. On a world scale, however, the reign of Times New Roman, with its tested prestige and now vast panoply of letters, signs, and symbols is hardly diminished and is assured of extending into the next millenium. The article traces the evolution of Morison's celebrated typeface from its introduction in the London newspaper's columns forty years ago.

The Matthew Carter drawings following page 167 were reproduced offset-litho by Gilchrist Brothers Ltd and printed by Lund Humphries on Polyart, opaque and translucent, both supplied by Bakelite Xylonite Ltd.
Line engravings on pages 166, 170, and 171 were also made by Gilchrist Brothers Ltd. The specimen type settings on page 173 are by The Monotype Corporation Ltd.

Almost exactly forty years after the introduction of Times New Roman, three sizes of Times Europa were introduced on 9 October 1972 for the news columns of *The Times*. For some months the newspaper still used Times New Roman in its larger and smaller sizes, thus prompting one reader to write how reassuring he found it that one could still die in Times Roman – provided one was not famous. Even this comfort will be denied in 1973, when larger and smaller sizes of Times Europa are brought into use by *The Times*.

A vast amount of printing, however, continues to appear in Times New Roman, and hardly a month goes by without the design being added to a new typesetting system. Here we shall examine the reasons for the introduction of the type in 1932, and why it has since become such a world-wide success for book printing, magazine printing, jobbing printing, and many other purposes quite different from those for which it was originally conceived.

When *The Times* published on 29 October 1929 a special number devoted to 'Printing in the Twentieth Century', it contained an article by Stanley Morison entitled 'Newspaper Types: A Study of *The Times*' in which he commented that the type then used by the newspaper was the same as it had used when its previous printing supplement had been published in 1912. His dissatisfaction with that state of affairs was expressed with far greater vehemence before a group of senior members of *The Times* staff, to whom he proposed that the types used by the newspaper should be 'redesigned and brought up to the standard obtaining in the average book as brought out by London publishers'. So rapidly was the group convinced that the newspaper's typography 'compared very unsatisfactorily with that of the contemporary novel, biography, or text-book' that a committee was promptly set up to consider the desirability of changing the founts used by *The Times* for text and headings. For the guidance of this committee, Morison prepared a long and extensively illustrated printed, *Memorandum on a Proposal to Revise the Typography of 'The Times'*. In this he summarized the background to the problem, and the nature of the particular problem to be attacked. Then, by his use of historical and technical data, he showed how he proposed to solve the problem. He also dwelt on the 'lack of correspondence between the book and newspaper branches of printing; the reason for low standards of typography in newspapers; desirability of an improvement in newspapers.' A change in *The Times*, he wrote, was a necessity which was 'comprehensible only historically' – a very Morisonian line of attack.

Rejected modified version of 'Monotype'
Perpetua.
This version of Eric Gill's typeface was
modified so that the 11 point size could be
cast on a 9 point body. Morison observed
that the effort to economize in depth failed
because there was insufficient space
between the lines to give comfort in
reading : 'The Perpetua stared at the reader'.

TRIAL NO. 2.   PERPETUA. 316-9   26-11-30
10½ SET.   COMPOSITION.

The desire of communicating ideas seems to be implanted in every
human breast : the two most useful methods of gratifying this desire are
by sounds addressed to the ear, or by marks or representations made to
the eye, or in other words, by speech and writing.   The first method was
rendered more complete, by the invention of the second, because it
opened a door to the communication of ideas through the sense of sight
as well as that of hearing.   Speech may be considered as the substance
and writing as the shadow that follows it.   The uses of a legible language
are too various to be enumerated.   By the wonderful invention of writing
we are enabled to record and to perpetuate our thoughts for our own
benefit, or give them the most extensive communication for that of others.
Without this art, the labours of our ancestors would have been lost to us
in every branch of knowledge.   Tradition, being so nearly allied to fable
that no authentic history can be compiled but from written or printed
materials.   Therefore generations have been enabled to add to the stock
they received from the past and to prepare the way for future acquisitions.

BY THIS HAPPY MODE OF COMMUNICATION DISTANCE IS AS IT
WERE, ANNIHILATED AND THE MERCHANT, SCHOLAR AND
STAESMAN BECOME PRESENT TO EVERY PURPOSE OF UTILITY
IN THE MOST REMOTE REGIONS.   THIS RAISES MAN FROM THE
BRUTE CREATION AND RAISES HIM TO A PRE-EMINENCE ABOVE
THAT OF THE SAVAGES OF HIS OWN SPECIES.   WE MAY CON-

ABCDEFGHIJKLMNOPQRSTUVWXYZÆŒ&
abcdefghijklmnopqrstuvwxyzæœfffiflffiffl   .,''-:;–!?—

First trial of 'Monotype' Times New Roman.
Although headed 'Times Old Style' this
setting shows Monotype 'Times New
Roman' in its first trial state, composed in the
column measure for which it was intended
to be used in *The Times*. Among the many
characters subsequently altered, note the
C G and S. The 'set' was later reduced to 9.

TIMES OLD STYLE   327-9   9¼ SET.   LINE .1325   22-4-31

CANBERRA (by mail)

Two currents in Australian politics have
been running on almost parrallel lines,
only now and again converging.   The
Labour Party, for instance, dominant in
the Federal Parliament and in the States
of New South Wales, Victoria, and South
Australia, is concerned as deeply with its
own internal troubles as it is with a policy
for the sorely stricken country.   One
arises out of the other, but in the struggle
for supremacy neither faction makes any
headway with constructive legislation.
The outlook of the opposition forces
is   scarcely   more   encouraging.   The
Nationalist Party and the Country Party
are each " separate entities," with their
contentions on political programmes and
the claims of each to particular con-
stituencies.   The pressure of the times
forces   the   minds   of   the   public   into
unusual   channels.   Western   Australia

talks of secession, and competent authorities assert that if a vote were taken in
that State a majority of the electors
would favour secession The agitation for
new States in Queensland and in New
South Wales has been given an impetus.
Riverina, the large agricultural terri-
tory in southern New South Wales, has
been incensed by Mr. Lang's repudiation
policy, and at enthusiastic meetings demands were made for a new State. Some
electors want to have all the State Parlia-
ments abolished, and there are others who
are asking why 6,000,000 people should
want seven Governors. None of these
things amounts to much in itself, but in
combination they precent the focusing of
the   public   mind   on   questions   which
urgently call for settlement. The truth is
that   our   forms   of   government,   over-
weighted as they are, offer no insuperable
obstacle to good government.

He also discussed the question of legibility which he admitted was surrounded by many imponderables. His designs were later subjected to what he called a 'medical examination' by a number of experts, notably Sir William Lister, consulting surgeon oculist to the King. Morison even found some support for his proposals in *The Legibility of Print*, a report by R. L. Pyke which had been published by His Majesty's Stationery Office in 1926.

As typographical adviser to the Lanston Monotype Company, Morison was particularly impressed by Pyke's verdict on the high legibility of three particular Monotype series, two of them Old Face and one Modern. These findings were not conclusive but they were sufficient to justify Morison in writing that 'the scientific investigation of legibility proves therefore, if it proves anything, that the ideal type should be simple, fairly broad, with fairly good thicks, with some but without too much contrast between the thicks and thins, set with fairly wide spacing'. From this Morison argued that 'any type which was not too strongly contrasted as between its thicks and thins would be "satisfactory", i.e. will be easy, agreeable, and therefore "legible" to the bulk of the readers of *The Times*.' He ended his memorandum by proposing to submit a design to a meeting to be held on 27 November 1930.

Morison was fortunate in being able to produce a new type for the newspaper at great speed, and with a high degree of technical excellence. At the Monotype Works at Redhill, an exceptionally able team had been built up by Frank Hinman Pierpont (1860–1937), an American martinet of wide experience. He had been managing director of the Typograph AG in Germany before joining the Lanston Monotype Company in 1899 as manufacturing manager. When Pierpont came to England, he brought with him several members of his highly skilled staff with whom he had perfected an unrivalled system for producing matrices. Thanks to these technicians, Morison had no problem with the manufacture of his new type; but first he had to decide exactly what kind of a design was required for it. When the committee met at *The Times* on 28 January 1931, Morison did not bring to it any new design, but instead submitted a number of experimental settings, two of which were set in Monotype Plantin and Monotype Perpetua. Monotype Plantin had been made by Pierpont in 1916 before Morison's appointment as typographical adviser, Perpetua had been cut experimentally by hand, following designs which Morison had bought from Eric Gill, and which had subsequently been recut by

OQCG

OQCG

OQCG

Similarities between Perpetua and Times New Roman.
The top row shows Perpetua, with Times New Roman in the centre (and Plantin below for comparison). Not only were Perpetua's sharper-shaped serifs incorporated in the design of Times New Roman: the proportions and angle of shading of Perpetua capitals were also influential.

Pierpont; both versions had very sharp serifs, in marked contrast with Monotype Plantin. After examining the various settings submitted, the committee decided that a new type for headlines would be necessary: a type which must appear to be larger, but because it must not take up more space would have to be either taller and more condensed, or have more colour. Further, it was agreed that the type should have the 'squareness' traditional to *The Times*, by which the committee meant that it must fill the body. (In making this stipulation the committee was not entirely wise, for reasons which will appear later.)

Morison was asked to prepare (a) a specimen of 'modernised Plantin', i.e. Plantin approximated to present Times practice, with sharper serifs and (b) a specimen of thickened Perpetua. The reason for insisting upon sharper serifs was that blunt serifs did not produce a clean effect after the types had been stereotyped for newspaper printing, especially when it became necessary to increase the number of plates made from the same flong. Perpetua had the right formation of serifs, but its design was found to be unsatisfactory after it had been modified to meet the committee's requirements for changes in its proportions.

It was therefore decided that Plantin should be modified to correspond with the committee's preferences. It might be thought that this would have been a mild conversion and a simple matter. In fact it proved to be a major operation of design, which amounted less to a partial conversion of the original character of Plantin than to its complete transformation.

How was all this achieved? Morison once declared that he pencilled the original set of drawings for Times New Roman, and handed them to a draughtsman employed by *The Times*, Victor Lardent, who Morison considered capable of producing an unusually firm and clean line. But it is very doubtful whether Morison ever pencilled a complete set of original drawings for this type. More probably he provided Lardent with a printed specimen of a type cut by Robert Granjon, which

Pierpont had used as the basis for Monotype Plantin. After receiving Morison's oral or written instructions, Lardent then produced outline drawings on which Morison indicated the alterations he wished to be made. Lardent's finished drawings were closely followed in the first trial cutting produced by The Monotype Corporation. The order was put in hand on 8 April 1931, and trial proofs were printed on 22 April 1931. The overall effect of the first trials was remarkably close to the type introduced in October 1932, but certain letters underwent important changes as can be understood from the accompanying illustrations.

To have produced a design of such excellence at such speed is a rare feat. Yet the speed of its inception, and the fact that the pioneer work was entirely carried out at the Monotype Works, are the reasons for two of its defects as a newspaper type. Although Morison was well aware of the problems, he seems to have overlooked the difficulties of adapting his basic design to the requirements of producing a related bold, as well as a series of related headline types.

The production of a bold version impelled him to respect the limitations of line-composing machines which *The Times* used far more extensively than Monotype composing machines. Since line-composing machines use duplex matrices to combine roman and bold letters on a single matrix, the bold for Times New Roman had to be designed without allowing any letter to be drawn wider than the roman. In the design of the bold, Morison used horizontal serifs which are discordant in close juxtaposition with the oblique serifs of the normal roman. Moreover Times Bold is too congested a design for easy reading in its smaller sizes.

Modifications of design and serif treatment. The blunt features of Plantin (above) have been refined to produce Times New Roman (below). The idiosyncrasy of the open-bowled P has been abandoned, so that the upper bowls of P B and R become consistent. The serifs of the S below match the C and G in the illustration opposite.

PBRS

PBRS

When war-time restrictions on paper supplies impelled a more economic use of materials, the exceptional space-saving qualities of Times New Roman brought it into far wider use for every kind of printing. The type was also acclaimed in America, where the Crowell-Collier Company adopted it for the text of *Collier's Magazine, Woman's Home Companion,* and the *American Magazine.* After the Crowell-Collier Company made this change in 1942, it issued a handsome quarto pamphlet entitled *Letter Perfect* extolling the virtues of Times New Roman. In 1953 the type was adopted by the Chicago *Sun-Times* daily newspaper and it has since been adopted by *Time* and *Life* magazines, and by *Sports Illustrated.*

Morison consistently held the view that Times New Roman succeeded because it was an economical type: it packed in the greatest possible number of letters, while their design ensured they were more legible than other types requiring more space. He maintained that as main stems and curves were thicker, his letters carried more ink, and so looked blacker on the page, and consequently were more clearly outlined against the paper on which they were printed. Thus increased perceptibility – not the same thing as legibility – was assured. In legibility research it is a platitude that people read most easily the types which they are most accustomed to read. Morison's accustomed standard was formed by reading books. Hence his concern in 1930 had been to bring the typographical standard of *The Times* (read of course by literate 'top people') 'up to the standard obtaining in the average book published in London'. Post-war surveys of reading habits in many countries have revealed that there exist a mass of readers who seldom, if ever, read a book, but who regularly read a newspaper. Consequently it is not surprising to see that Times New Roman, originally designed as a newspaper face for a special class of readers, is now going out of fashion for certain kinds of journalism, although the type remains in constant demand for book, jobbing, and display work. The type has become more widely available in recent years after being copied by makers of filmsetting machines, photographic display gadgets, transfer sheets, letters for signs and exhibitions, and so on.

The displacement of Times New Roman by Times Europa in the columns of *The Times* is not to be lamented. Fundamental changes have occurred since the war in the quality of paper used by that newspaper, and in the standards of presswork applied to its printing. Morison's type no longer shows to advantage in the newspaper for which it was originally created. On the other hand, over a period of forty years,

Varieties of 'Monotype' Times New Roman

If the conditions $\dfrac{4\pi L^2}{a_1 a_2 \sin^2 \omega} \gg 1$ are fulfilled, then

$$\sum_{k}^{\infty}{}' K_0\left(\frac{|\boldsymbol{r}-\boldsymbol{r}_k|}{L}\right) = \frac{2\pi L^2}{\sigma}\left\{1+\frac{\sin^2\omega}{4\pi^2 L^2}\sum_{v_1,\,v_2}{}'\frac{e^{2\pi i\left(\frac{v_1}{a_1}x+\frac{v_2}{a_2}y\right)}}{\left(\dfrac{v_1^2}{a_1^2}+\dfrac{v_2^2}{a_2^2}-\dfrac{2v_1 v_2}{a_1 a_2}\cos\omega\right)}\right\} \qquad (13.2)$$

σ is the area of the lattice-cell; a prime means that the term with $v_2 = v_2 = 0$ must be dropped.

Series 569 Times 4-line Mathematics.

Ἐξ ὅλων τῶν μεγαλυτέρων καὶ πλέον χρησίμων ἀνακαλύψεων, ὁ Πλάτων, τὴν ἀνακάλυψιν τῆς ἀλφαβητικῆς γραφῆς, δὲν τὴν *Ἐξ ὅλων τῶν μεγαλυτέρων καὶ πλέον χρησίμων ἀνακαλύψεων, ὁ Πλάτων, τὴν ἀνακάλυψιν τῆς ἀλφαβητικῆς γραφῆς, δὲν τὴν εἶδε μὲ*

Series 565 Times Greek Upright and
Series 566 Times Greek Inclined.
Series 567 Times Greek Bold Upright and
Series 667 Times Greek Bold Inclined.

Ἐξ ὅλων τῶν μεγαλυτέρων καὶ πλέον χρησίμων ἀνακαλύψεων, ὁ Πλάτων, τὴν ἀνακάλυψιν τῆς ἀλφαβητικῆς γραφῆς, δὲν τὴν *Ἐξ ὅλων τῶν μεγαλυτέρων καὶ πλέον χρησίμων ἀνακαλύψεων, ὁ Πλάτων, τὴν ἀνακάλυψιν τῆς ἀλφαβητικῆς γραφῆς, δὲν τὴν εἶδε μὲ*

Платон не слишком благосклонно относился к величайшему и наиболее полезному из всех изобретений, изобретению *Платон не слишком благосклонно относился к величайшему и наиболее полезному из всех изобретений, изобретению буквен-*

Series 327 Times New Roman (Cyrillic) and Series 334 Times Bold (Cyrillic).

Платон не слишком благосклонно относился к величайшему и наиболее полезному из всех изобретений, изобретению буквен- ***Платон не слишком благосклонно относился к величайшему и наиболее полезному из всех изобретений, изобретению буквен-***

Series 327 Times New Roman (standard characters).

Meine Eltern lebten nur die Sommermonate in Deutschland, den größten Teil des Jahres in Paris, wo mein Vater als einer der Inhaber die Niederlassung eines alten hamburgischen Kommissions- und Bankhauses leitete, das seit dem Anfang des achzehnten Jahr-

Series 727 Times New Roman (light capitals).

Meine Eltern lebten nur die Sommermonate in Deutschland, den größten Teil des Jahres in Paris, wo mein Vater als einer der Inhaber die Niederlassung eines alten hamburgischen Kommissions- und Bankhauses leitete, das seit dem Anfang des achzehnten Jahr-

Series 327 Times New Roman (standard characters).

A l'occasion du Festival de RIGA, on projettera des œuvres aussi différentes que *La Quête du Graal* de GRÉGORY QUINN, *La Ronde,* et un court métrage indien, *Rikki-tikki-tavi,* d'après RUDYARD KIPLING. Ce festival sera placé sous le patronage du MARQUIS DES

Series 827 Times New Roman (French): with alternative characters for CÇGQRcçgqrGQRgk.

A l'occasion du Festival de RIGA, on projettera des œuvres aussi différentes que *La Quête du Graal* de GRÉGORY QUINN, *La Ronde,* et un court métrage indien, *Rikki-tikki-tavi,* d'après RUDYARD KIPLING. Ce festival sera placé sous le patronage du MARQUIS DES

Times New Roman has been provided with so vast a panoply of letters that its use now extends far beyond its original intention, and it is extensively employed for composition in Greek, Russian, and other languages. Moreover it has been equipped with an exceptionally comprehensive range of special characters, signs, and symbols for the composition of mathematics, chemical formulae, and other kinds of scientific composition. This unparalleled range of type-faces, now available in an unrivalled diversity of composition and display systems, will ensure its continued use well into the third millennium.

Composition '72

L. W. Wallis

1972 was a year of solid commercial progress in the application of new composing technology, as well as one of far-reaching technical innovation. Industrial growth was especially strong in phototypesetting, whereas the concentration of ingenuity and inventiveness seems to have been diverted momentarily into computer systems controlling visual display terminals and mass-storage peripherals for data entry, retrieval, and editing purposes.

Greater realism seeped into phototypesetting during 1972. There was no longer a morbid preoccupation with hardware and the nuts-and-bolts of the subject; instead the spotlight turned to the essentials of producing marketable composition for a reasonable profit. Accordingly, the qualitative and quantitative assessment of output from the various systems, together with the related subjects of phototypography and composition software, assumed rightful positions of prime importance.

More than one hundred phototypesetting units (suitable for the setting of continuous reading matter) were installed in the United Kingdom in 1972, a development equal to an annual growth of 47 %. The comparable statistic for 1971 was 20%. The total population of tape-controlled photo-units in the country approaches 420 spread over some 280 plants. Significantly the proportion of electronic units has risen to 70 %, while the sales of the sole surviving mechanical system ('Monophoto' Filmsetters) have slowed down in the last few years.

Easily the most dominant supplier on current form is International Photon Limited. No fewer than thirty-nine Photon Pacesetter machines (introduced at IPEX 71) had been earmarked for thirty British installations over the ten-month period from January to October inclusive, the transactions amounting to a value of around £400,000 for photo-units alone. Though sounding somewhat glib, the reasons for the quick commercial acceptance of the Photon Pacesetter are a low capital cost allied to comprehensive technical facilities. Recognition of the equipment has come from different areas of the industry. Web-offset newspapers figure predictably among the buyers. Some have operational experience with superseded Photon 713 equipment, such as the East Midland Allied Press and the Bedford County Press. Others are fresh converts from hot-metal composition, for instance the Bucks Free Press, Swale Press Limited, and the *Chester Chronicle*. Outside newspapers the Photon Pacesetter equipment has gone into some quality-conscious environments of the stature of Alden & Mowbray Limited (Oxford), Alabaster Passmore & Sons Limited (Maidstone), and Headley Brothers Limited (Ashford). It will be a big task for International Photon Limited to service effectively and promptly the proliferating industrial installations, especially as low-priced equipment is not bolstered by generous profit margins.

Having captured more than 30 % of the total British market for tape-controlled phototypesetting machinery in 1972, International

Photon was way ahead of its nearest competitor, Addressograph-Multigraph Limited. As an office equipment supplier, the professional printer has been reluctant to credit Addressograph-Multigraph with serious intentions in phototypesetting, but a transition in attitude is gradually taking place. It was in the summer of 1972 that Addressograph-Multigraph launched (with unwarranted panache) a couple of new photo-units, namely an AM 744 and AM 747. Royalties on sales are payable to Photon Inc. in the USA, since the machines are of its design. In the post-DRUPA period, Addressograph-Multigraph reportedly obtained orders for more than a dozen of the new machines, the first AM 747 going to Multiform Limited in Cardiff. Apart from this spurt of orders, the early part of the year saw a steady ticking over of sales for the now defunct AM 725 interlarded with a few AM 707 machines.

After a faltering and ponderous beginning, the Linofilm VIP is slowly attracting patronage. Exhibited in the UK for the first time late in 1970, the initial installation was deferred until the autumn of 1971 to be followed by another two in the same year. Some acceleration occurred in 1972, the aggregate of machines reaching eleven. Among the recruits are newspapers and general printers, such as the *Annandale Observer*, Dragon Press Limited (Luton), Blackfriars Press Limited (Leicester), and Jolly & Barber Limited (Rugby): the latter is a particularly interesting installation because the firm has been weaned on the quality product of a 'Monophoto' Filmsetter.

Other systems scored isolated and fitful successes during 1972. It was noticeable that interest in the Diatronic slackened, possibly because the high sales levels of 1971 could scarcely have been sustained by the market and because Berthold HG announced at DRUPA an impending tape-driven version of the machine which distracted attention from existing lines. On the other hand, the Diatronic S is not expected to appear in the UK until April/May 1973. It is significant that the tradesetting area of the market continues to show the most interest in the Diatronic, as witnessed by a recent installation at John Swain & Co. Limited. Another system enticing to tradesetters is the Alphatype, a machine that has been operational in the USA for more than a decade. It was launched in Europe at IPEX 71 by Stephenson, Blake & Co. Limited and has secured support from three London Trade houses, namely, Apex Typesetting Limited, Letterform Ltd, and Photoscript Limited. Abroad, the Alphatype has been installed in Brussels and Dusseldorf. Some general printers such as the Millbrook Press Limited

(Southampton) and the Studio Press Limited (Birmingham) plumped for the Diatronic and Alphatype systems in 1972. In many respects the Diatronic and Alphatype equipment falls short of the ideal system; the former is over-complex and the latter somewhat crude technically, but both of them are supported by good phototypography and by a commonsense systems design permitting the setting of a wide range of copy. Neither system is fashionable with whizz-kids, a race of people that have a knack of losing other people's money!

After a blank 1971 for orders in the UK, the Linotron 505C experienced something of a resurgence when the *Financial Times* and the *Liverpool Daily Post & Echo* made commitments to the equipment following the DRUPA exhibition. Demand from abroad for the British-designed machine continued to be very brisk. On the other hand, the Magnaset 226 from Crosfield Electronics Limited (principal rival of the Linotron 505C) wallowed in the doldrums and still awaited a British buyer in November 1972, though the initial shipment to Ernst Klett Druckerei of Stuttgart took place in December. Another machine gaining scant success in the UK during 1972 was the 'Monophoto' 600 and field experience with the system has been chequered. One of the happiest users is Santype Limited of Salisbury, a trade house that exports a good deal of technical and mathematical composition to the USA, but other firms have been less enchanted with the equipment. Total users in the UK have still to reach double figures after more than three years of availability, an unusually lukewarm response to a Monotype product even allowing for a price tag in excess of £27,000. Only one system fell temporarily by the wayside in the UK last year when the Pershke-Price organization jettisoned the agency for the American-manufacturered CompStar. Main reason for the decision was the sparseness and poor quality of photo-typography offered from across the Atlantic. It seems incredible that the gulf between European and American typographical requirements is still not fully realized in some quarters. Come November, the CompStar agency had rebounded to Crosfield Electronics.

Technical developments in phototypesetting mercifully slowed down in 1972 after several previous years of fever-pitch activity. In the main, the advances that did take place were refinements and ameliorations to existing equipment lines, though the odd exception added spice to the mixed bag of achievement. Some important trends emerged as well.

Photon Inc. enhanced the specification of the Pacesetter series of machines with a Mark 2 version, even though the original equipment was introduced only in the middle of 1971. The latest machines have quoted speeds of ninety lines per minute when dressed with four or eight type styles of 112 characters each, though reduction of the phototypography to two and four type styles permits the output speed to be quickened to 150 lines per minute by repeating characters of high-frequency on the photo-matrix disc. Earlier models rated at forty and fifty lines per minute will continue to be marketed aided by a price differential of some £2,000. Hence, a printer requiring additional volume of throughput will pay a surcharge for the facility. North Wales Newspapers of Oswestry installed the first Pacesetter, Mark 2, in the UK. It is useful to note that some slack still exists in the specification of the Pacesetter, since the increased speed of the Mark 2 has been obtained by employing faster motors on the drives to the character escapement and photo-matrix, by more economical software, and by reducing the variety of stored photo-typography to accommodate repeat characters for the fastest throughput.

While conceding that the Pacesetter, Mark 2, consolidated the competitive posture of Photon Inc. and added credence to its claim as a market leader, a number of other technical innovations by the company could bring longer term benefits. At the ANPA/RI exhibition in Atlantic City, a Photon 561 laser typesetter emerged as a first-ever public attempt to break out of the straitjacket of wet processing the exposed machine product. There is nothing new about the typographical aspects and working principles of the Photon 561, a machine that began life as an electro-mechanical Photon 560 before undergoing conversion to solid-state electronics. However, the Datawrite laser unit made by the Datalight Corporation is new to the Photon 561 and the two combined represented a prototype exhibit in Atlantic City, possibly as a market research exercise to gauge the reactions of potential buyers. Seemingly the laser emits a bright green beam, readily visible, and requires minimal precautions, despite the lethal nature that one usually ascribes to this form of energy. Used in conjunction with the laser is a dry-silver emulsion paper manufactured by the 3M Company, a material developed by the application of heat exceeding 200°F in a special processor or warming oven on-line to the Photon 561. It is asserted that the 3M dry-silver material is appreciably slower in reacting to light than the conventional phototypesetting emulsions. Hence the need for a laser which provides a much greater flash intensity than a traditional xenon source.

As one expert eyewitness emphasized, the 'machine is a prototype and not yet for sale. That may well have been the original intention, but a laser machine was installed at the *Hartford Courant* in the USA during November. Briefly stated, the advantages of laser technology applied to phototypesetting relate to the dry-silver paper which comes out some 30 % cheaper than customary materials, eliminates processing chemicals, yields a dry and instantly-usable end-product ready for page make-up, and permits handling in normal daylight without the encumbrance and inconvenience of wet processing and darkrooms. On the other hand, the laser unit is somewhat expensive and will tend to inflate the capital prices of phototypesetters, though volume production would have the effect of reducing the unit costs. Some improvement in output quality must occur too before the trade will bestow the final seal of approval on the development.

Two other 1972 announcements from Photon Inc. were encouraging and indicative of current trends. Firstly, a photo-matrix disc consisting of eight separate segments was formally released and expected to be produced for the Pacesetter series of machines in 1973. Hitherto the photo-matrix disc has constituted a most inflexible form of character store and because of its immutability has imposed severe constraints on printers. It is impossible in some kinds of composition to forecast precisely the typeface combinations and character sets likely to be required by the market tomorrow, let alone in future years. Yet a succession of phototypesetting machinery manufacturers has insisted on designing systems with rigid photo-matrix stores, often comprising large numbers of characters. If a given combination of type styles or characters were demanded for a job but omitted from the store, a further expensive photo-matrix disc, drum etc. would need to be purchased and the inevitable delivery delays suffered. Over the last two or more years, a trend toward fragmenting photo-matrix stores has gained momentum, as evidenced by the pi-carousel on the 'Monophoto' 600, by the segmented drum on the Linofilm VIP, and by the individual glass matrices with paired characters on the Linofilm Europa. Each of the eight segments on the projected Photon Pacesetter photo-matrix discs contains 108 characters and screws firmly into the hub, thereby allowing any permutation of type styles and characters.

Consistent with the same philosophy, the other 1972 pledge from Photon Inc. concerned a pi-matrix system for the Pacesetter machines: another manifestation of fragmenting phototypography. The concept is somewhat crude and smacks of a palliative, yet the method will suffice for incorporating the occasional extraneous characters in a composition, particularly where alignment and fit are not too critical. Every fifth position in the outer row of characters on the photo-matrix disc consists of a transparent window, coupled with a register mark. The pi-matrices are prepared on pressure-sensitive film which enables them to be mounted on the disc and positioned in the apertures guided by the register marks.

Photon Inc. did not monopolize the action in phototypesetting last year. Various constituent companies in the Linotype Group actively enhanced the specifications of established products. In Britain, Linotype-Paul Limited almost doubled the speed of the highly-regarded Linotron 505C by unveiling a TC version; an appellation truly evocative of the hastening process! Rated as a 320 newspaper lines per minute machine, the Linotron 505TC accomplishes greater productivity by writing out characters on the forward and reverse sweeps of the scanning carriage, whereas the earlier machines exposed characters on the forward traverse only. Another encouraging feature of the Linotron 505C and TC systems is the accumulation of composition software runnable on the Honeywell 316 controller which now extends to disc file maintenance programs for classified advertisements as well as to the formatting of mathematical formulae.

Not to be outdone, the Mergenthaler Linotype Co. enriched the Linofilm VIP range to ten diverse models. Instead of operating at thirty-two lines per minute as the original machine, the most recent models turn out fifty lines per minute. Additionally the maximum line length has been stretched from 36 picas to 45 picas. And the newer models are no longer confined to a single photo-matrix drum, but can incorporate one, two, or three to give an upper limit of eighteen type styles of ninety-six characters apiece automatically accessible from tape command. Pinnacle of the latest development is a Linofilm VIP 7245/3: a daunting model number denoting a largest point size of 72, a widest line length of 45 ems, and an availability of three photo-matrix drums housing a maximum of eighteen type styles. At the time of writing, a multiple drum Linofilm VIP has not appeared in the UK, though delivery of a 7245/3 is scheduled for the Dragon Press Limited and a two-drum machine is expected by Copyset Ltd.

Another machine introduced with unrestrained ballyhoo and swagger was the Eurocat marketed by Bobst Graphic S.A. and sold in the UK by Oscar Friedheim Limited. Despite the fanfares, the Eurocat is essentially an expanded incarnation of the long-standing

CAT (Computer Actuated Typesetter) designed and made by Graphic Systems Inc. of Lowell, Massachusetts: the company which constructs the Photomix series of machines for Singer-Friden. Typographical nucleus of the Eurocat is a photo-matrix drum with interchangeable quadrants each of 108 characters, inclusive of some floating accents. Either 10 or 15 point sizes can be accessed automatically and intermixed. When dressed with ten sizes, the type-size range stretches from 6 to 18 points, while the five additional sizes extend the span from 6 to 36 points. Maximum measure is 47 picas.

Central to the Eurocat is a Data General Nova 1200 computer. Seemingly the main memory can be expanded from 8K to 64K (16-bit words), the capacity varying to suit programming and systems requirements. Justification routines and hyphenation by logic rules 'in all European languages' are claimed to be available. Other, more specialized, software is said to exist. Indications are that Deltaconsult of Frankfurt has undertaken to write the software package. Quoted speed of the Eurocat is 80,000 characters per hour, while the price bracket goes from £8,000 to £30,000 according to the precise systems configuration.

Harris-Intertype appears to be in a state of internal turmoil as far as phototypesetting is concerned. Rumours of a rift with Purdy and McIntosh gain in strength and, by publication time, may have taken public shape. Meanwhile the Fototronic 600 (a PM brainchild) remains somewhat elusive, though a couple of production machines have reached the field in the UK and many more are claimed to be operational in the USA. Hearsay suggests that the delays have arisen from policy disagreements between the American and British companies with the former running out as winners. It is a pity that the British invention may have been hampered by non-technical issues because prototypes of the Fototronic 600 seem to be working satisfactorily at QB Limited (Colchester). Goodwill to Harris-Intertype abounds in the industry and some Fototronic 600 orders have been outstanding for some time. Wellwishers hope that a more coherent policy will emerge for the Fototronic 600 in 1973 and that the company generally will project a more credible image to regain a dwindling share of the European phototypesetting market. Before the integrally-computerized Fototronic 600 had reached the market in final form, a slave version was launched at Northprint '72 in Leeds early last year. Designated the Fototronic 600S: the machine accepts computer-generated six-level tapes with doublets of codes for every character; stores a half-dozen type styles of 118 characters; spans type sizes from 5 to 24 points; runs at eighty lines per minute; and accommodates measures up to 42 picas. Price is around £4,000.

One of the most curious trends to develop in recent years has been the growing numbers of phototypesetters offered with on-line keyboards, a trend re-emphasized in 1972 by the Photon Compositor and CG Universal (Compugraphic Corporation) which follow in the footsteps of the Diatronic, CompuWriter and ACM 9000. It is absorbing to speculate on the reasons for the phenomena, especially as the commitment to multiple inputs servicing a photo-unit through control tapes has strengthened enormously over the past decade. One can resurrect and apply the old arguments for the manually-operated linecaster and point to the economy of a one-man system and the instantaneous availability of copy after keyboarding, but suspicions of other motives for on-line systems come to mind. There has been some disenchantment in the trade with approaches involving non-justifying keyboards producing endless data for formatting by computer software, irrespective of whether the programs are resident in a free-standing computer or in a phototypesetter. Certain kinds of work pose problems for this method, for instance difficult tabular matter, displayed advertising, and corrections. Some technicians feel that a return to counting keyboards for these jobs has many virtues, since the operator can make decisions and exercise discretion beyond the facilities of most composition programs. It could be that the uprush of on-line keyboards to phototypesetters represents a revival of justifying keyboards in a novel or trendy form thought to be appropriate and assimilable in modern times. In the years ahead, the keyboard manufacturers may be stimulated to come up with some economical and attractive counting units to meet a growing market need. Presently a reasonable justifying keyboard costs in excess of £2,500, but programmable technology promises to expand and cheapen the scope of future equipment. In the meantime, M. H. Whittaker & Son Ltd has sold nearly a score of CompuWriter and CG Universal machines, even though the tape-driven Compugraphic products have had a quieter time during 1972.

Somewhat ironically, Berthold HG chose to join the mainstream in phototypesetting by introducing the Diatronic S, a tape-operated version of a machine previously worked exclusively from an on-line keyboard. Many questions about the system remain to be answered, but commercial applications in 1973 should divulge some useful information. Tape-merging equipment was also inaugurated with the Diatronic S, the interim proof being a typewritten hard copy that has proved to be more acceptable in the German market than in the UK. The first tape-controlled Diatronic in the UK will go to Photo +Graphic +Art in Glasgow. Rumour-mongering as to the expected participation of MGD Graphic Systems in the so-called pre-press area reached a shrill level by the autumn of 1972, a situation that perhaps persuaded the company to make an official announcement of future plans to end the speculation. News came in the form of puffy press releases that were designed to titillate, rather than to instruct. In phototypesetting, a Metro Set system was promised, a piece of equipment that will cost less than $100,000 and output some 1,000 lines per minute. Using CRT techniques, the machine will store 100 founts in digital form for reproduction between 4 and 72 points over measures up to a maximum of 66 picas. Seemingly the characters will be written out on the CRT at same size, something attempted by no other system using similar technology. The images from the CRT are conveyed to the photographic material by means of a fibre-optics faceplate. European release of the machine is not anticipated until 1974. Knowing the way schedules go adrift, the Metro Set may be a little further away than that.

Optical character recognition
Last year in THE PENROSE ANNUAL, the technical survey devoted a good deal of space to reviewing the three OCR systems that had surfaced forcefully on the composition scene, namely the Autoreader by ECRM Inc., the Compuscan 170 by Compuscan Inc., and SETYPE or Dataflow by the Datatype Corporation. All three systems have consolidated their industrial footholds since then. By the autumn of 1972 some 35 installations involving fifty-eight ECRM Autoreaders were claimed to be operational in the USA, compared with forty-six Compuscan 170 machines in the field and around thirty-two installations with banners nailed solidly to the mast of Dataflow. As usual the manufacturers outbid each other with regard to alleged orders. Though the movement toward OCR was not so pronounced in Europe, a number of plants got underway. ECRM Autoreaders started as front-runners at N.V. Drukkerij Periodica in Brussels, at Sydsvenska Dagbladets A.B. in Malmo, at *De Telegraaf* in Amsterdam, and at *Berlingske Tidende* in Copenhagen; but as the year progressed the European population of Compuscan 170 machines gradually closed the gap with installations at Saxon Lindstrom in Stockholm, at VNU in Eindhoven, another installed

at Frankfurt in October, and outstanding orders to be fulfilled elsewhere. Uncertainty hung over the Dataflow system in the UK, principally because of the collapse of the agent Total Input Limited. Datatype Limited, a marketing subsidiary of the American manufacturer, was inaugurated to push the Dataflow, but the latest word is that the equipment has been taken under the wing of BOAC (if the phrase will be pardoned): a temporary arrangement until a more credible graphic arts' outlet can be found.

On the technical front in OCR, a couple of noteworthy events took place. Perhaps to fend off increasing competition, ECRM Inc. reduced the price of the Autoreader from $89,000 to $69,500 for the model which has a scanning rate of 700 words per minute. Additionally an Autoreader 1200 was released with a price tag of $79,500 and with a reading speed of 1,200 words per minute. It is stated that the speed modification can be retrofitted to Autoreader 700 models for $10,000.

Rather more radical was the entry into the OCR arena of a fourth machine jostling for the composition market, namely a Textreader made by Cognitronics Inc. and marketed in Europe through the outlets of Bobst Graphic S.A. in Lausanne. Oscar Friedheim Limited handle the equipment in the UK. Specification of the Textreader suggests a character recognition speed of 120 characters per second, an optimum throughput of eighty-five characters per second, a variable document size from $2 \times 3 \cdot 25$ in. to $8 \cdot 5 \times 14$ in., a facility to recognize OCRA as well as ten handwritten digits and a few alphabetic characters, and an alleged error rate of 1 in 10,000 characters. For scanning purposes, the machine employs a laser spot which is swept horizontally across a line of typescript by means of a rotating eight-sided mirror. Forty-eight horizontal traverses of the laser are made for every line, a number that encompasses the need to track skew. Reflections from the document are gathered by a silicon diode which converts the samplings of blackness and whiteness into digital information for comparison with stored idealized characters. In the USA the Textreader is sold by Graphic Systems Inc., but MGD Graphic Systems announced a Metro Reader at the same time as the Metro Set, a piece of OCR equipment which sounds very similar to the Cognitronics product.

In Britain, the interest in OCR has been of a wistful nature because the attitudes of the trades unions involved were expected to be prickly. Without doubt, the concept of OCR is potentially far more radical in terms of its implications for labour than computers and phototypesetting have ever been. Consequently, a passive situation developed and only the foolhardy or unsqueamish were expected to grasp the nettle. In spite of expert predictions and the general air of defeatism, the *Nottingham Evening Post* took the plunge and installed a Bobst/Cognitronics Textreader in the post-DRUPA period for scanning classified advertisements prepared on electric typewriters.

It is very easy to get caught up in the excitement of new technology, especially in a subject like OCR which has plenty of intrinsic interest. One must not lose sight, however, of the main question: is OCR a better method *technically* of inputting and editing copy for composition systems? That there is a danger of OCR being installed for the wrong reasons cannot be denied. Some will see OCR as an implement for bashing the trades unions and for solving other management problems without technical roots. Other issues come to the fore as well. Can creative skills (i.e. journalism and authorship) be *efficiently* combined with the convertive skills of OCR typewriting in a single person? Is there not a possibility that both aspects of the work will suffer when married, particularly as the standards of print quality, cleanliness and geometry required in OCR documents are exacting? Can printers produce jobs quickly and efficiently on a typewriter, an instrument serving as a microcosm of the limitations of OCR in applications involving assorted character sets and complex typographical commands of high frequency? These and other questions have to be unequivocally answered by commercial empiricism before the industry can confidently embrace OCR as an economic proposition or panacea.

Visual display terminals

Three video display terminals were reported fully in THE PENROSE ANNUAL last year, from both the technical and applications standpoints. Still leading the way is the Harris 1100 equipment with more than 150 units installed by May 1972: a third of them delivered to United Press International. Ignoring the news agency, about 75 % of the installations are in newspaper plants, the remainder going to commercial printers. Again excluding the UPI units, approximately 80 % of the Harris 1100 units are employed in off-line or stand-alone configurations with paper tape input and output. The rest are utilized on-line to a computer. Parallel headway has been made by the Hendrix 5200 equipment which had chalked up 100 installations by last May. And the CorRecTerm M/100 from the Mergenthaler Linotype Co. has kept pace with its two main rivals and aggregated around 150 installations by August 1972. All the commercial action has not been confined to the USA, as witnessed by a Hendrix 5200 entering production at the East Midland Allied Press in Peterborough, by a CorRecTerm finding a place at the printing department of the Kent County Council in Maidstone, and by a Harris 1100 at Waterloo Web Litho. All three units contain hard-wired logic and are somewhat expensive, the Harris 1100 and Hendrix 5200 costing in the region of £9,500 and the CorRecTerm some £6,250. For stand-alone operations, the capital costs are exorbitant, especially if a proofreader and copyholder constitute the agreed work team for the unit. Where a single 'corrector' only is allowed to manipulate the equipment in order to give effect to a marked proof, the nub of the problem then becomes the provision of that proof and the attendant economics. Undaunted by the prospect, a number of other off-line terminals joined the ranks of the established trio over the past twelve months, notably the Mohrtext 1200, the Composer 15, and the Varicomp.

In the USA, the Mohrtext 1200 Editing/Proofing Terminal is manufactured by Omnitext Inc. and sold by Mohr Enterprises. The same item of hardware constitutes part of the System 1 package marketed by Graphic Systems Inc., the Mohrtext being transmogrified into a System 1 Editor. Technically the Mohrtext is something of a hybrid. It does not rely exclusively on hard-wired logic as the Harris 1100, Hendrix 5200, and CorRecTerm M/100, neither does it go overboard for software operation as the Composer 15. Instead the unit represents a half-way house, the video terminal itself undertaking buffer storage and character generation and refreshing, but the software in an integrated Data General Nova 1200 computer governs the editing functions. Such a solution allows the single minicomputer to service five on-line terminals. Characters for display are generated on the basis of a 7×11 dot matrix on a screen with a 14 in. diagonal and a green phosphor against a black background. Between 104 and 128 characters make up the set. Capacity of the display is a maximum 2,560 characters presented as thirty-two lines of up to eighty characters each. The buffer memory holds 5,120 characters (twice as many as can be displayed), but extra modules can be added to a ceiling of 10,240 characters. Reverting to the Data General 1200 controller, an 8K (16-bit) memory will enable five terminals to be serviced for editing functions and for hyphenation and justification. Magnetic discs can be interfaced to the system for file maintenance work. Prices for the Mohrtext start at $12,900. Last July some dozen Mohrtext terminals were said to be operational in the USA.

Moving on to the Composer 15 terminal from the IMLAC Corporation, the inclination toward software is quite pronounced: the characters being created and refreshed by program out of core. Consequently, the fount content of ninety characters can be easily changed. Another feature of the system is the proportionally-spaced characters, as opposed to every other terminal mentioned having monospaced images. Further evidence of software elasticity is implicit in the option of four image sizes for display. The screen of $8\frac{1}{2} \times 11\frac{1}{2}$in. will display approximately 1,000 characters, the longest line length holding an average of 120. Buffer capacity starts at 5,000 characters, but can be expanded to 21,000. Distinctions between type styles are accomplished by underscoring for italic and by increasing the brightness to 2:1 for bold characters. It is fair to say that the Composer 15 rocketed to public attention as the first stand-alone display terminal to incorporate justification/hyphenation logic, thereby enabling programmed word breaks to be checked for acceptability and the effects of overruns to be validated by visual inspection. Price of the Composer 15 is $20,000.

Breakthrough is an overworked word beloved by writers on technical matters, but the emergence of the Varicomp 2000 and 3000 editing terminals from Varisystems Inc. at £3,600 could be genuinely described as an economic breakthrough that competing suppliers will feel obliged to match. Sold in the UK by International Photon Limited, the Varicomp lacks the sophistication of some alternatives, but for many applications the technical facilities will suffice with the persuasion of a third to a half cut in normal prices. Only 576 characters can be accommodated by the display, the usual word wraparound feature is missing, and the images lack the quality seen elsewhere.

As competitors catch up in the stand-alone terminal application, the seasoned manufacturers have moved on to place the VDT within a systems context. There seems little doubt that the most fruitful use of video display technology will occur with the units on-line to a computer reinforced by backing stores for holding information to be updated, corrected, edited, verified, and generally organized. Such a concept presupposes a dialogue between operator and system, the VDT functioning as an interactive device permitting the interrogation of information files and providing a means for visually verifying any changes. It can display questions too, which the operator is obliged to answer before proceeding, thereby imposing a fail-safe situation guaranteeing the proper completion of data.

Reference was made last year in THE PENROSE ANNUAL to the Hendrix EDS/3400 system which has the same philosophical concepts as those outlined. That system has now been re-named the Hendrix TPS (Text Publishing System), a psychological manoeuvre intended to be interpreted as a new product. At the heart of the TPS system is a PDP-11 computer with an 8K memory for the composition and editing software, supported by a fixed-head VR 1016 magnetic drum (made by Vermont Research) capable of housing 2 million characters. This 'assemblage' is placed on-line to a second PDP-11 with software for handling up to sixteen of the EDS/5700 terminals usable as data entry and editing devices. Overall the hardware configuration represent a data management system for the maintenance of files.

Harris-Intertype came stridently into the identical segment of the market during 1972 with a 2500 system, a development prompted by the same philosophical principles as the Hendrix TPS, though the sales emphases might suggest otherwise. In essence, the system proposes the origination of news and advertising copy at VDT terminals under computer control, the work taking place in the newsroom, editorial and tele-ad departments. Accordingly the composing room is relieved of all data entry responsibilities and simply handles the phototypeset output for page make-up. Centrepiece of the Harris 2500 system is a PDP-11 computer connected to a fixed-head disc store for holding data files. An important component of the system is a Harris 1500 terminal interfaced to the PDP-11 computer by way of multiplexors. Four of the terminals can be hooked up through a single multiplexor. As eight multiplexors can be accommodated, a total of thirty-two Harris 1500 terminals can be embraced on a time-shared multi-programming basis.

Character generation and refreshing of the display is executed within the Harris 1500 terminal which also embodies a buffer store for 960 characters. The maximum number of characters that can be displayed is 800 (ten lines of eighty characters each), but the operator can scroll through to the limits of the disc file by transferring blocks of data between the terminal buffer and the computer backing store. Images on the screen extend to a fount of 128 characters generated on the basis of a 9×12 dot matrix. Characters enter the screen from the bottom, a feature designed to give the effect of a video typewriter when a journalist is originating copy at the device. At the time of writing, projections indicate that the first Harris 2500 system should be fully operational by the end of 1972 at the *Today* newspaper in Cocoa, USA.

Apart from Hendrix Electronics and Harris-Intertype, other projects have been treading parallel paths in the development of computer-controlled interactive terminal systems. Among the companies showing their hands during 1972 were Xylogic Systems Inc. using a GRI 909 computer, together with Delta Data Telterm visual display units. First users of the Xylogic systems are the *News Journal* at Daytona Beach and the *Daily Times* at New Mexico. Digital Equipment Corporation, the company manufacturing the central processing units for most of the other VDT systems, decided to jump on the bandwagon with a Typeset-11 package encompassing a PDP-11 computer and VT-20 terminals. Keeping pace with the rest is Tal-Star, an American software house, using General Automation computers, disc files, and Delta Data Telterm editing units. In Europe, the development of computer systems with interactive peripherals has been far from static. In conjunction with the *Express* & *Star* in Wolverhampton, PIRA has been responsible for the design and programming of a classified advertisement handling system.

Numerous projects are in train for undertaking page make-up under computer control. Most notable move in this direction during 1972 was a link up between Hendrix Electronics Inc. and Typlan Systems Project Oy Ab of Helsinki, the joint effort spawning the Hendrix PAL System (the initials signifying Page and Ad Layout). Apparently the programs have been written in Fortran IV, but will be converted to the PDP-11 assembler language at some future time. Apart from the PDP-11 central processor, a configuration will include EDS/5700 editing terminals, a 2·5 million character magnetic disc, a Rand Tablet for delineating on input the extent of copy blocks, the entire package being planned to cope with page dummying, interactive displayed advertisement mark-up, and the more mundane editing functions.

One final development last year brings us to the threshold of composition in 1973: the Harris 2200 Display Ad Video Terminal. Again the nucleus of the system is a PDP-11 computer (without backing store) which will handle up to four 2200 terminals. In the memory are stored the character widths for the various founts to be used in the displayed advertisements, along with the programs for activating the manipulations demanded from the terminals. The screen is divided into two zones by a vertical line, the left-hand field being reserved for typographical commands or parameters with the right-hand field restricted to copy or data. It is envisaged by the Americans that copy will be fed into the terminal as raw input tape devoid of typographical instructions and that the command strings will be summoned from the terminal as a format in computer store. Such an approach is valid for American practice where the standardization of display advertising is sympathetic to format storage. In Europe, the alternatives might be for a set of arbitrary parameters (not too precise) to be keyboarded at the terminal or at the original tape stage.

In the left-hand field on the terminal, the parameters consist of an operational code (quad left, right, centre), a measure, a fount, a point size, a film advance, and a horizontal displacement from the left-hand margin of the setting. In effect, the data area on the screen represents a 45 picas square, though scrolling permits the depth to be increased.

Once the parameters and data have appeared on the screen, an execute control causes the character images to be enlarged to the required sizes and to take up the commanded positions in the composition area. Thus, the terminal provides a good graphic representation of an advertisement with regard to relationships between point sizes and to inter-linear and horizontal spacing arrangements, though the images are in a single typeface only.

If a line of copy does not fit, the data and associated parameter will flash on the screen as if clamouring for corrective treatment. To alter a layout, the cursor of the terminal is positioned on the parameter requiring modification and the operator applies the changes from a series of control keys. There are pairs of controls which, when depressed, will increment and decrement point size in one-point steps, lengthen or shorten measures, increase or decrease leading, and shift horizontal displacements to the left or right. As the control keys become active, so the parameter concerned is automatically modified and visual effect is given to the commands in the data area for operator approval and verification. Price of the Harris 2200 system starts at around $55,000 and will rise to some $150,000, depending upon the number of terminals, the capacity of the controller, and the scope of software. Seemingly the prototype system is destined for the *St Petersburg Times* in Florida.

One thing is certain, 1973 will witness a continuing proliferation of VDT technology within a computer systems context, rather than the pedestrian off-line applications that have predominated hitherto.

Computer-aided design: an exploration

Aaron Marcus

Programs have been written in Fortran to control a photo-typesetting machine connected to a digital computer in a joint venture by the Computer Science Department and the Department of Graphic Design at Yale University.
With this system new forms of visual communication have been explored and the author describes the methods used and problems that have arisen.

The blocks illustrating this article were made by The Lyth Engraving Co. Ltd.

The availability of photo-typesetting machines connected to digital computers offers the graphic designer-artist high-quality type and images at great speed. The machines may be photo-mechanical or photo-electronic. All offer varying fonts, sizes, and leadings of type; some can handle half-tones or linework. The achievement of this state of technological art means that many new and imaginative approaches to typographic composition become possible. Typographic features unused since manuscript forms were replaced by mechanical ones may again become valid features of mass-produced typographic communication, for example, handwritten letterforms, variable-width letterforms, and/or typographic abbreviations similar to those common in Gutenberg's time.

The attitude of most producers of computer-controlled photo-typesetting equipment has been to focus on bringing to perfection Gutenberg's methods without realizing that they have entered an entirely new age of sign[1] composition. The conservative attitude of the producers of typesetting machines can be seen in the retention of many features and of nomenclature from mechanical typesetting. Also indicative of this attitude has been the sequential rather than the parallel development of the typesetting machine as a photo-setting machine. Existing equipment does, however, make possible experiments to show the potential scope of computer-assisted photo-typesetting. Because no interactive computer graphics systems oriented specifically for graphic designers[2] are available, it is necessary to use the slower methods of non-interactive communication with the computer (either on-line or off-line). Consequently, instead of the smooth process of eye, mind, hand, pencil, and paper familiar to the designer-artist, the sequence is broken up artificially into segments of think, look, write/compute, display/think, look, write. The designer-artist must then balance several competing forces: (1) the demands of content (both syntactic and semantic), (2) the demands of one's own aesthetic, (3) the demands of the hardware (computer and display equipment limitations), and (4) the demands of software, especially the immediate programming requirements.

While each factor places restrictions on visual form, each factor can also stimulate new discoveries about intra-sign relationships, possibilities for meaningful communication, and the nature of the designer-artist's aesthetic. This aspect is especially important, because one's aesthetic must continually confront the hardware and software demands mentioned above. The designer-artist must recognize explicitly aspects of an aesthetic that will dominate and control the final form.

The author has recently written programs in Fortran IV for a PDP-10 computer that can control a Mergenthaler Linofilm Quick photo-typesetting machine either off-line through the use of paper tape or on-line through the mediation of a smaller computer, a PDP-11. The equipment is located in the Computer Science Department of Yale University but is used jointly by this department and the Department of Graphic Design in the Yale School of Art, which owns the Quick. The Quick is capable of setting type at three different magnifications from any one of four glass negatives on which appear two complete fonts of type, e.g., roman and italic or roman bold and italic bold, or roman and roman bold, etc. A separate system program easily converts data from PDP-10 coding to standard teletype coding in order to properly command the Quick.

These programs attempt to explore the capabilities of the Quick in unconventional ways and to join to them the power of the digital computer to manipulate and to transmit information. The programs themselves result in typographic compositions. The desired relationship between man and machine is one of symbiosis in which the designer-artist and the computer reach an integrated compromise in the creation of visual form. The human being provides the necessary human qualities of imagination and judgment. The computer performs some decision-making tasks as well as the laborious carry-through tasks resulting from previous decisions.

The computer can make decisions only on the basis of mathematical and logical conditions. For example, if a number is greater than four, it may take option A; otherwise, it may take option B. The designer-artist-programmer's task is to relate simple mathematical and logical relationships (causes) to visual statements (effects). Option A may be to write a particular character or set of characters. Option B may be to move vertically down the field before writing some other character. The computer's ability to execute many such decisions within a fraction of a second allows it to approach human qualities of positioning and decision-making. However, lacking the human being's capacity for complex pattern recognition, an uncontrolled computer generates only useless, empty, chaotic form, vividly described in jargon as 'garbage'. As in everyday life, some so-called garbage may be valuable, but it is the human being's sensitivity to the unrealized potential of objects and processes that transforms the useless into the useful, the insignificant into the significant.

In the programs, the designer-artist provides the necessary framework of control by specifically describing units of form and possible interactions or sequences of such units. These units of form may involve decisions on type size, placement, weight, horizontal and vertical position, and the frequency of appearance of the unit. A more sophisticated set of controls may state explicitly or implicitly conditions under which normal interactions may be superseded by alternative ones. For example, a letter normally printed in regular weight may change density or size if it is one of a special set of letters. The computer is given the task of operating upon incoming information and transforming it or recomposing it according to the program. Alternatively, it may generate its own information, e.g., it may generate an ordered or random sequence of letters, numbers, or other characters. The program may specify that at certain times a random choice between visually equal or unequal alternatives may be made. This is one way of introducing formal surprises and complexities. It is an approach that is appropriate for dealing with large-scale data flows within electronic media. This conception of the creation of form assumes that the human being is working within an environment of such a scale that not every minute detail can be predetermined or controlled. The designer-artist does, however, retain control over primary qualities of form and over the decision to call a work finished. As in modern physics, a continuous boundary or limit to the concept of form replaces precise yes/no contours.

The accompanying illustrations show the visual results of these experiments in computer-assisted typographic and calligraphic composition. They are essentially drawings which take the form of visual poems in those cases in which word elements predominate.

In the Weather Report series (Figs.1, 2, 3) the computer randomly reorders the headline segments of the front page of a newspaper which it reads from a file of headline data. The computer then positions the segments within a predetermined grid, with predetermined probabilities for the number of lines at any of sixteen grid positions. At the same time, a predetermined change of letter weights for certain alphabetic characters takes place. By these processes a viewer is able to create new patterns of meaning from a conventional phenomenon. The programmatic and electronic basis of the form suggests that the system (hardware and software) could be coupled to the regular appearance of the newspaper thereby providing a simultaneous poetic filtering of the daily reality.

Figure 1

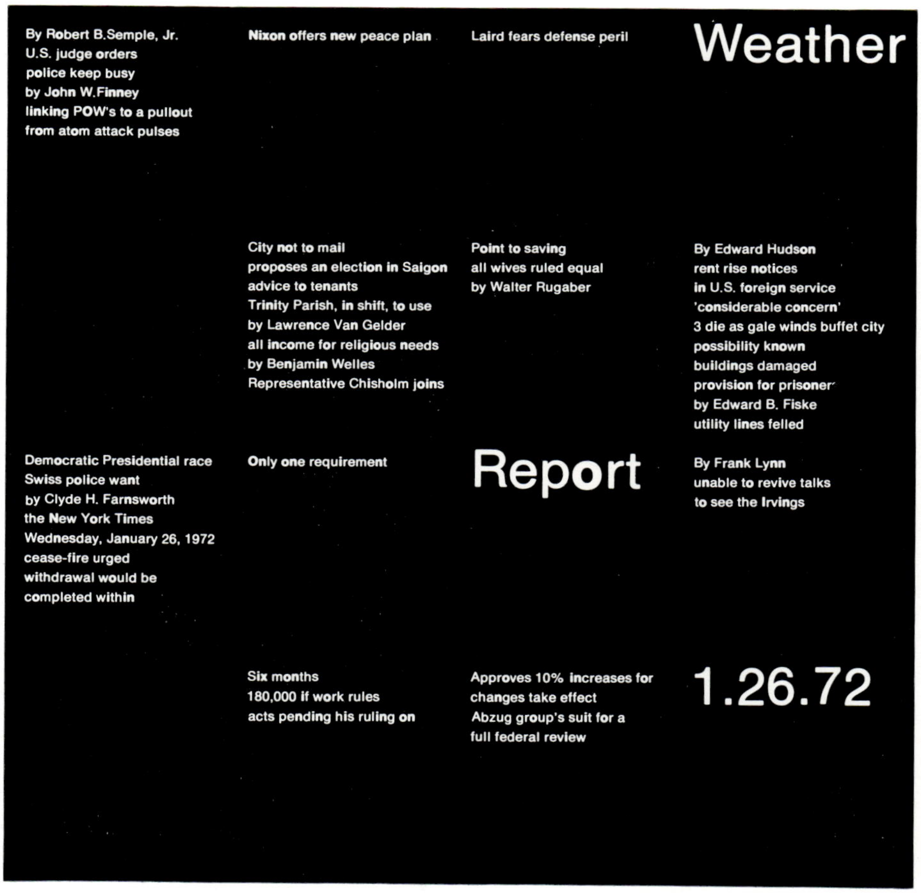

Figure 2

Figure 3

Figure 4

The Weather Report drawing (Fig.4) uses essentially the information sequence of the Weather Report poems but adds to it the capability of the Quick to use calligraphic as well as typographic elements in its optical system. At this stage the information content is almost totally abstract. The drawing indicates further possibilities for guided translations of structure by which new form relationships may emerge.

The series of abstract typographic poems (below) explore the concept of visual evolution by specifying changes that a group of rhythmic units is to undergo. The units, e.g., /./ or /// / or 00/00, etc., are selected in a random process to create gradually changing sequences of lines whose rhythm echoes a language of intonation or of connotation. These compositions convey no specific or explicit information but rather attempt to call up in the viewer a resonance with unconscious responses to human forms of utterance, i.e., with outward vocal and visual manifestations of inner experience.

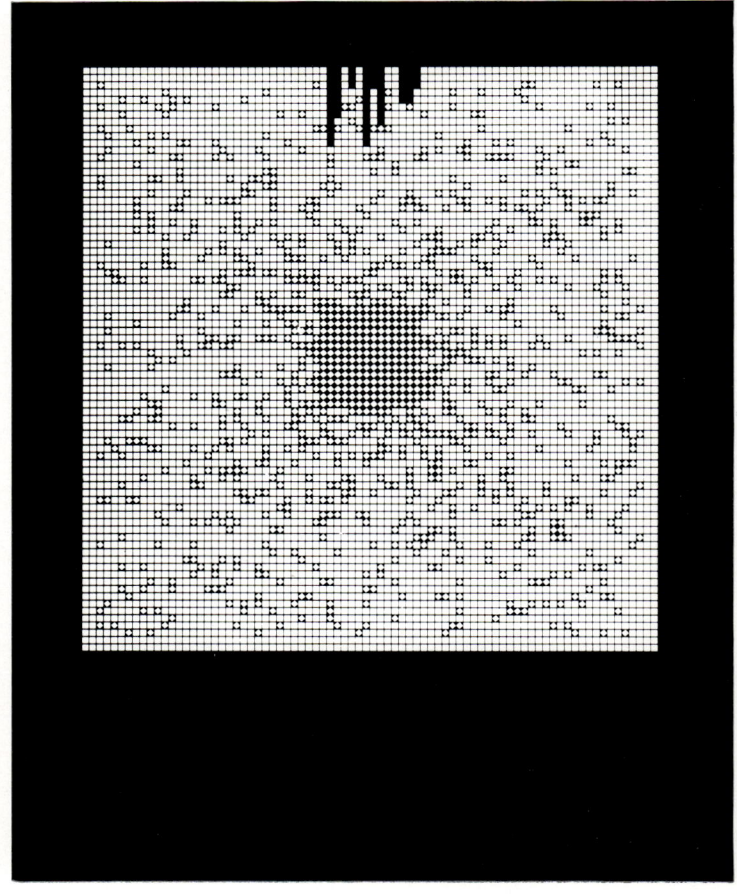

The multiple examples of the Weather Report series, of the abstract typographic poems, and the other poems⇌drawings, demonstrate the ability of the computer to synthesize many possible variations on a theme. In the end, however, it is man, not the machine, who discovers the meaningful in the meaningless.

These experiments in composition have made clear several points in relation to this form of man-machine interaction. A designer-artist who wishes to approach the creation of visual form via the computer must accept the fact that a great amount of time may be spent without achieving visual results or with only partial results. This is the nature of program development. However, once an effective program has been achieved, many variations of form can be tried with a minimum of effort. It is in the long run that program development is worthwhile.

Program development takes so long because one is usually trying a fundamentally new approach, and there is little program reference

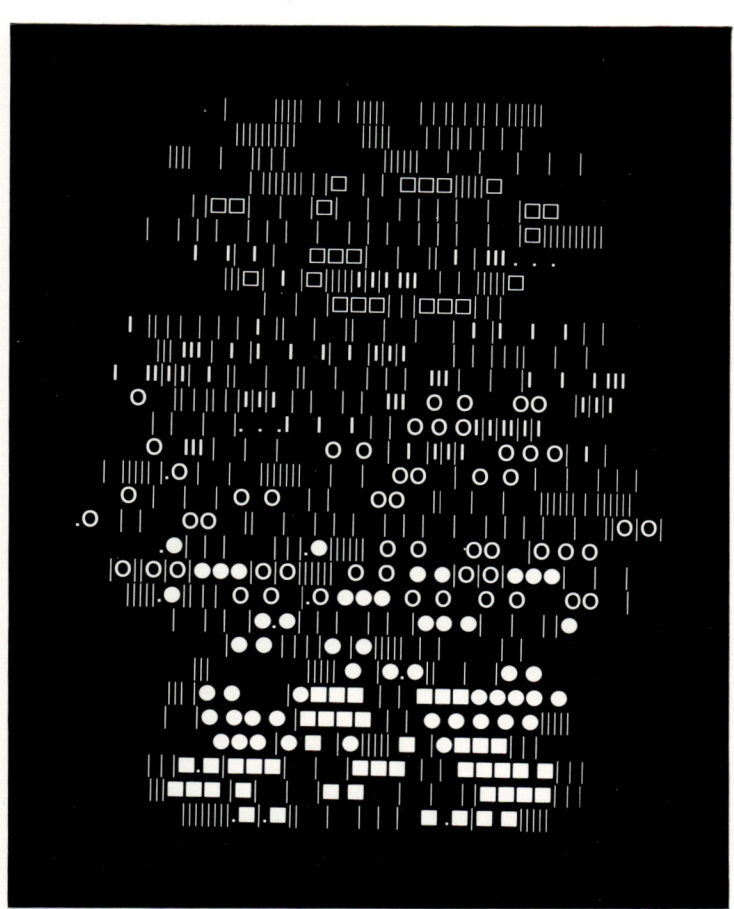
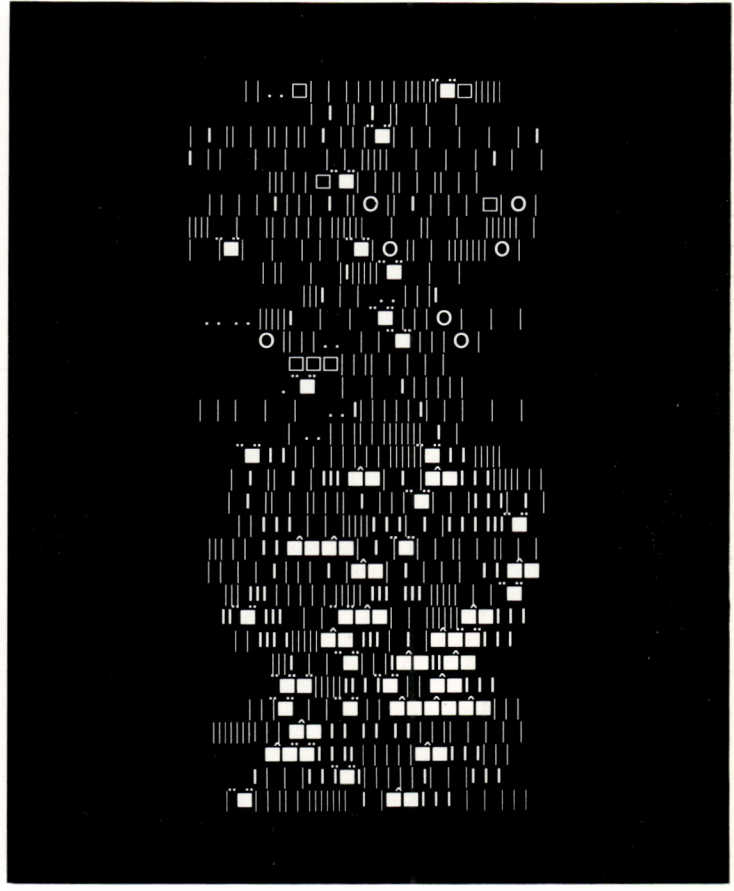

literature to consult. In addition, a good part of the time must be spent in adapting one's work to the limitations of the display devices, often circumventing careful and elaborate limitations built into the equipment because of its narrowly conceived *raison d'être*. For example, the Quick is intended to advance to the right on a field, then move down a certain increment and return to the left, There is not available at present a possibility for moving left or upward from a given position, although the mechanics of such movement are essentially within the machine. Such devices are not well-equipped for certain ways of drawing with type. Through appropriate programming, however, some simple but difficult drawing activities can be accomplished.

There is a paradox associated with the designer-artist's use of the computer. Giving over the programming control to someone else means losing many opportunities for making mistakes and discovering new possibilities of form. As an interactive display becomes more and more sophisticated, certain aspects of the visual forms become more and more predetermined. On the Linofilm Quick, for example, the magnification sizes are set at three given enlargements, as opposed to a continuum of sizes.

On the other hand, if the designer-artist does involve himself with the programming, much time and energy must be spent on developing an explicit and logical framework by which visual form is realized. This does not preclude expressive, manual and/or random aspects. It does imply that the designer-artist can understand and describe the essential structure of the work. For this reason, working directly with the computer via programming can be a valuable educational experience as well as a means of exploring new possibilities of visual communication.

[1]'Sign' is used in the semiotic sense and includes both 'formal' and 'symbolic' aspects of visual communication.
[2]Aaron Marcus, 'A Prototype Computerized Page-design System', *Visible Language*, Vol.V, No.3, Summer 1971, describes a prototype solution to this problem.

Press coatings

William A. Rocap

Pollution problems face print like other industries and are likely to become more pressing everywhere. The director of research and engineering of the US firm of Meredith Printing, Des Moines, describes the press coatings method of trapping hydrocarbons and combustion products in the printed page so that they need no longer be driven out into the atmosphere.

Press coatings is a method of printing designed to solve the problem of industrial emissions raised by web heat-set printing. In this method, the paper-ink-coating-equipment system retains all the ink components on the sheet of paper instead of driving them out into the atmosphere. Provided that each component of the system is properly chosen, it should be economically and technically feasible. The environmental problems that face the printing industry, particularly web printers, include emission of smoke, odour, and the hydrocarbons released by the high-temperature drying required to drive off ink solvents or other reaction by-products. Approaches to the solution of these problems have included thermally catalysed inks, ultraviolet setting inks, electrostatic precipitation, direct-flame afterburners (with and without catalysts), low-emission inks, and press coatings. In the United States the printer is obliged by Federal, State, and local regulations to eliminate hydrocarbons, smoke, and odour emissions from his web press operations and he can be sued for nuisance if he breaks them.

United States Patent No.2,696,168, dated 7 December 1954, registered a claim by John P. Costello to a method of protecting wet-ink films on printed surfaces by applying to the surface, over the wet ink, a continuous, thin, transparent film-forming coating solution, and passing the printed surface – on which the ink is wet – in direct non-wiping contact with a solid contact surface, wet with a thin film of the solution; the solvent constituent of the solution is volatile and the solution is a non-solvent for the wet ink. Since Mr Costello's work, which was done before 1954, a number of developments have been made in coatings, inks, and equipment. A presentation was made at the 27th annual national forum of the Packaging Institute, 30 September 1965, by Hugh Dunn of Inmont Corporation. The name of this process was Project GROW (*G*et *R*id *O*f *W*ax), and it suggested an aqueous sealer and coating to eliminate anti-static sprays and provide tough, low-cost, glossy, mar-resistant overprint lacquers.

The paper for the press coating system should have a smooth surface and should be capable of running successfully in the printing process used. The system should be effective in either the letterpress or offset process. In either case, since the coating may contribute gloss and finish to the overall printed sheet, it may be possible to use less coating and have less gloss in the paper itself. Since the inks will not be removed but will remain entirely on the surface of the sheet, sealed in by the coating, it may be advisable to include in the paper a barrier to prevent penetration and possible 'ghosting' of one side, due to penetration from

Three types of coater:
The Dahlgren liquid application system, right;
the Inta-Rota gravure type coater, centre;
and the Packer flexo-coater.

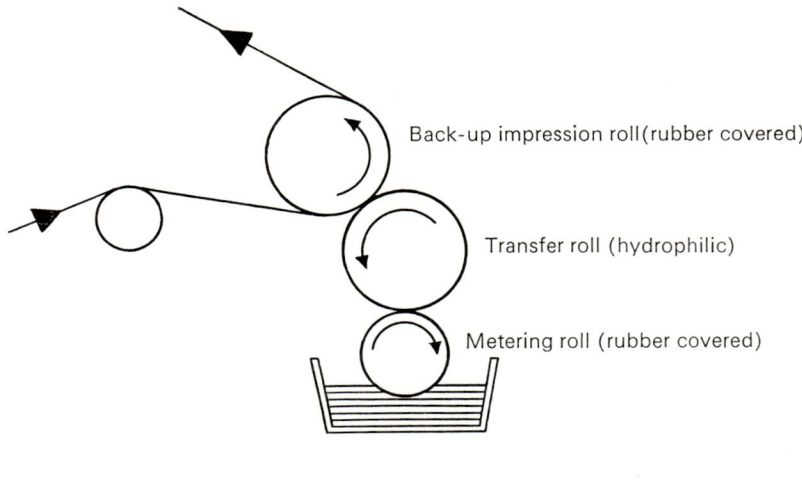

Back-up impression roll (rubber covered)

Transfer roll (hydrophilic)

Metering roll (rubber covered)

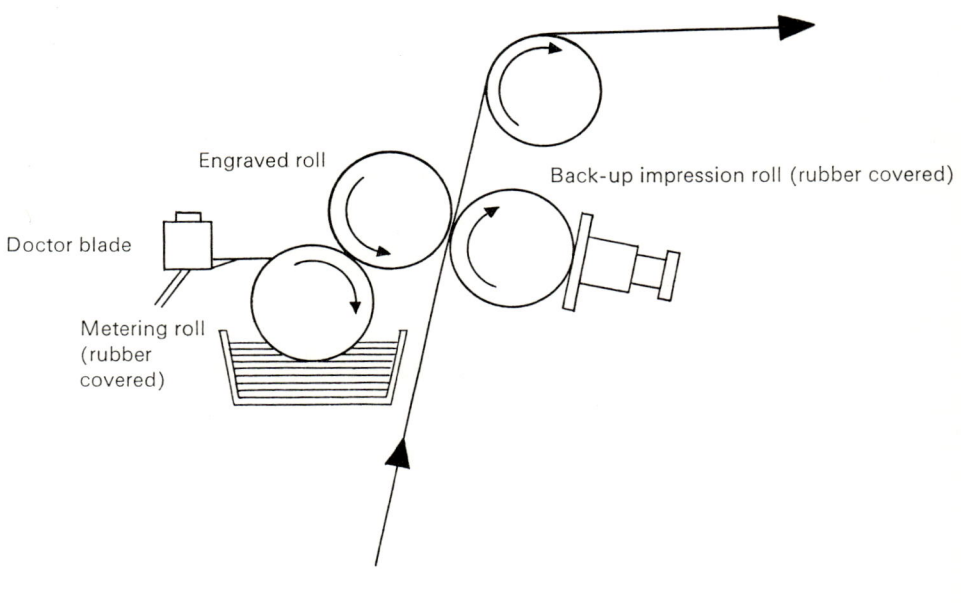

Engraved roll

Back-up impression roll (rubber covered)

Doctor blade

Metering roll
(rubber
covered)

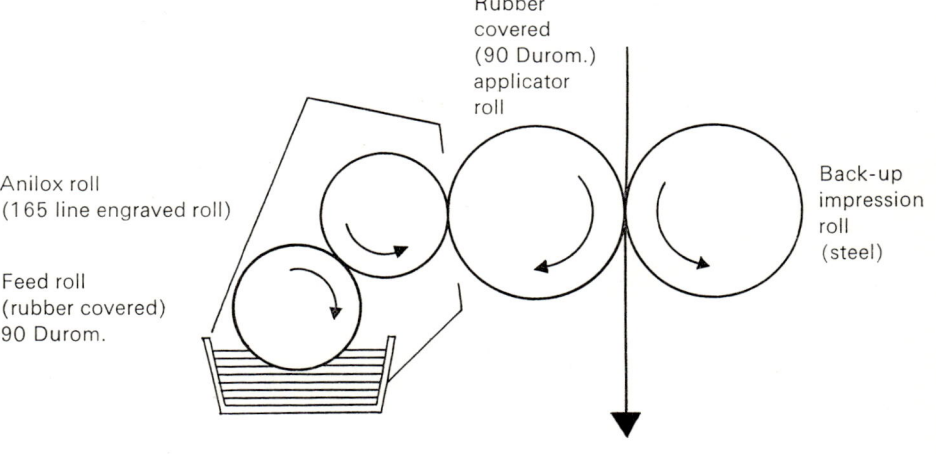

Rubber
covered
(90 Durom.)
applicator
roll

Anilox roll
(165 line engraved roll)

Back-up
impression
roll
(steel)

Feed roll
(rubber covered)
90 Durom.

the other side. In other words, ingredients in the paper coating may serve to prevent migration of the ink components.

The paper will not be heated to any great extent – perhaps to no more than 160°F. It will not therefore be necessary, for faster drying of the coating, to build heat resistance into the paper and this may allow a cheaper sheet of paper to be used. Other qualities now required in the paper, because of the heat to which it is subjected, may cease to be necessary.

It may also be feasible to incorporate in the paper coating materials which will accelerate the drying of the ink film. For example, if an oxidative drying system is used for the inks, the rate of oxidation or polymerization of the inks might be accelerated by catalysts incorporated in the paper coating. Hitherto coatings have been successfully applied to ordinary publication cover and insert papers from 40# to 60# basis weight. Paper manufacturers have been invited to consider how they might help in perfecting the press-coating process.

Inks used in the process, apart from the properties required for the press used – whether letterpress or offset, high speed or slow – need not contain the usual materials which are now added for surface properties. For example, materials such as waxes, oils and silicones, which are at present added to produce surface slip, mar resistance and so on, can be eliminated since the inks will be covered by the press coating. The ink selected for the press coating process should provide the very best dot formation on the paper surface and have good binding properties to the paper and good trapping characteristics. It should be an ink that will work well with the surface coating used. For example, if an alcohol soluble propionate (ASP) coating such as the one produced by Eastman Chemical Company is used, pigments and toners which would bleed when this coating is applied over them in their wet form must not be used. The inks should set as rapidly as possible initially, on the paper surface; however, while still in the press distribution system they should have good stability. They should then have the ability to 'through-dry' to a hard film in a minimum time after being printed. The oxidative oil type of ink has been the most successful in trials made to date; it would be feasible, however, to use any type of ink which met the requirements of the press coating system.

The primary requirements of the press coating are: that it should be possible to apply it to the wet ink film on the paper without causing the ink to bleed or mark, and to protect it from marking as it travels through the press, impression, and folder; it should serve as a protective, attractive, glossy coating to the overall page, both on the printed and non-printed areas, without adding excessive weight to the paper; it should not inhibit the ink under it from completely setting to a hard film and could contain a catalyst to accelerate the drying of the ink. The press coating should also be economically feasible to use, and repulpable. One basic material which seems to meet most of these requirements is the Eastman ASP. This forms a tough, semi-permeable film which permits oxygen to penetrate to the oxidative inks and it is de-inkable.

Finally, it will be necessary to find a means of applying the press coating uniformly to the wet ink film on a production press. Several types of coaters have been tested and found to be quite adequate. Three of these are the Dahlgren liquid application system (LAS) coater, an Inta-Rota gravure type coater, and the Packer flexographic type coater, all diagramatically illustrated on page 200. Press coatings have been applied on these coaters at web speeds as high as 1600 feet per minute with satisfactory results.

In conclusion, the press coating system can provide a practical solution for the problem of environmental control which letterpress and offset web printers now face: it eliminates the present driving out into the atmosphere of hydrocarbons and combustion products. The press coatings can be applied and dried by simple, low-cost equipment, at low temperatures. And it will be possible to use less gas as well as to reduce paper problems associated with the necessity to subject the web to high temperatures in drying ovens. If a press coating with an appropriate gloss level is used, it is possible to produce an attractive protective-coated printed sheet at a competitive price.

Cathode ray consoles in composition

Collier A. Elliott

Cathode ray tube systems, serving as a kind of electronic window enabling editors to see exactly what is in storage and facilitating correction, will play an increasing part in the composition process. The author examines developments in this field by Hendrix Electronics and Harris-Intertype in the United States.

The block illustrating this article was made by Vantage Engraving Co. Ltd.

The cathode ray tube console, now frequently referred to as the video display console or terminal, is a relatively simple electronic device of considerable usefulness in the composition process. The generic name also covers other kinds of displays, such as those which use 'storage tubes' for long-lasting displays which cannot be changed except by rewriting the entire screen. Others are mainly used to display graphic representations such as curves derived from mathematical computations. This article will deal only with CRTs which display alphanumeric characters which can be modified from the device's keyboard on an individual character basis.

Physically, the device consists of a standard television picture tube with raster scanning circuitry, a keyboard, an electronic storage memory, input, output character generation, and instruction execution logic circuitry, and the requisite power supplies, all neatly encased as a desk-top unit. Early CRTs tended to be small, displaying only a few lines consisting of a few all-cap. characters. They were used for inter-communication with computers and were usually dependent on the host computer for memory storage, character generation, and periodic refreshment of the screen images. Lacking lower case alphabets, they were of no interest to the printing world. Even with lower case capability, displays were so limited that no serious consideration could be given them as adjuncts to the composition process.

The recent widespread adoption of photo-composition as the method best suited for work intended to be printed by offset-lithography or by rotogravure – processes which require camera shots for plate-making – brought the time, labour, and materials costs of corrections to photo-composed material to the shocked attention of production executives. Photo-comp corrections were found to be exorbitantly expensive in comparison with hot metal corrections.

Many ideas for circumventing this difficulty were tested but none proved fully satisfactory. It remained for the predecessors of present-day CRT consoles to show the way. The first such machine was a big step forward. It presented an acceptably large display – twenty-four lines of eighty characters – and a full complement of upper and lower case letters, numerals, punctuation, and symbols reasonably representative of typesetting idiosyncrasies such as the standard fixed spaces, leaders, quadding functions, and the like. It also offered a self-contained memory with attendant character generation and screen refreshing capability so that it was dependent upon the host computer only for an initial loading of text and for a destination for completed work. The computer was not required to spend part of its time taking care of the functional needs of the CRT. In fact, in the interval between loading and unloading this new CRT, the device was on its own, completely out of communication with the computer.

In this 'local' mode, the keyboard could be used to direct any desired modification of the displayed material. An incorrect character could be instantly replaced by the correct one. The replacement took place within the CRT's own memory and since the content of that memory was used to refresh the screen sixty times per second, the operator had visual proof of the content of the CRT's memory in the display he saw on the tube face.

Other circuitry provided for insertions ranging from a single character to phrases, sentences and, in fact, as much as the operator desired. The previously displayed material was obligingly moved away to the right as characters were inserted one by one. In similar fashion, the machine carried out deletions with material to the right of the character(s) deleted moving leftward to close up what would otherwise be a gap.

The place in the CRT's internal memory where these operations were to take place was displayed by a screen character called a 'cursor'. Usually a blinking underline, readily located by the operator, the cursor was controlled by a set of keys on the control keyboard which could move it up, down, left, right, or 'home' – the name given to the upper left character in the display.

This first practical CRT was produced by the firm which has now evolved into Hendrix Electronics. Its initial offering was a CRT console coupled to a paper-tape reader and to a paper-tape punch with optional availability of direct attachment to a disc storage unit which was, in turn, interfaced to press wire service lines. The control elements were hard-wired (single purpose as opposed to programmable) electronics.

As Hendrix was developing its unit, the American Newspaper Publishers Association's Research Institute, having learned of extensive earlier involvement with military applications of CRTs by a company which had been acquired by Harris-Intertype Corporation, encouraged Harris to exhume some of Radiation Incorporated's prior technology as a basis for a text editing and correcting device. Harris responded and the Harris 1100 was born. It, too, was a tape-in, tape-out system but it had an optional interface connexion which could be used to tie it to a computer.

cursor was controlled by a set of keys on the control keyboard which could move it up, down, left, right, or "Home" the name given the upper left character in the display.

With some refinements and embellishments, these are still the characteristics of present day CRT Consoles.

The first practical CRT, described above was produced by the predecessor firm which has now evolved into Hendrix Electronics. Its initial offering to the printing world was a CRT Console coupled to a paper tape reader and to a paper tape punch with optional availability of direct attachment to a disc storage unit which was, in turn, interfaced to press wire service lines. The control elements were hard-wired (single purpose as opposed to programmable) electronics.

As Hendrix was developing its unit, the American Newspaper Publishers Association's Research Institute, having learned of extensive earlier involvement with military applications of CRTs by a company which had been acquired by Harris-Intertype Corporation, encouraged Harris to exhume some of Radiation, Incorporated's prior technology as a basis for a text editing and correcting device. Harris responded and the Harris 1100 was born. It, too, was a tape-in, tape-out system but it had an optional interface connection which could be used to tie it to a computer.

Both of these developments were aimed exclusively at the Graphic Arts market. Consequently, research and development costs had to be recouped from relatively fewer potential sales than those of CRT manufacturers which targeted much larger more general markets. The lower priced CRT Consoles offered by the latter firms were found to be adequate for the work involved in so far as editing and correcting text is concerned. True, specialized symbols for specialized composition functions were not available, but the math symbol for "less than"—a V shape pointing to the left made a usable replacement to indicate "Quad Left" and the "equals" sign wasn't hard to understand as Quad Center. Designed for computer interfacing, such commercial CRTs are now in use in pioneering editing and text-perfecting systems now in successful operation in U.S. newspapers.

Such systems are based upon control minicomputers which handle the traffic from input devices such as press wire service lines, paper tape readers, direct-coupled input typewriters and Optical Character Recognition devices in custom designed combinations of some or all of these to storage in a disc storage system.

Stored material is called to CRT Consoles and corrections and-or editing changes are carried out by an operator at the Console. Completed ("text perfected" is a term coined by the author for such) work is restored and subsequently output directly to photocomp typesetting machines or to paper tape punches which produce tape-formatted by the computer control program specifically for a given photocomp typesetting machine. Some editors have indicated a desire to do their own editing on CRT Consoles but not many are interested in combining this work with proofreading and correcting the text. It is questionable whether two CRT processing steps—one for editing and the other for proff-correction—is the most efficient procedure.

Other editors have considered CRTs as input devices. One in fact, ordered one to write his editorials on. In the author's opinion, CRTs are extravagantly expensive

cursor was controlled by a set of keys on the control keyboard which could move it up, down, left, right, or "Home" — the name given the upper left character in the display.

With some refinements and embellishments, these are still the characteristics of present day CRT Consoles.

The first practical CRT, described above was produced by the predecessor firm which has now evolved into Hendrix Electronics. Its initial offering to the printing world was a CRT Console coupled to a paper tape reader and to a paper tape punch with optional availability of direct attachment to a disc storage unit which was, in turn, interfaced to press wire service lines. The control elements were hard-wired (single purpose as opposed to programmable) electronics.

As Hendrix was developing its unit, the American Newspaper Publishers Association's Research Institute, having learned of extensive earlier involvement with military applications of CRTs by a company which had been acquired by Harris-Intertype Corporation, encouraged Harris to exhume some of Radiation, Incorporated's prior technology as a basis for a text editing and correcting device. Harris responded and the Harris 1100 was born. It, too, was a tape-in, tape-out system but it had an optional interface connection which could be used to tie it to a computer.

Both of these developments were aimed exclusively at the Graphic Arts market. Consequently, research and development costs had to be recouped from relatively fewer potential sales than those of CRT manufacturers which targeted much larger more general markets. The lower priced CRT Consoles offered by the latter firms were found to be adequate for the work involved in so far as editing and correcting text are concerned.

True, specialized symbols for specialized composition functions were not available, but the math symbol for "less than" — a V shape pointing to the left — made a usable replacement to indicate "Quad Left" and the "equals" sign wasn't hard to understand as Quad Center. Designed for computer interfacing, such commercial CRTs are being used in pioneering editing and text-perfecting systems now in successful operation in U.S. newspapers.

Such systems are based upon control minicomputers which handle the traffic from input devices such as press wire service lines, paper tape readers, direct-coupled input typewriters and Optical Character Recognition devices in custom designed combinations of some or all of these to storage in a disc storage system.

Stored material is called to CRT Consoles and corrections and editing changes are carried out by an operator at the Console. Completed ("text perfected" is a term coined by the author for such) work is restored and subsequently output directly to photocomp typesetting machines or to paper tape punches which produce tape formatted specifically for a given photocomp typesetting machine by the control computer program.

Some editors have indicated a desire to do their own editing on CRT Consoles but not many are interested in combining this work with proofreading and correcting the text. It is questionable whether two CRT processing steps — one for editing and the other for proof-correction — is the most efficient procedure.

Other editors have considered CRTs as input devices. One in fact, ordered one to use

Both these developments were aimed exclusively at the graphic arts market. Consequently, research and development costs had to be recouped from relatively fewer potential sales than those of CRT manufacturers whose target was much larger, more general markets. The lower-priced CRT consoles offered by these firms were found to be adequate for the work involved in so far as editing and correcting text was concerned.

True, specialized symbols for specialized composition functions were not available, but the mathematical symbol for 'less than' – a V shape pointing to the left – made a usable replacement to indicate 'quad left' and the 'equals' sign was not hard to understand as quad centre. Designed for computer interfacing, such commercial CRTs are being used in pioneer editing and text-perfecting systems now successfully operating in American newspapers.

Such systems are based upon control minicomputers which handle the traffic from input devices such as press wire service lines, paper-tape readers, direct-coupled input typewriters, and optical character recognition devices in custom designed combinations of some or all of these to storage in a disc storage system.

Stored material is called to CRT consoles and corrections and/or editing changes are carried out by an operator at the console. Completed work ('perfected text' is a term coined by the author for this) is re-stored and subsequently output directly to photocomp typesetting machines or to paper-tape punches which produce tape formatted specifically for a given photocomp typesetting machine by the control computer program. Some editors have indicated a desire to do their own editing on CRT consoles but not many are interested in combining this work with proofreading and correcting the text. It is questionable whether two CRT processing steps – one for editing and the other for proof-correction – are the most efficient procedure.

Other editors have considered CRTs as input devices. One editor ordered a CRT for use in writing his editorials. CRTs are extravagantly expensive typewriters which may be all well and good as a reward and status symbol for a valued executive editor but which are certainly not for the staff reporter. CRTs, without additional equipment, do not produce hard copy, which is still considered essential for many reasons. Thus, their use for generation of copy which must be reviewed by a copy editor, is not advisable. On the other hand, CRTs offer a useful capability for classified advertising ad takers.

CRTs for such application should have 'format' capability. This is the ability to protect selected areas of the display while other areas are variable. The protection is extended to the captions of an ad order entry form which the computer places on the screen. The areas to be filled in are variable. When the ad is agreed upon, the computer unloads only what is in the variable areas, leaving the protected captions on the screen for the next transaction.

Again, in such cases, hard copy must be produced by a printer of some sort, but this can be handled by the computer as time is available. Similar information on other (contract) ads where the advertiser knows what he wants to say, are properly taken care of by direct-coupled typewriters. CRTs, of course, should be used to correct any errors in ad copy before typesetting.

Display advertising is minimally served by application of CRTs. The copy, itself, like all copy to be photo-typeset, should be perfect before going to the typesetting machine. The CRT can be used to insert mark-up designations or format numbers which the computer can translate into the long strings of instruction codes required by display photo-typesetters.

In commercial work, pre-correction is just as important as it is in newspaper work. Again, here, when large amounts of text are involved such as are normal in books, publications, and brochures, maximum benefits are derived. In book-work, serious consideration should be given to suitably larger storage devices such as magnetic tape instead of disc storage. A text-perfected book on magnetic tape requires practically no additional work if the text is to be reformatted for a paperback.

Systems available include the Hendrix and Harris tape-in, tape-out systems mentioned above. Depending on memory size and other options, they run from $15,000 upward. Mergenthaler Linotype has such a system at $12,500. Input speed on all of these is limited to the speed of the tape reader and the systems are not expandable because they are all based on hard-wired controllers.

Widespread use of integrated circuitry has brought down the price of modern minicomputers; the author has recently quoted $12,500 for a tape-in, tape-out system controlled by an all solid-state computer. This system will load the screen at the speed of the tape reader only for the first screenful. After that, the reader will have stored the next screenful in the computer memory and subsequent unloading and loading will be completed in less than a second. In addition, the computer is expandable and can be re-programmed so that the system itself can expand to meet its owner's future needs. This will be the trend; evidence of it is found in the incorporation by Hendrix of a minicomputer in its more advanced and complex systems.

Further evidence of the shape of things to come is found in two interesting, albeit expensive, CRT systems recently put on the market. One is a text machine which provides a display in which the letters occupy space proportionate to their counterparts in a unit cut, TTS typeface. This machine, the Imlac Composer-15, incorporates a minicomputer which justifies the text upon command and displays it as it will be typeset – hyphenations and all. Any incorrect hyphenations can be corrected while the material is displayed.

Another new CRT system, the Harris 2200, is a display advertising system. Copy is displayed in proportionate size and in position relative to the margin of the screen. The special computer incorporated in the system generates full sets of area typesetting instruction coding which is incorporated in the output tape with the copy so that the Fototronic sets the whole ad as it was displayed. For a substantial additional fee Harris will provide instruction coding for other than Harris Intertype typesetting machines.

As the skills now embodied in experienced ad mark-up men die out, such devices become increasingly useful. Now, however, with a 2200 controller, one CRT and a Fototronic adding up to more than $100,000, there will be something less than universal acceptance. The controller, incidentally, will handle four CRTs, which makes the price somewhat more palatable.

To sum up the usefulness of the CRT, the reader may wish to think of it as an electronic window which allows him to see exactly what is in storage and to change this material to his satisfaction. Such changes are far more acceptable psychologically than those which require the merging of correction information out of sight inside the 'black box'. When you make a change using a CRT, you see what has been done and, if you have made an error in your correction, you can correct your error easily and directly. For these reasons, CRT corrections are preferable to those provided by manufacturers of optical character recognition devices. Use OCRs, if the circumstances justify the cost, but forget OCR correction procedures and handle corrections in a CRT.

CRTs will be key devices in future composition systems. It will be advantageous to keep well abreast of further hardware and application developments.

Tension control for web-offset

John R. Martin

The president of the US firm of Martin Automatic analyses tension and stretch requirements for good register in web-offset printing, and describes the firm's 'inertia compensated' dancer roller and associated equipment offering the printer freedom from his great dependence on 'paper variation'.

The illustrations in this article were engraved by Kings Town Engraving Co. Ltd.

When tension is applied to a rubber band, it stretches: when tension is applied to a steel band, it also stretches, but much less. The relationship between tension and stretch is a function of the material which we will call its modulus. The modulus of paper is not constant; constant tension does not produce constant stretch, nor does constant stretch produce constant tension. It is because of this, and because printers have always tried to hold the wrong thing constant, that the black art of web handling has remained such a mystery.

It is obviously necessary that the web should not break, or accumulate in great loops, or wander sideways. Apart from this, the only reason for maintaining constant tension (or is it stretch?) is the need for good register. The following diagram will help us to analyse cut-to-print register in a perfecting offset press.

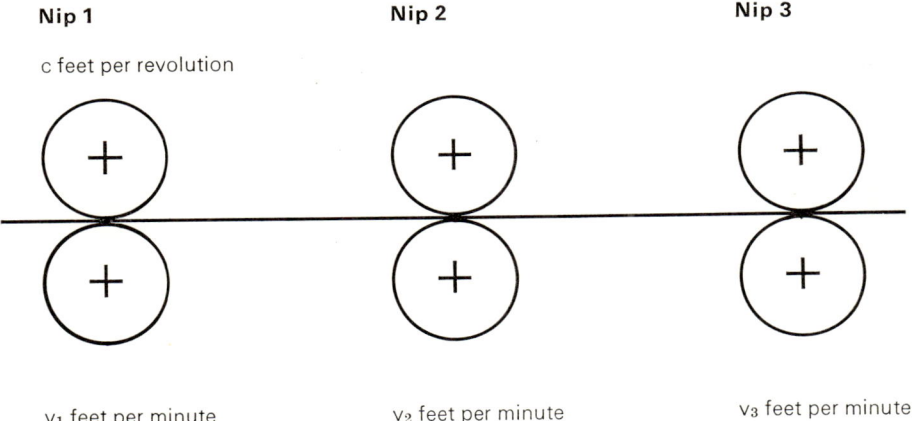

Nip 1 will represent the last printing unit, printing one mark per revolution at a speed of v_1 feet per minute with a circumference of c feet and therefore printing $\frac{v_1}{c}$ marks per minute. Obviously, if $\frac{v_1}{c}$ marks per minute are being printed, a measurement at any point downstream will yield $\frac{v_1}{c}$ marks per minute also, as we cannot expect to deliver more or fewer signatures in a minute than the number we print.

The figure of $\frac{v_1}{c}$ marks per minute must then hold true at Nip 2 which will represent the chill rolls. *If*, however, the chills are driving the web at a speed of v_2, the only way in which $\frac{v_1}{c}$ marks per minute can pass

209

the chills at a speed of v_2 feet per minute is for the marks to be spaced $\frac{v_1}{v_2} c$ feet apart. Putting the matter another way, we can say that after the marks were printed at a spacing of c feet, the web was stretched by $\frac{v_2}{v_1}$ ($\frac{v_2}{v_1}$ can be less than, equal to, or greater than 1).

If the web is uniform between Nip 1 and Nip 2, and *if* the web in the span between Nip 1 and Nip 2 is not subject to any other forces, then the stretch at Nip 2 must apply at all points between Nip 1 and Nip 2. This must be so, because a non-uniform stretch within a span would imply a non-uniform tension within a span and this is impossible because the sum of the forces at any point in the span must equal zero. This means that the spacing of marks in the span between Nip 1 and Nip 2 is equal to $\frac{v_2}{v_1} c$ just as it is at Nip 2.

Now, *if* $\frac{v_1}{v_2}$ is a reasonable value, i.e. if it ensures that the web will not break or accumulate, and *if* $\frac{v_1}{v_2}$ remains constant both short term and long term, and *if* the distance which the web travels between Nip 1 and Nip 2 does not change, the registration at the chill rolls will not change. Similarly, subject to the same *ifs*, the mark spacing between Nip 2 and Nip 3 (Nip 3 represents the folder nip) will be $\frac{v_3}{v_1} c$. Thus, the register does not change between Nip 2 and Nip 3 or between Nip 1 and Nip 2; therefore the register does not change between Nip 1 and Nip 3 and cut-to-print register is constant.

Cut-to-print register will be constant . . . 1. *If* the chills drive the web at v_2 . . . in fact if all drive points are non-slip; 2. *If* the web is uniform in any given span; 3. *If* the web in any given span is not subject to any intermediate forces; 4. *If* gains are reasonable; 5. *If* all drive points have a constant relative speed; 6. *If* the web path between nips does not change.

It is significant that, in the above analysis, tension was not a consideration. In fact, it emerges clearly that *for constant register the stretch between nips must be maintained constant.*

Now let us consider colour-to-colour register using the same diagram, with Nips 1, 2, and 3 now representing printing nips. The arguments concerning cut-to-print register still apply, i.e. constant stretch between nips, etc. is still necessary. There is, however, a new

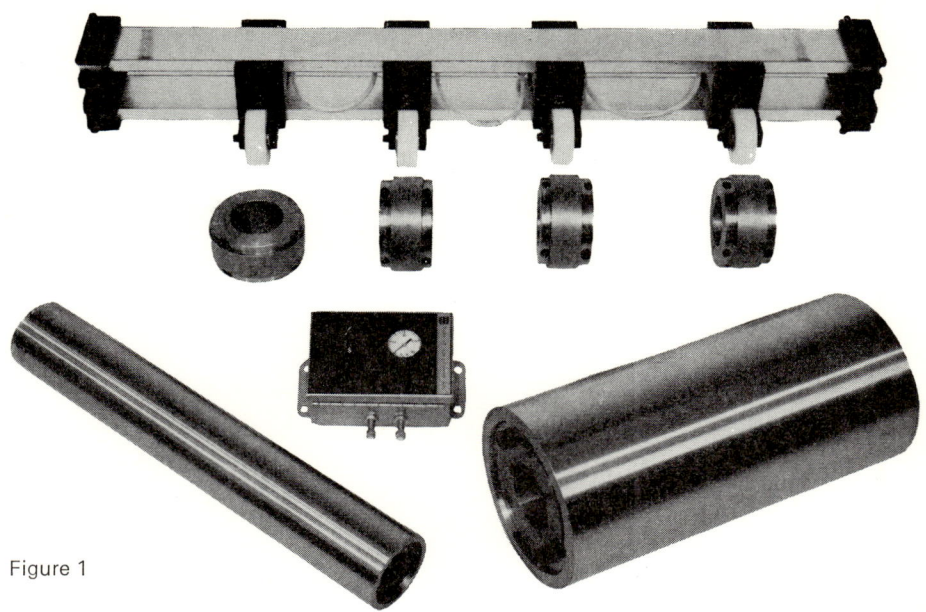

Figure 1

difficulty in satisfying the sixth *if*. The web will not leave the blankets tangentially, but will 'follow' the blanket in an amount determined by the 'stickiness' of the blankets and the tension in the web. *If* the blanket stickiness remains constant, and *if* the web tension remains constant, then the web length between units, and therefore colour register, will remain constant. We still have the requirement of constant stretch between nips and have now added the requirements of constant tension to produce requirements which seem to be mutually exclusive; how can both tension and stretch between nips be constant when they are related by a variable, i.e. the modulus? The only way is to set the stretch between nips equal to zero (all printing units 'feed' the same) so that the tension produced by the stretch between nips is zero. Obviously, we cannot print with zero tension, so the web must be pre-tensioned before it enters the first nip (the first printing unit). In other words, whatever tension and stretch exist in the web while it is being printed are established before the web enters the first printing unit and are simply maintained by a one-to-one drive through the units.

In actual practice the application of water to the web tends to reduce the tension as the web passes through the units. Fortunately this reduction tends to be constant in time and our requirement for constant tension is not violated – even though the tension between Unit 1 and Unit 2 is not quite the same as that between Units 2 and 3.

So, to maintain colour register, we may further define the sixth *if* by:
6a. *If* stickiness of the blankets remains constant; 6b. *If* tension of the web entering the first printing unit is constant.

We now seem to have a formula for good register if our *ifs* can be satisfied. Let us consider them one by one.

1. *If* all web drive points are non-slip.

Disregarding blanket nips which are normally non-slip, this condition can be ensured by gripping the web at the drive rollers with sufficient force. The 'trucks' supplied with new presses are normally incapable of supplying enough force. The American firm of Martin Automatic, Inc. supplies high-pressure pneumatically loaded trolleys (trucks) which are self-aligning and capable of ensuring enough traction to prevent slip (Fig.1).

2. *If* the web is uniform within spans.

The requirement here is only that the web shall be uniform within a given span, not from roll to roll or within a roll. Fortunately, the modulus of paper, although not constant, is sufficiently uniform within short spans for the error introduced to be well within commercial tolerances. The worst situation is the step-change in modulus which occurs when the outside of a new roll is spliced to the inside of the previous roll. Even then, if all the other *ifs* are satisfied, the typical error in cut-off can be as small as 1/32 of an inch and return within approximately twenty signatures.

3. *If* the web in any span is not subject to any intermediate forces.

The only danger here is that of 'driven' or 'drag' rollers or slitters which have a high gain and significant wrap or trucks. The solution could be simply to idle these rollers, but in practice web-up becomes simpler if they are driven. Therefore it is recommended that the diameter of these rollers be established at web speed.

4. *If* gains are reasonable.

It should be emphasized that reasonable gains have not been predicted by the theory but have been determined empirically. For offset perfectors, sufficient experience dictates that folders should drive at bearer speed. For other types of presses and chill rolls on perfectors, the safest route has been to measure precisely the speed of the running web and to match the drive roll gains to the web. For these measurements, Martin Automatic has developed instrumentation with the required precision.

5. *If* all drive points have a constant relative speed.

This requirement can be divided into long-term and short-term aspects. Short-term requirements indicate that drive trains should not show significant 'wrap-up' with a changing load, which changes tension. Fortunately, standard printing press design has satisfied this requirement. Long-term requirements indicate the undesirability of adjustable ratio transmissions. In a typical offset perfector, a change in chill roll gain of $0 \cdot 1 \%$ will affect the stretch of the web in the dryer (typically 20 feet) to produce a cut-to-print misregister of $0 \cdot 1 \% \times 20$ ft. (240 in.) $= 0 \cdot 24$ in.

Required stability is seen to be in the order of $0 \cdot 005 \%$ – a figure which is unachievable with conventional variable ratio transmissions. Martin Automatic has replaced many of these transmissions with

Figure 2

constant ratio timing belt drives to produce significant improvements in cut-off register (Fig.2).

6. *If* the web path between nips is constant.

With the exception of *ifs* 6a and 6b, this requirement reduces to permanently locating all drive and idler rollers.

6a. *If* the stickiness of the blanket remains constant.

Experience indicates that normal care in handling inks satisfies this condition adequately.

6b. *If* tension of the web entering the first printing is constant.

There are a number of ways to control the tension of the web entering the first printing unit. The indirect methods – trying to control tension by controlling stretch – should not be considered, because of the variation of the modulus.

For direct control of tension there are two main classes of mechanisms. One uses a tension-sensing device and, through an appropriate control system, controls the speed of a nip to maintain the output of the sensor constant. This type of system has no 'storage' and its response time limits its ability to adjust for rapid changes. Attempts to speed up the response time and improve the capabilities usually involve complications which yield no commensurate improvement. The other main class of tension control is the dancer or 'floating roller' type of system. The dancer should not be confused with the tension-measuring roller. *The dancer does not measure tension – it establishes it.* When a tension-measuring roller is out of position by as little as a few thousandths of an inch, usually the tension is different. When a dancer

Figure 3

is out of centre, this does not mean that the tension is different. Since the dancer establishes tension by pushing on a loop of web, it is desirable that this push should remain constant.

There are three possible sources of error in the design of the dancer:

1. Position. The geometry of the dancer should be established so that the tension is independent of dancer position. In the case of a pivoted dancer, long dancer arms and long web leads help. The dancer should be counterbalanced or move essentially in a vertical direction to minimize gravitational errors. Geometric accuracies better than plus or minus 1/8 % are easily achieved.

2. Speed. Dancers should be designed so that their push on the web does not change when the dancer is in motion. A well-known example of poor practice is the use of a shock absorber on the dancer, with the aim of stabilizing the system. It is true that many dancer systems require stabilization, but this can be better done with rate response in the control element.

3. Acceleration. It has long been realized that a dancer, because of its inertia, will not completely absorb tension transients. Martin Automatic Inc., with its patented 'Inertia Compensated' dancer roller, has now made it possible to cancel out the effects of inertia completely. The firm understood that a physically realizable dancer has both rotary and translational inertia and that the effects of these are opposite. The outcome of this understanding is a dancer in which these opposite effects are made equal and therefore cancel each other out.

The Martin dancer can act as a perfect filter of tension disturbances; upstream transients are absorbed by the dancer and not transmitted downstream. This principle is used in the Martin Constant Tension Infeed and Martin Tension Control (Fig.3).

Summing up the Martin Automatic experiences, there are two main conclusions to be drawn. The first is that the conventional practice of seeking constant tension at the delivery defeats the requirement of constant stretch (because of the changing modulus). The second is that the common practice of controlling infeed tension with the constant stretch characteristics of an adjustable ratio infeed defeats the requirements for constant tension (again because of changing modulus). The firm hopes it has established that, by controlling the desired parameter, printers can rid themselves of their tremendous dependence on 'paper variation'.

Water-based printing inks

Hugh Dunn

A discussion of the growing concern about print and pollution and the methods being used in the US industry to deal with the problem. The author examines in detail American experiences bearing on the viability of water as a replacement for organic hydrocarbon solvents in printing ink formulations.

The worldwide problem of air pollution is receiving particular legislative attention in the United States. Almost all local, state and Federal laws include nuisance clauses dealing with contamination of the atmosphere by smoke and odours. Some localities, notably Los Angeles County in California, adopted very stringent regulations controlling organic hydrocarbon emissions as long ago as 1966. Other cities and states have followed suit and it would appear that with the help of the Federal Government all offending situations will receive attention shortly. The time-table for such action has, in large part, been mutually agreed upon by all the states and the Environmental Protection Agency of the US Government.

The printing industry, particularly those sections where heat is used to dry printed ink films, is obviously affected by the anti-pollution rules. Heatset web letterpress and heatset web-offset are two prime examples; others include the flexographic and rotogravure processes used in publishing and packaging and the lithographic printing and coating of tinplate for can fabrications.

Almost all heatset or heat-dried inks and coatings contain solvents which are driven off during the drying cycle by heat in such forms as hot air, open gas flame, steam drum, and infra-red radiation. It is the emissions generated by these operations that prompt strict regulations to be framed. Hydrocarbon solvent emissions which are photochemically reactive can form smog through a complex reaction with sunlight, ozone, and nitrogen compounds in the atmosphere. The various air pollution control regulations aim to prevent the formation of smog injurious to plant and animal life. Other kinds of air contaminants like particulates (dust), carbon monoxide, sulphur and nitrogen oxides are also regulated. The regulations controlling the emission of hydrocarbon solvents are a major concern to the industry because all the printing operations referred to earlier use these solvents in the inks employed.

Los Angeles Rule 66 limits the discharge of organic materials into the atmosphere to 15 lb per day or 3 lb per hour if there is contact with flame or the materials are baked, heat-cured, or heat-polymerized in the presence of oxygen and the discharge has not been reduced by at least 85 %. A photo-chemically reactive solvent is any solvent with an aggregate of more than 20 % of its total volume composed of the chemical compounds classified below, or which exceeds any of the individual percentage composition limitations, in relation to the total of solvent:

1. A combination of hydrocarbons, alcohols, aldehydes, esters, ethers or ketones having an olefinic or cyclo-olefinic type of unsaturation: 5 %.
2. A combination of aromatic compounds with eight or more carbon atoms to the molecule except ethylbenzene: 8 %.
3. A combination of ethylbenzene, ketones having branched hydrocarbon structures, trichloroethylene or toluene: 20 %.

The fifty states have all submitted implementation plans for control of air pollution, and roughly half have included some form of hydrocarbon emission control requirement for existing emission sources. In general, most of the state regulations follow Los Angeles APCD Rule 66, or some modification of it, for existing plants. Many rural sections of the country, however, will have no controls over hydrocarbon emissions.

Methods of dealing with the problem
To comply with existing and proposed regulations, the heatset printer has several alternatives which vary in cost and effectiveness:
1. *Incineration* – afterburner equipment operating with approximately 95 % efficiency at 1,200–1,500°F which essentially reduces the hydrocarbon effluent to innocuous water, carbon dioxide, and nitrogen oxide mixtures. Catalytic afterburners are also used requiring lower operational temperatures (650–900°F) and obtaining better economy through fuel savings.
2. *Solvent Recovery* – absorption of the hydrocarbon effluent on activated charcoal beds. Steam is then blown over the beds to strip the solvent. This method is generally well suited to the emission control of hydrocarbons. Absorption or scrubbing equipment can also be used, particularly when the effluent is soluble in water, e.g., alcohol vapours.
3. *Ink Formulation* – Several approaches exist:
(a) Eliminate the use of volatile solvents or other components which will create objectionable volatile effluent during the drying or curing cycle. Examples of such formulations include ultraviolet curing systems, plastisols, hot melt and electrostatically applied dry powder inks and coatings. Some of these systems have been described in earlier editions of THE PENROSE ANNUAL.
(b) Replace objectionable hydrocarbon solvents with exempt solvents or those with known levels of acceptability.

Water-based ink formulation – basic principles
The main question this article will discuss is the viability of water as a

substitute for organic hydrocarbon solvents in printing ink formulations. Although water would appear to have certain behavioural traits which preclude its use in letterpress and lithographic printing, it has been used quite successfully in some flexographic and rotogravure applications. But first it will be useful to outline the basic principles of water-based ink formulation. All inks of this type contain colorants, vehicular components, and additives for special purposes. Printing ink is basically designed to impart colour to a substrate. Therefore, the colorant used is a prime component. The vehicle serves two purposes; the first is to transfer the colour in wet form from the ink fountain to the substrate being printed, and the second is to hold it there. Additives serve to aid dispersion of pigment, prevent foaming, and improve rub resistance, and other special purposes.

Colorants include organic and inorganic pigments as well as dyes. The most commonly used pigments are:

Inorganic types	Organic types
Titanium dioxide	Benzidene yellows
Chrome yellows	Red lake C
Molybdated orange	Barium and calcium lithols
Iron blue	Phthalocyanine blues
Iron oxide yellows and reds	Rhodanine reds
CARBON BLACK	Victoria blue
	Methyl violet

Larson's *Industrial Printing Ink* gives fuller details of these pigments.

Vehicles provide the means whereby the colorant is transferred and bound to the substrate. The relative degree of efficiency of this transfer is called printability. The vehicle must have a certain amount of tack, supplied by solution viscosity, to transfer the colorant properly in the printing operation. Water-based latex paint will not print properly by either flexo or gravure because the paint vehicle does not have solution viscosity. These paints are generally fine dispersions of resinous or polymeric materials in water. A good working water-ink vehicle must be a solution of resin or polymer in water. Yet, when the ink dries, the vehicle must no longer be soluble in water. Most water-based ink vehicles are solutions of acidic resins in alkaline media such as ammoniated water. A typical vehicle can be made by reacting ammonium hydroxide with shellac to form a product which might be called ammonium shellacate. When a solution of ammonium shellacate is dried, the ammonia evaporates, leaving the original acidic shellac which is no longer water-soluble. It forms a tough adherent film which binds the pigment to the printed surface. Numerous types of acidic resins are used in printing ink vehicles. They can be classified in three categories: hard resins, proteins and polymers.

Hard resins are typically shellac, fumarated rosin and esterified fumarated rosins. With the exception of shellac, these resins are of moderate price and can be made into high solids, low-viscosity solutions providing excellent printability. Modified rosins are hard and brittle and not conducive to providing good rub resistance.

Proteins are typically casein and alpha protein. These form higher viscosity solutions which, in comparison with other resins, do not help in transfer or printability. They do provide excellent heat resistance, however, and are widely used in inks for printing coated liner board which must subsequently be corrugated. Proteins provide good rub and fair water resistance.

Polymers, sometimes referred to as acrylics, include reaction products of ethylene or styrene and carboxylated (acid containing) monomers such as maleic, acrylic, or itaconic acids. Sometimes shellac is used as the acid monomer. Such vehicles provide good printability, excellent rub resistance, fast drying and good water resistance.

Additives include wax compounds, defoamers and adhesion promoters.

Wax compounds containing paraffin, microcrystalline, or polyethylene waxes are used to impart rub resistance to the ink film. They accomplish this by imparting slip or lubricity.

Defoamers are used to retard the formation of bubbles generated by the soapy character of some ink vehicles. Typical defoamers include fatty esters, silicones and higher alcohols such as octyl alcohol. Excessive use must be avoided to prevent poor ink lay or 'fish eye' formation.

Lattices are used in inks as adhesion promoters but also serve to improve wet and dry rub resistance. Typical lattices include: polystyrene, vinyl chloride/vinyl acetate copolymers, vinylidene chloride and acrylics. We generally consider these polymers as additives since they do not contribute to the printability function of a vehicle.

Auxiliary solvents are commonly used in water-based ink systems to adjust solution viscosity and to adjust the drying speed of the ink on press. Typical solvents are alcohols, and glycol ethers. Ethyl alcohol must not be used too freely because it can evaporate from the ink fountain too quickly and cause an unduly rapid increase in ink viscosity. Also, relatively low concentrations (5–10 %) can lower the flashpoint, which may be of concern in some corrugated plants.

We should now be better able to evaluate the possibilities of putting these materials into use in water-based inks in the various printing systems that traditionally employ hydrocarbon solvent modified inks.

Letterpress web printing is designed to print with conventional ink systems generally composed of a resin, hydrocarbon solvent and a pigment mixture. The drying is done by applying heat in the form of hot air, steam drum contact, open gas flame impingement, or a combination of these. The hydrocarbon solvent is vaporized and forcibly ejected from the stack either in its original chemical form or modified through cracking or chemical reaction in the high temperature dryer environment.

The hydrocarbon solvent generally used in this type of ink has a relatively high boiling range to prevent evaporation from the inking rollers on the press. The number of inking rollers can range from a dozen to two dozen and these are used to distribute the ink film uniformly in its passage from the ink fountain to the printing plate. A typical distillation range for the hydrocarbon solvent used would be 470–515°F having a vapour pressure of only 0·40 mm of mercury at 150°F. Compare the evaporative stability of this solvent to that of water and the problem involved in using water as a replacement becomes obvious. Water has a vapour pressure of 187 mm at 150°F. A serious roller stability problem can, and does, occur if one tries to use water-based inks on this type of equipment. If a simpler letterpress roller distribution system could be employed to approximate that used in flexography, then perhaps a water-based ink could be used. The ink formulation, of necessity, has to be quite fluid to work on a flexo roller system, and this would probably work against the achievement of rheological properties deemed important to high-quality dot reproduction and gloss associated with publication letterpress printing.

A new concept of 'press coatings' now being explored is designed to solve the problem of hydrocarbon emissions created by web heatset printing. An aqueous coating is applied over wet ink and the coating is dried at a relatively low temperature. The ink is protected by the thin coating film and is expected to resist the marring normally caused by turn bar contact, nose cone formers, folders, and so on. The ink, if it is of an oxidizing type, can be expected to dry even though it is covered by a thin film. Practicality for web printing has yet to be proved but the technique is working successfully in some instances on sheet-fed equipment. In these cases the method has been called Project GROW.

Web-offset lithography
The roller stability problem applies here also. Even if there were no stability problem, the use of a water-based ink would be impractical in the lithographic process. There must be a controlled immiscibility between lithographic ink and the fountain solution which is an acidic, aqueous mixture to prevent inking of the non-printing area of the lithographic plate. Metal decoration on lithographic sheet-fed or dry offset printing equipment would also be ruled completely impractical because of the roller stability problem, unless dramatic changes could be made in the ink distribution or rheology of the inks used.

Water-based flexo inks
Water-based flexo inks have been the unglamorous workhorse of the packaging industry for more than twenty-five years. A conservative estimate of today's production of such inks by captive and commercial manufacturers would be in the range of 20–30 million lb annually. These inks are ideally suited for printing on absorbent paper and paperboard substrates and not generally recommended for films and foils, mainly because of poor adhesion and low gloss.

Typical large-volume applications of water-based flexo include printing of such goods as paper bags, shopping bags, gift wrap, wrapping paper, labels, corrugated liner board, paper towelling, bathroom tissue, facial tissue and carrier cartons. There has been a steady improvement in the performance of water-based flexo inks over the past ten years, particularly with regard to end product resistance. The use of more highly sophisticated polymers and copolymers to replace the natural binders like casein and alpha protein used years ago has contributed largely to better performance.

Although water is the main solvent used in all three types of inks to be discussed, it should be understood that some water-based ink formulations use organic cosolvents such as alcohols and glycol ethers to provide special performance characteristics like improved printability and drying speed. (The drying speed of water-based flexo inks printed on absorbent papers has never been considered a serious problem, mainly because flexo is a letterpress method of printing from rubber plate surfaces and the printed substrate is not dried until *all* colours have been transferred.)

Water-based gravure inks

These inks have been used for a number of years but limited to specialized applications such as printing corrugated liner stock, writing paper, paper to be laminated in post-curing operations, wallpaper, bleached kraft and other absorbent stocks, to upgrade quality. The major advantages noted are non-flammability, easy wash-up and dilution with water, lower insurance rates and minimal residual odour in the printed product. Another obvious advantage is the non-polluting character of such formulations.

Among the major disadvantages noted in the past are slow drying speed (compared with organic solvent based inks), low gloss, limited adhesion to various substrates (particularly non-absorbent types), distortion of stock and swelling cellulosic fibres, poor film properties, poor printability and relatively high cost compared with solvent-based inks. Many of these problems have been overcome in the light of today's formulations.

It is probably fair to say that air pollution regulations, actual and to come, and the wish to eliminate fire hazards are the two main reasons why printers are evaluating the use of water-based systems today. The concerted and co-operative efforts of the printer, ink-maker, cylinder, paper, press and dryer manufacturers will be required to overcome all the problems confronting us. However, considerable progress has been achieved in recent months through the successful R & D effort of ink-makers.

The relative drying or evaporation rate at room temperature of various solvents used in gravure inks is listed in Table 1. The figures represent the time necessary to evaporate 1 cm³ of solvent from a filter paper. The evaporation rate of a solvent is a function of vapour pressure and latent heat of vaporization. Both properties vary with change in temperature and are different for each material (Table 2). One can conclude from these data that more energy input is needed to evaporate 1lb of water than to evaporate an equivalent weight of any of the organic hydrocarbon solvents listed. The actual drying speed of an ink is determined by the drying rate of the solvent and the solvent release of the binder dissolved in this solvent. The solvent release of different binders varies widely and final selection for ink usage depends on many factors other than solvent release, for example gloss, printability, and cost. Water-based inks in general should require greater heat energy input and a longer dwell time to approximate the drying speed of solvent-based inks. This means more efficient hot-air ovens having larger air volume throughput to develop the necessary level of heat transfer.

Table 1

Solvent evaporation rate

	Time in seconds
Water	1,102
Toluol	180
Lactol spirits	110
Ethyl alcohol	240
Methyl ethyl ketone	100
Ethyl acetate	85

Table 2

Vapour pressure and latent heat of vaporization of some common rotogravure ink solvents

	Vapour pressure at 86°F mm Hg.	Latent heat of vaporization at 77°F btu/lb
Water	31	1,043
Toluol	36	177
Heptane	70	157
Ethyl alcohol	79	368
Methyl ethyl ketone	119	182
Ethyl acetate	120	184

One of the very real problems with the acceptance of water-based inks is their slow speed of drying in comparison with solvent-based inks, and this is accentuated by the relative inefficiency of dryers on presses that are more than six years old. Maximum achievable press speeds have been in the range of one-half to two-thirds the speed of conventional solvent ink drying.

Help in getting water-based inks to dry more quickly has come through the successful use of radio frequency (RF) dryers or boosters. The water molecules in water-based inks and coatings are excellent absorbers of RF energy. The effect of this absorption is molecular rotation that produces heat of friction and uniform heating of the ink film, resulting in rapid drying due to flash evaporation of the water content. Although proved effective under practical conditions, RF drying equipment currently costs about $1,000 per kW per inch of web-width. Each gravure colour station requires an RF booster in addition to the regular hot-air dryer to provide the synergistic drying efficiencies noted. At least double the drying speed has been observed with an RF booster installed. Microwave equipment can also produce the same improvement in drying speed but the capital investment and operating costs are much higher than R F costs.

In a further effort to resolve the drying speed problem, the Inmont Corporation has worked very closely with the cylinder engravers to develop jointly an optimized system which depends at present on specially formulated, higher strength pigment inks. For example, we have observed at Inmont that a 175–200-line screen will produce an excellent half-tone effect with water-based ink reduced to a viscosity close to that of water. Wiping characteristics are good, provided that the chrome cylinder surface has been properly prepared. Striation is minimized or eliminated in the line or mass-tone areas. We are now investigating the use of shallower-etched cylinders which have shown promise in the marked improvement of drying speed through a reduction in the amount of ink deposited, with correspondingly less water to be evaporated, or absorbed. Applying less ink will also help to eliminate fibre swell, embossing, distortion and creasing – all of which have proved troublesome in the past.

Water-based publication gravure inks
Publication gravure printers are also very eager to comply with air pollution and fire hazard safety regulations. Some have already installed expensive solvent recovery systems or other engineered means of complying with air pollution regulations. Many have yet to do either. We believe that publication gravure printers would convert to water inks tomorrow if they could obtain the same printing quality, dry as quickly, and pay no more than the cost of the solvent inks now used. The standards of the publication gravure printing industry are very high because it must be competitive with web-offset and letterpress as well as with other gravure printers. So far, water-based inks have not been considered good enough to meet publications standards. Considerable time and effort has been directed during the past five years to overcome these valid objections. The ink manufacturer has concentrated on improving gloss, printability and reducing cost. A systems approach has been adopted – including optimization of the paper, cylinder and dryer aspects – to ensure successful and commercially viable answers.

On the basis of a number of commercial field trial results using conventionally etched cylinders, and comparing regular solvent-based publication gravure inks to water-based inks, the following conclusions can be drawn:

The gloss of water-based inks on coated stock is better than that of conventional solvent-based inks designed for supplement printing.

The gloss of water-based inks on groundwood papers is approximately equal to that of conventional solvent-based inks designed for supplement printing.

Print quality, smoothness and dot structure are slightly inferior to organic solvent inks but are being improved.

Scuff resistance is better than with conventional inks.

The present bulk ink cost is roughly 10–25 % higher than the cost of solvent type supplement inks.

With some exceptions, water is the only solvent used in these formulations. Therefore no air pollution hazard or need for restriction exists.

The drying speed of high-strength water-based inks from shallow-etch cylinders is greatly improved and commercial field tests should confirm their equivalence to the drying of conventional solvent from shallow-etch cylinders.

The drying speed of normal strength water-based inks from conventional etch cylinders can be 30–50 % slower than that of solvent inks using low-efficiency drying equipment. One commercial trial experience with modern, efficient H V H A dryers proved that water-based inks could be dried satisfactorily at 1,600 ft/minute on both coated and uncoated stocks – an unexpected result!

A standard specification system for print production

Maurice Goldring and Angela Hackelsberger

'Standardisation is not an impediment to the development of civilisation, but, on the contrary, one of its immediate prerequisites. A standard may be defined as that simplified practical exemplar of anything in general use which embodies a fusion of the best of its anterior forms.'
Walter Gropius:
The New Architecture and the Bauhaus.

Designers, typographers, editors, and printers in the technologically advanced countries are becoming aware that the traditional practices of specifying for print are no longer adequate in relation to management and production techniques in the printing industry.

The traditional practice of specifying can best be characterized as informal. The information needed for the production of a job is transmitted using various visual modes, usually in specification notes, letters, and memoranda, and in annotations to authors' copy, designers' layouts, and printers' proofs. Such information is also transmitted verbally, perhaps at second hand, as telephone messages.

Information is not transmitted in a comprehensive, coherent form from the outset, but by degrees. This can and does work so far – at a cost – but what are the disadvantages and limitations of this practice of specification as opposed to a more formal approach, such as would be possible by the application of a standard specification system as we will call it, which will be outlined below?

At present, printers meet with unnecessary difficulties and uncertainties in scheduling, planning, and co-ordinating their operations, also in estimating their production costs reliably.

Traditional specifications usually have to be assembled and transcribed, and sometimes translated, by someone other than the specifier for use at the various levels of skill and by the various trades involved in the print production process. This represents a potential source of factual error and misinterpretation of the designer's or print buyer's intentions, moreover the duplication of effort incurred is wasteful. Such specifications do not facilitate consistency of specified information, especially in the event of amendments and alterations. Nor do they facilitate effective and systematic quality control or reference for further use.

One of the most urgent reasons for considering a standard specification system is that the traditional practices of specifying are not compatible with computer applications and with the requirements of the evolving new techniques in printing.

The limitations listed above not only concern designers and print buyers. All members of the design/production team (author, editor, designer, publisher, printer) are affected by them as well as, to some extent, the manufacturers and suppliers of materials, machinery, and equipment.

Let us now consider what a standard specification system is, how it would be applied, and what it could offer. We shall then see how the construction industries in two countries benefit from standard specification systems in their field.

A standard specification system for print production would be both a method and a physical object. As a method it is the rationalized and effective means by which a specification for a particular job, a standard job specification as we will call it, can be arrived at. This contains all the particulars needed for the production of the projected work.

As an object the standard specification system can be imagined on the one hand as an information store in the form of a handbook, loose-leaf file, card index, or even a computer data bank. It would need to present the information in the concise verbatim form required; easily accessible, permitting the relevant selections of information to be found rapidly and to be extracted neatly. It has to be flexible, allowing for amendments to be made.

On the other hand we have – *horribile dictu* – a set of forms and guidance notes or, at any rate, some formalized means by which to set down the items of the standard job specification formulated from the information store, in the right sequence, using agreed preferred terms, with duplicates as required. Such forms would have to be well structured and designed with the efficiency and convenience of the production side kept foremost in mind.

These forms would be filled in largely by the 'professional customer' (designer, print buyer, editor, etc.), if need be in consultation with the production side. Other parts of the forms are for the production side to complete, namely, those concerning technical aspects which can and must properly be left to them to decide upon, and which are covered from the 'professional customer's' point of view by his specified performance requirements.

The advantage of such forms lies in having one document containing all agreed, duly recorded, and readily accessible information which, together with manuscripts, artwork, and production drawings form the source material for the realization of a job. A form is sometimes seen as a constraint, but if it is well made it is a prompter for information to be established and for decisions to be taken. It is thus an aid to discipline and to good communication.

The information store would contain the comprehensive descriptive lists of materials, equipment, and print production processes. It would also contain statements of performance requirements. For example, a printing ink's lightfastness rating, say LF8, or its spirit varnish resistance rating, say SVR5, both maximum ratings (according to

British Standard BS 4321 : 1969 Methods of Test for Printing Ink), could be seen both as qualities of an existing ink and as performance requirements for an ink that has as yet to be found or to be made up. A maximum permissible tolerance, for example, of typographic measure, could also be seen as a performance requirement and be specified as such.

The information contained in the store should be of high technical quality, presented in concise, clear language, using agreed preferred terms. It should be the most comprehensive assemblage of such information available. It should therefore list all materials, equipment, and processes that are in use, and all currently attainable performance requirements.

This information would be presented in the form of standard specification data groups. From these data groups the appropriate items would be selected and be incorporated verbatim into the standard job specification.

It is possible that a standard job specification would be assembled in a manner so that each production section (i.e. typesetting, illustration processing, printing, binding, trimming, etc.) could receive its own extracts copied out of the standard job specification document. This master copy could also be agreed to have a contractual function in conjunction, of course, with the manuscript, layout, drawings, artwork, estimate, and production schedule.

A typical sequence out of a standard job specification, which is dealing with the paper to be used and which has been assembled from information contained in the standard specification system, might read as follows:

Type	Woodfree off-machine coated
Size	SRA1 (640×900 mm)
Weight	120 g/m²
Colour	White
Coating	Air-knife, trailing blade
Surface	Super calendered, high gloss, two sided
Sizing	Hard, engine sized
Printing	Letterpress
Cutting	Guillotined four edges
Wrapping	Kraft wrappers

Variables such as the brand name of the paper, its price, quantity required, etc., could also be written into the standard job specification where necessary.

The items given in the example above follow the pattern long established by the British trade journal *Paper Facts & Figures* which is now generally accepted by paper manufacturers as well as by printers, print buyers, and designers as providing a good basis for the presentation of factual, comparable information on paper and boards.

The standard specification data groups would be classified and notated using an appropriate notation system (possibly alphanumeric). This would allow the data groups to be arranged systematically for storage, selection, and retrieval for use in standard job specifications.

Such a system of notation would provide a shorthand method of specifying where instead of the full data group only its notation might be given. This would be useful in many ways, to give one illustration: where production in a foreign country under foreign language conditions was involved.

Presupposing that a standard specification system could be agreed, eventually, on an international basis, a job could be specified, say, in the German language version of the system, referred to by notation and produced, say, in Britain using the English language version corresponding to the notation.

This necessary approach of classification and notation should also – and most urgently – have an exemplary effect on the whole field of technical information related to print production, especially on the disparate body of manufacturers' and suppliers' trade literature, and on sample distribution. Trade literature is, of course, competitive in its nature but nevertheless it can become co-operative to the extent of offering itself pre-classified and bearing the appropriate notation. It would also be an advantage if the format of such trade literature could be standardized to the A4 size and be pre-punched for filing. The user – designer, print buyer, technician – could thus much more effectively shape all the available source material, or have it shaped for his use in a library, into a ready tool of up to date reference and learning. Moreover the materials, processes, and products which competing manufacturers offer in their promotional literature appearing under the same notation would invite and facilitate comparison.

The first steps have been taken in holding consultations with relevant professional, trade, standards, and research associations to agree the need for, feasibility, and extent of a standard specification system. These bodies include ICOGRADA (International Council of Graphic

Design Associations) and, in Britain, the Society of Industrial Artists and Designers, Institute of Printing, BFMP (British Federation of Master Printers), British Standards Institution, and PIRA (Research Association for the Paper and Board, Printing and Packaging Industries) which has proposed to undertake the necessary research and development work subject to adequate funding and support.

The response of these and other bodies – as well as of a number of the largest publishing houses and printing firms – has been interested and encouraging with one exception, that of the BFMP. Their doubts must be considered helpful in that they are model doubts about any attempted innovation in the context of a long tradition.

The BFMP's Technical Committee, while agreeing that communications between customers and printers need to be improved generally, fear that a formalized system would interfere with flexibility and freedom of decision in printing firms. They fear that technically unqualified people would disturb well established practices with unreasonable demands and that half-qualified people would be tempted into overspecifying. While all these pitfalls could be overcome in an intelligently constructed, mutually agreed and safeguarded standard specification system, one side question remains: how do printers and designers wish to see each other?

Does the printer see the designer as an artist unfettered by technical concerns, thus supposedly able to concentrate all the more on creativity? Is the designer to see the printer as the kindly magician who will somehow print what the designer intended? Too many mistakes and misunderstandings happen for such idylls to remain aglow. Printers might realize that more and more professional designers get involved in their industry and are an integral part of it. Most of these have been encouraged, ever since William Morris and then the Bauhaus, to know well the techniques not only of designing, but also of manufacture, and to let themselves be stimulated and guided by this understanding. Today the Society of Industrial Artists and Designers requires both creativity and technical/professional competence from designers applying for membership under its Direct Admission Scheme. Further, the Institute of Printing is now considering admitting suitably qualified designers to its membership.

One of the main problems is the complexity and diversity of the printing and associated industries. How has a comparable though larger industry, also with long and proud traditions, which has to face a

References

Tony Allott
NBS : a progress report, *PIBA Journal*,
February 1971, London.

Maurice Goldring
Can the typographer assist printing
technology, *Institute of Printing Bulletin
No.12*, 1966, London.

Maurice Goldring
The functional relationship between
typographers and keyboard operators,
Printing Technology, Volume 12, No.1,
April 1968, Institute of Printing, London.

F. L. LaQue
Standardisation and quality control,
BSI News, October 1971, London.

Bruce Martin
Standards and building, Royal Institute of
British Architects, 1971, London.

Martin Scheele
*Punch-card methods in research and
documentation*, Interscience Publishers Inc.,
1961, New York.

similar challenge started to deal with the need to rationalize its methods of specification?

The Swedish construction industry led the way with the publication of *Bygg-AMA* in 1950. This is a general specification of building materials and workmanship which was agreed and adopted throughout the industry. It is recognized in Sweden that it has proved valuable to use a unified general specification and that it has been beneficial to get a common pattern of specification for all trades. Apart from the Swedish *Bygg-AMA* being the first standard specification for the construction industry to be adopted, it also pioneered the use of the SfB system for the arrangement and coding of its contents.

The SfB system is a method of classification and notation devised for all aspects of building. It uses a series of alphabetical and numerical symbols denoting conceptual groups covered by tables which form the basis of all permutations of the system. The SfB system originated in Sweden after the Second World War. Within a few years it spread to the other Scandinavian countries and to Britain, where it is now thought to have its widest use. The system is also in use in many other countries throughout the world.

Twenty-two years after the Swedish initiative in publishing *Bygg-AMA*, the British construction industry will in 1973 be adopting its own standard specification system, the *National Building Specification* (NBS). This is being prepared by NBS Ltd, a subsidiary company set up for this purpose in 1969 by the Royal Institute of British Architects. The NBS has the support of the representative organizations of the construction industry. Its aim is to improve the quality of job specifications, making them more consistent, relevant, and reliable. Standard specification clauses will be provided which can be incorporated into job specifications. They will be classified and notated using a development of the SfB system – CI/SfB. The NBS will be suitable both for manual and for computer applications.

As the construction industries in two countries find that a standard specification system brings many advantages and benefits, the time seems to be appropriate for serious consideration to be given to the creation of such a system in the printing and associated industries. Once the standard specification system and its related classification and notation system together with the dictionary of preferred terms were created, an organization responsible for publishing them and for promoting and advising on their use would need to be set up. This could well be an international venture.

Advertisements

"True . . . in the old days you did know the printing game inside out."

Coverex lasting good looks that are bound to succeed

Coverex the tough cover material by Winterbottom

Coverex is a NON-WOVEN cover material made from exceptionally strong latex-saturated base stock with the famous Winterbottom coating of nitro-cellulose (pyroxylin).

The dignified colour of Coverex

Coverex is available in ten classic shades and seven embossed grains, giving a wide choice of beautiful finishes. Of course, as with all our products almost any shade can be matched for reasonable making quantities. And it doesn't stop there. For the connoisseur, Coverex Antique – sheer luxury in five shades.

Made to stand the strain of hard use

The good-looking toughness of Coverex gives both durability and good appearance even to much-handled works of reference. And more: Coverex resists scruffs and scratches, water and adhesive penetration. It has good light fastness and high edge-tear strength, and blocks perfectly. Coverex will fold, crease, and can be used with all standard adhesives. All desirable features for use with books that are made to last. And because of these superb qualities Coverex is also used by slip case manufacturers and manufacturing stationers.

1 Spencer-Bower and Turner, Res Judicata, (2nd Edn) Published by Butterworth and Co. (Publishers) Ltd. Coverex Coachhide
2 Pettit. Equity and the Law of Trusts (2nd Edn) Published by Butterworth and Co. (Publishers) Ltd. Coverex Morocco.
3 W. E. Vine. Expository Dictionary of New Testament Words. Published by Oliphants. Coverex Crush.
4 Jamieson, Fausset and Brown Commentary. Published by Oliphants. Coverex Levant.
5 The Amplified Bible. Published by Marshall Morgan & Scott Coverex Crush.
6 Mathew Henry's Commentary (Broadoak edition) in one volume Genesis to Revelation Published by Marshall Morgan & Scott. Coverex Levant.

This is Coverex binding a promise of lasting good looks

Change to Coverex now. Don't hesitate, send for a pattern card OR a trial piece OR be bold – and order a roll of Coverex now.

Once again Penrose Annual is bound in Art Canvas—another Winterbottom product that's bound to succeed.

If you'd like to check out our range of Art Canvas or Coverex, or any of our Textured Bookbindings, send for free details, colourways and samples.

Winterbottom Products Ltd.,

Victoria Mills, Weaste, Salford M6 5RH, Lancs.
Tel : 061-736 5265   Telex : 668812

our coloured papers speak for themselves!

art and technology

by

Gilchrist Brothers Ltd
litho & letterpress platemakers
and full supporting services

Leeds ■ London ■ Glasgow ■ Manchester ■
Leicester ■ Bristol ■ Tel Leeds 0532-20463

1700

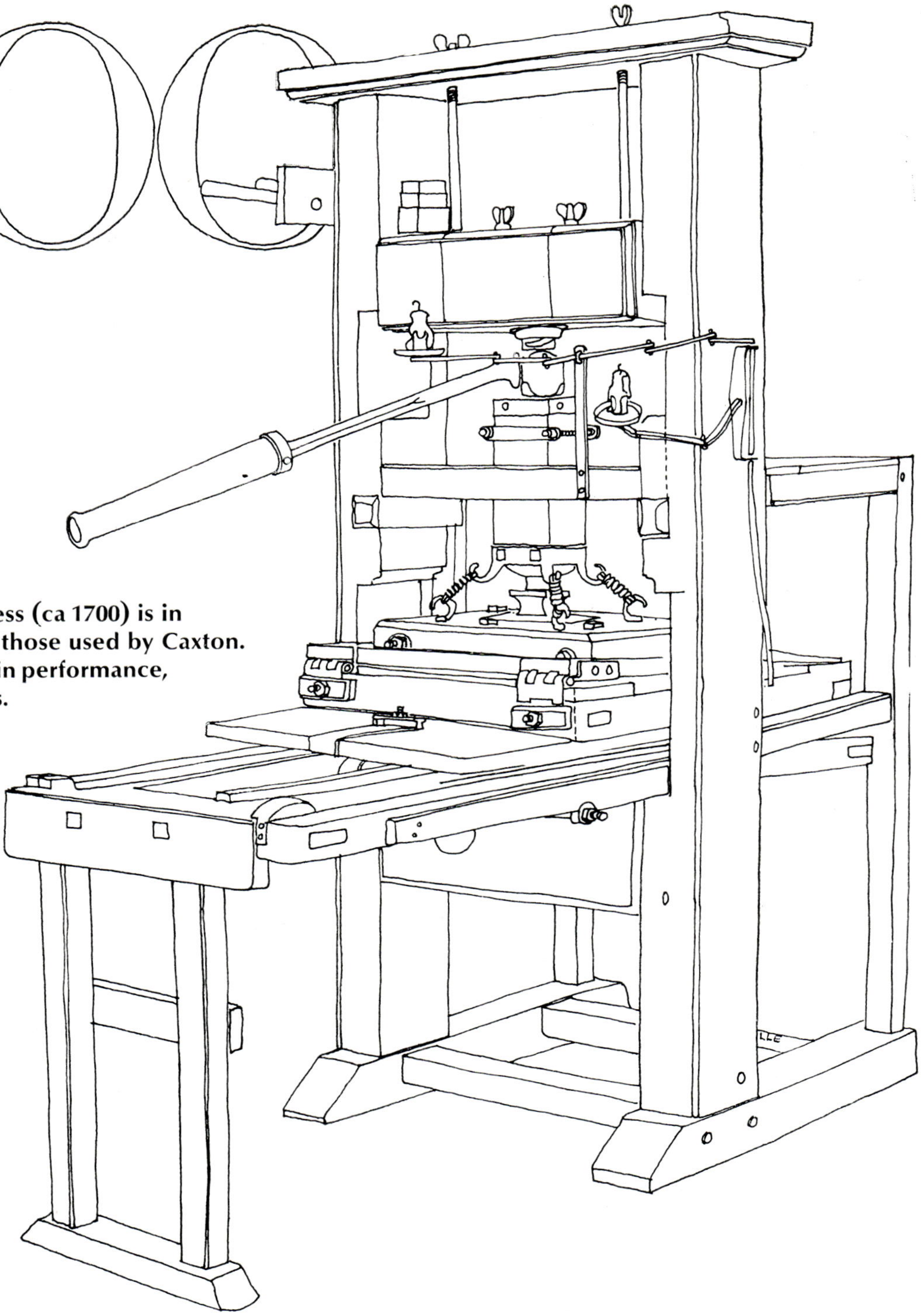

This early printing press (ca 1700) is in many ways similar to those used by Caxton. As presses improved in performance, so did printing metals.

Today, the consistency of Plus printing metals is your best safeguard against perplexity and frustration. As Britain's leading supplier of printing metals we maintain unrivalled facilities for research and quality control, as well as a tradition of customer service.

Plus Printing Metals Ltd *formerly Pass Printing Metals (London) Ltd* Dominion Buildings, South Place, London EC2M 2RE
Telephone: 01-628 8030 Telex: 885737 Telegrams: PLUSPRIMET LONDONEC2

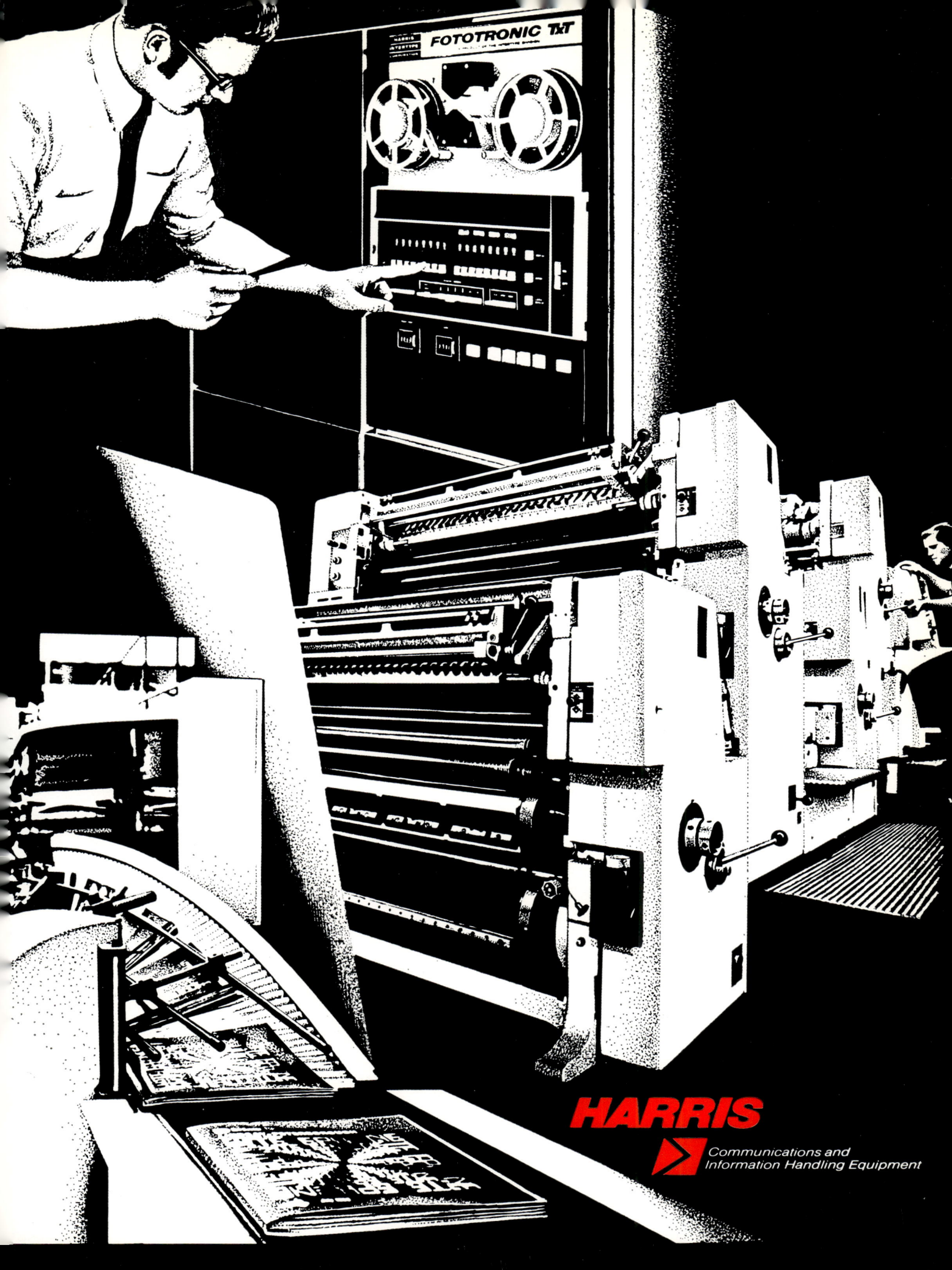

FOTOTRONIC TXT

HARRIS
Communications and
Information Handling Equipment

HARRIS-INTERTYPE LIMITED · PO BOX 27 · FARNHAM ROAD · SLOUGH SL1 4XD   SLOUGH 34666

Photographer: Rex Bamber
Client: Good Housekeeping
Material: Kodak 'Ektachrome' Film
Separations: Gee and Watson Ltd.
Processor: 'Kodalith' Film Processor Model 324-N

From original to printed page...

...Kodak materials for every stage

**Photographic film
Graphic arts films
Phototypesetting materials
Automatic processors
Chemicals
Colour proofing materials
Printing plates**

Graphic Arts Sales Department, Kodak Limited,
PO Box 66, Hemel Hempstead, Hertfordshire.

Kodak, Kodalith and Ektachrome are trade marks

6

The Timson Way
You know the machines.
But not their performance.

Not any more.

Timsons have taken their three most successful machines and up-dated and up-rated them – to give even greater performance efficiency and profitability than ever before.

The Wun-Up Mark III

– as versatile as ever, but with still more improvements, to make it the only possible choice for profitable, long-run form production. What more can you do to a machine that already runs at up to 1,000 fpm (305 mpm) re-reeling and only marginally less for sheeting and zig-zag folding. And prints by letterpress, letterset and offset-litho? Ask us and find out.

The Zig-Zagger

Economical production for the in-plant printer, and greater flexibility for the continuous stationery printer. The new version of this superbly simple machine goes even faster now. And greater output means greater profit.

The Verti-Collector

– streamlined production of multi-part sets – paper and carbons are now crimped or hot-melt gummed together more efficiently. To give a better product – faster.

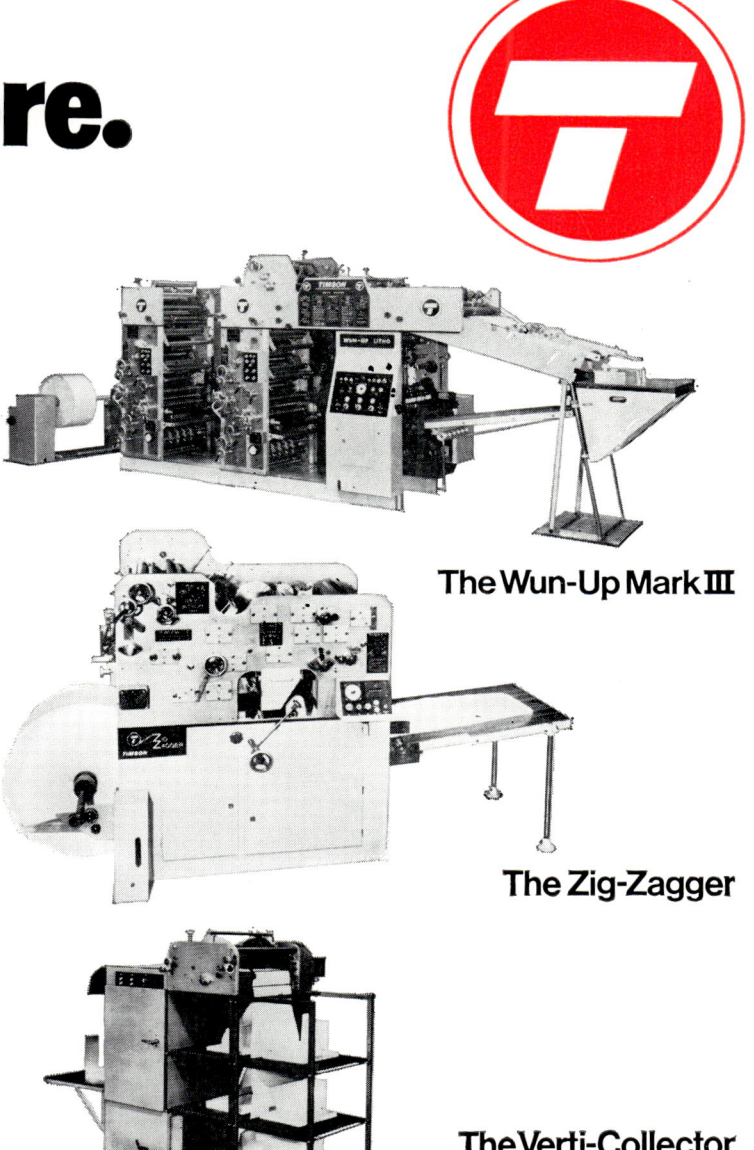

The Wun-Up Mark III

The Zig-Zagger

The Verti-Collector

Timsons (Exports & Sales) Limited of Kettering and Panton House, 25 Haymarket, London, SWI. Telephone 01-839 4781

THIS SHEET OF SOMMERVILLE'S BLUE LAID HAS BEEN PRINTED BY THE STELLAR PRESS. DEVICE FILMSET BY CRANMER BROWN LTD. DESIGNED BY PETER GUY.

DU PONT

CROMALIN*

The new CROMALIN 4 Color Proof System

What the CROMALIN 4/C proof system is

A photopolymer laminate that is stripped to the proof sheet prior to exposure and toning.

An extremely thin laminate. All four colors total about a thousandth of an inch in thickness.

A positive proofing system. Exposure through a halftone positive hardens the non-image area, leaving a tacky positive image that accepts the color toner.

A dry proofing system. No liquids, inks, or solvents are required.

What CROMALIN can do

Full color printed results anticipate your press run

Toners blended to match process inks in use

Clean background proofs; no grey appearance

Quickly made proofs —
11″ x 14″ 4/C proofs in less than 15 minutes
25″ x 38″ 4/C proofs in less than 30 minutes

Reproducible proofs
Exact duplication, time after time
Consistent results, job-for-job

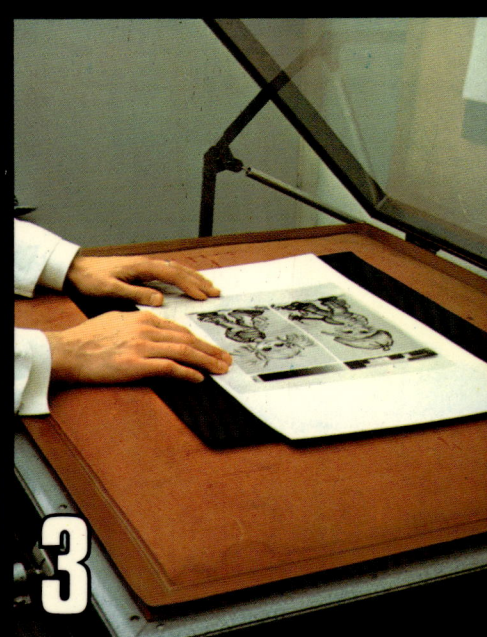

How it is done

The steps are simple and easily done by craftsmen. Cleanliness and care in applying toners are the basic essentials.

Mix toners, if necessary, to match the inks in use. If press inks are standardized, bulk toner quantities can be prepared. Color matching is excellent since the toner pigments are the same as those used in making process inks. Standard 7500° K illumination is recommended for best control when color matching. (Note: 5000° K is commonly used for color evaluation. 7500° K is preferred for color matching.)

Prepare laminator for use. Switch on power switch. Laminator will not run until operating temperature is reached (about 10 minutes). Load with desired width of CROMALIN material.   Place a sheet of proof paper on the bed of the laminator and feed it into the roller nip. The sheet should be slightly wider than the CROMALIN film.   Switch drive motor on. (Pilot light will glow when roll is heated and drive is operative.) Feed the proof sheet to the roller nip and allow it to pass through the laminator. Stop drive motor when the proof sheet extends about an inch beyond the rollers. Trim off film close to the proof sheet using a sharp blade.

Place the sensitized proof sheet in the vacuum frame. Position the first color positive, correctly oriented on the proof sheet. When exposing through the base of positives, use a concentrated light source, masking off the reflector if necessary. Reestablish correct exposure for this condition. Use either pin register or visual positioning. (Note: Positives should carry or have attached, the usual color bars, control strips, or other guides for measuring and evaluating the proofs.) Close the frame and wait for good vacuum contact. Twenty to twenty-five inches vacuum is required.   Expose the CROMALIN proof. Exposure will be with: 2 kw. pulsed Xenon at 60″, 20 sec. Expose within 5 minutes after CROMALIN is laminated to the proof paper.

Where you can use CROMALIN

Color etching proofs to guide progressive dot-etching

Preview of ganged color proofs when press combinations compel compromise between inks

Alternate ink colors for proofs when several different inks are to be evaluated for art director's or customer's decision

Superior quality proofs to submit to your customer or agency

4

5

Transfer CROMALIN proof sheet to toning console. Remove the protective MYLAR* cover by first separating it and then quickly pulling it away parallel to the surface of the proof.

Apply the first color using the lamb's wool applicator that has been dipped into and has a slight excess of the first color toner. Move applicator lightly and quickly back and forth and sideways without pressure until the entire proof area has been covered. Carefully wipe off the excess toner with a wad of cotton followed by a final wipe with a clean cloth. Also, wipe off the back of the proof sheet.

Notes:

Toner application should be within two minutes from time of exposure. If the first color down is yellow and visual registration is to be used, apply dabs of cyan or black toner to the register marks with the aid of the finger or a Q-TIP. Wipe excess toner away from job.

Return proof sheet to the laminator. Apply the second layer of CROMALIN film. Register the positive. Expose and tone as was done for the first color.

Repeat for the remaining colors.

Apply a protective cover film of CROMALIN, if desired. Expose this protective layer for about two minutes.

CROMALIN equipment and materials

CROMALIN Laminator 2700
Designed to give trouble free operation and requiring only a minimum of table top space.

CROMALIN Toning Console
Required for optimum cleanliness during application of toners. Surplus toner is drawn off and filtered by built-in down draft system.

CROMALIN Applicator
and Toning Box
For easy handling of toners.

CROMALIN
Quick Kit Roll Changer
For use when more than one size material is required.

CROMALIN 4/C Film —
Order Code C4/C
6 Sizes
12" x 100' (30,4 cm x 30,4 m)
20" x 100' (50,8 cm x 30,4 m)
25" x 100' (63,5 cm x 30,4 m)
12" x 300' (30,4 cm x 91,4 m)
20" x 300' (50,8 cm x 91,4 m)
25" x 300' (63,5 cm x 91,4 m)

Toners

Color	Designation	
Magenta (5 toners)	M 35	M 80
	M 35/2	M 80/2
	M 35H	
Cyan (4 toners)	C 28	C 22
	C 28/2	C 22/2
Yellow (2 toners)	Y 2	
	Y 2/2	
Black (2 toners)	K 5	
	K 5/2	

What the CROMALIN System can offer You
- Correct reading 4 color proofs from screened camera or contact positives
- A completely dry system — no liquids, inks or solvents
- Large proof size capability
- Consistant duplicate proofs
- Matched ink colors with intermix possibilities
- Quickly made proofs (A 4 size less than 15 minutes, A 1 size less than 30 minutes)

Printed from LYDEL* photopolymer offset printing plates
Cover picture: R. Angenendt, Dortmund

* Du Pont's trademark
Technical modifications reserved
Printed in the Federal Republic of Germany

I'm interested in CROMALIN and would like

☐ your representative call

☐ a demonstration at Du Pont

Company name and address:

....

....

Name: ....

Position: ....

Telephone No.: ....

DU PONT COMPANY (UNITED KINGDOM) LTD.
Hawksden Road
St. Neots
Huntingdonshire
Telephone Huntingdon 73881   pa

DU PONT DE NEMOURS (DEUTSCHLAND) GMBH
Photo Products Department
6 Frankfurt am Main 1
Opernplatz 2
Telefon (0611) 21951

DU PONT DE NEMOURS (FRANCE) S.A.
9, rue de Vienne, Paris VIIIe
Téléphone
387-59-19 / 387-49-29

DU PONT

Colour
spectacle!

Always looks better on **IVOREX**

IVOREX
Twin-wire Board

Smooth High White and Super White

Description	Substance g/m²
SRA2 450 × 640 mm	190
	224
	300
	355
	400
Royal 521 × 635 mm	190
	224
	300
	355
	400
	500
	600
Postal 572 × 724 mm	190
	224
	300
	355
	400
SRA1 640 × 900 mm	190
	224
	300
	355

Matt High White and Super White

Description	Substance g/m²
Royal 521 × 635 mm	190
	224
	300
SRA1 640 × 900 mm	190
	224
	300

Ivorex is matured at the Mill and waterproof wrapped.   All stock boards are LONG GRAIN.

IVOREX
The board behind the best printing jobs.
by Tullis Russell and Company Limited

Markinch, Glenrothes, Fife KY7 6PB, Scotland. Telephone Glenrothes (STD 0592–75) 3311. Telex 72213. Also in London, Manchester, Birmingham.

Printed on Ivorex smooth high white 355 g/m²

Our new symbol...

...and what it stands for

It marks the joining of two International Companies to form Littlejohn Graphic Systems Ltd. – a powerful new force in the graphic arts business.

It stands for a comprehensive range of equipment bringing fully integrated systems to every stage of the reproduction and plate making processes.

Backed by a pooling of talents and resources from Littlejohn and Cosmocord for even better things to come in terms of your production efficiency and profitability.

A single mark. A single name. A single address. And a singleness of purpose that will set new standards for service. Try us.

Littlejohn Graphic Systems Ltd.

16-24 Brewery Road, London N7 9NP. Telephone- 01-607 6681. Telex: 23735

City Engraving Co (Hull) Ltd
PO Box 17 Hull Yorkshire
Specialists in Letterpress Colour Half-Tone
Photolitho Reproduction and Platemaking
Advertisement and Repro Typesetting
Electros (College and Metal)

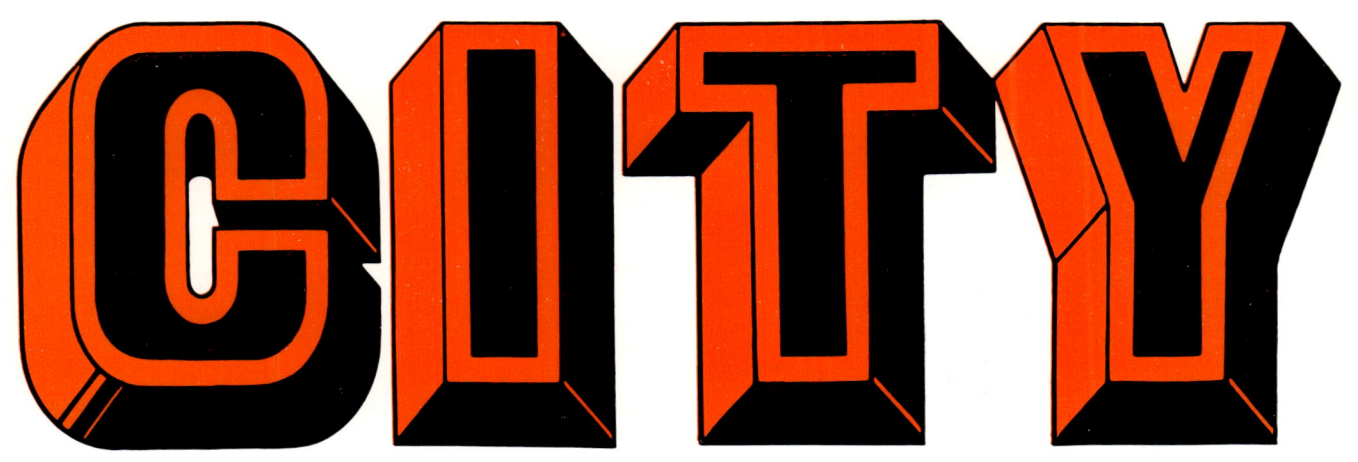

Artwork and Photography
Flexographic Plates
Nyloprint
Rubbers
Stereos

GRANGE FIBRE
-the Linson people-
have adopted
the new symbol
commemorating
the centenary of
their parent company,
Watsons at Linwood.

Wherever there are quality bookbindings, whether casebound or limp, you will find this symbol.

Take, for instance, a growth market like limp covers. Even a publication like The Penrose Annual now has a limp cover edition. So what do they bind it in? SNOLIN. In three standard weights, it is one of the whitest cover materials on the market and is another winner from the internationally famous Linson range.

So get to know this symbol. It is just about all you need to know about bookbinding materials.

THE GRANGE FIBRE COMPANY LIMITED · 20/26 WELLESLEY ROAD · CROYDON · SURREY CR9 2AL   Tel. 01 686 8051

R. & W. WATSON (CONVERTERS) LIMITED · LINWOOD · RENFREWSHIRE · SCOTLAND PA3 3DF Tel. JOHNSTONE 21543/7

LINOSCAN

the most cost effective system for colour reproduction

The Linoscan is the only electronic colour scanner on the market that can analyse, correct, enlarge, expose and direct screen all four colours simultaneously.
It can produce a complete four colour set in just over $3\frac{1}{2}$ minutes enabling you to bring the cost per set down to the minimum.

The design of the machine is simple, so its cost is modest, yet it offers all these facilities:
*built-in computer *unsharp masking
*colour correction *flesh tone control
*electronic masking
*automatic two-level drop out
*gradation control *enlargement
*undercolour removal *direct screening
*Linoscan has interchangeable drums so that a second job can be prepared while the first drum is being scanned.
*The machine can produce up to as many as 20 A4 formatted colour pages in one eight-hour shift.
*The drums and carriage are mounted on zero friction gas pressure bearings for consistent reliability, accuracy and low maintenance.

In short, the Linoscan is the answer to the many problems which still beset the industry in that it offers reliable, flexible, profitable and very fast colour conversion to the highest visual standard and at the right price.

Tell me about the Linoscan

Name

Position

Company

Address

Telephone

Brochure Representative Demonstration

post to Linotype Group Publicity
Department, Kingsbury Works,
Kingsbury Road,
London NW9 8UT.

13

the Linotype
HUNTER
an entirely new web offset press

Linotype have produced a completely new, compact, web offset press that's crammed with big machine features. We call it – THE HUNTER

The Hunter is designed to be

* Versatile
it will deliver double parallel book sections, quarter fold periodicals and magazines and tabloid or broadsheet newspapers– long runs or short runs.

*Fast running
up to 25,000 copies per hour

*Easy to extend
plug in, pre-wired units – can be stacked or in-line

*Accurately controlled
the latest refinements in printing technology have been built in to ensure the highest quality reproduction.

*Effortless to operate
a central console offers overall remote control although the operator has manual override. Access through the press during the run is unimpeded.

*Simple to maintain
unit design ensures simplified service and parts replacement.

*Economic to run
fast makeready and plate change; the new folder and preset inking and damping minimise wastage.

*Dependable
It's made by Linotype and backed by nearly a century of experience in the design and manufacture of printing machinery.

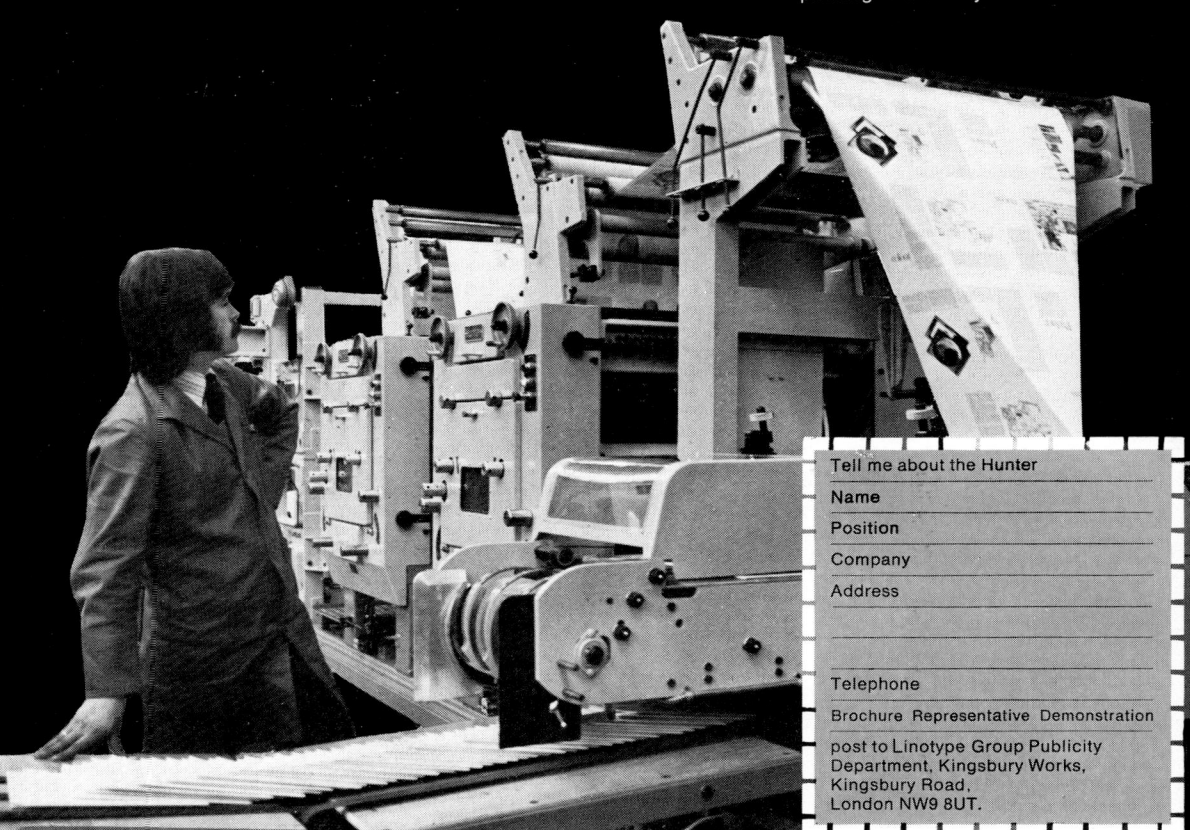

Tell me about the Hunter

Name

Position

Company

Address

Telephone

Brochure Representative Demonstration

post to Linotype Group Publicity Department, Kingsbury Works, Kingsbury Road, London NW9 8UT.

14

LINOTRON 505

the most widely used CRT phototypesetting system in the world

They say we don't shout enough about the LINOTRON so here goes:— close on 200 installed including 505C and TC. the most advanced and versatile phototypesetting systems all based on the proven TWIN CRT photo unit on-line to a control computer.

* 160 to 320 news lines per minute.
* 4 to 72 point with 23 sizes in between.
* 1088 distinct characters and signs on tap.
* Fast magnetic disc store — 12,500,000 characters capacity.
* 7 or 9 track magnetic tape read-write unit — 16,000,000 characters.
* 1200 news lines/min line printer.
* Paper tape readers and punches, etc. ALL ON LINE to the computer on a time sharing basis with VDU terminals available shortly.
* All the software to run that lot including:— full composition programmes, justification, hyphenation (every european language available except albanian and we'll write that too if we are asked) — disc storage, sorting, updating retrieval, classified ads without tears, maths without effort, ask us to tell you more.

Tell me about the Linotron 505

Name

Position

Company

Address

Telephone

Brochure Representative Demonstration

post to Linotype Group Publicity Department, Kingsbury Works, Kingsbury Road, London NW9 8UT.

15

Lettering as Drawing

NICOLETE GRAY

This book treats Western script and lettering as an abstract visual art comparable with painting in formal and expressive sensitivity and power. The author has brought together material from the whole range of calligraphic history, from Merovingian charters to modern magazine covers. The book is an aesthetic analysis intended for the general reader as well as for artists. Previously published in two paperback volumes, this edition is in larger format and has an appendix of additional illustrations.   188 illustrations   £6.50

Industrial Ceramics

Tableware
NEAL FRENCH

In order to design ceramics to be made by industrial processes it is vitally important that these processes should be understood. The author, who has had twelve years of experience working with Worcester Royal, describes the intricacies of the manufacturing methods and shows what scope they offer to the designer.   57 illustrations   £1.10
Oxford Paperbacks Handbooks for Artists

OXFORD UNIVERSITY PRESS

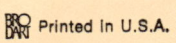